CU00544222

Fatal Flight

"**A fascinating story**, not nearly well enough known on the American side of the Atlantic, **artfully and engagingly told.**" G.J. Meyer New York Times bestselling author of *A World Undone: The Story of the Great War 1914 to 1918* & The World Remade: America in World War I

"Why does brilliant vehicle design sometimes end in tragedy? The crash of the intended flagship of the British Empire, the magnificent dirigible R.101, is not only **an absorbing human and technical story** as told by Bill Hammack. It is also a vital lesson in the risks of even apparently small compromises and unforeseen hazards to big projects when confronted by the forces of nature. Impressively documented, Fatal Flight should be required reading for engineers and political leaders alike." Edward Tenner Author of international bestseller *Why Things Bite Back* & *Our Own Devices*

"A **well-researched and gripping** look at Britain's greatest airship disaster from a new perspective: through the eyes of a man who built, flew, and died with the ship." Dan Grossman, Airship Historian author of *airships.net* and coauthor of *Zeppelin Hindenburg: An Illustrated History of LZ-129*

Other Books by the Author

Why Engineers Need to Grow a Long Tail
Bill Hammack • 2011

How Engineers Create the World
Bill Hammack • 2011

Eight Amazing Engineering Stories
Bill Hammack, Patrick Ryan, & Nick Ziech • 2012

Albert Michelson's Harmonic Analyzer
Bill Hammack, Steve Kranz, & Bruce Carpenter • 2014

Michael Faraday's The Chemical History of a Candle
Bill Hammack & Don DeCoste • 2016

Fatal Flight

The True Story of Britain's
Last Great Airship

Bill Hammack

Copyright © 2017 William S. Hammack
All rights reserved. No part of this book may be reproduced in any form by any electronic or mechanical means (including photocopying, recording, or information storage and retrieval) without permission from the publisher.

Articulate Noise Books

New York | info@articulatenoise.com
First hardcover edition: June 2017
William S. Hammack
Fatal Flight: The True Story of Britain's Last Great Airship /
Bill Hammack—1st edition (version 1.0)
ISBN 978-1-945441-01-1 (hbk)
ISBN 978-1-945443-03-5 (paperback)
ISBN 978-1-945441-02-8 (electronic)
1. R101 (Airship). 2. Airships—Great Britain—History. 3. Airships—History—20th century. 4. Aircraft accidents. 5. Airships—Design and construction—History. I. Title.

Never to lose an opportunity of reasoning against the head-dimming, heart-damping Principle of Judging a work by its Defect, not its Beauties. *Every* work must have the former—we know it a priori—but every work has not the Latter & he therefore, who discovers them, tells you something that you could not with certainty or even with probability have anticipated ....

Samuel Taylor Coleridge, *Coleridge's Notebooks: A Selection*, ed. Seamus Perry (Oxford: Oxford University Press, 2002), p. 36

CONTENTS

List of Illustrations

THE PERENNIAL PROMISE OF AIRSHIPS

A T FOUR IN THE AFTERNOON on Wednesday, October 28, 2015, a Pennsylvania State Police officer fired a hundred shotgun blasts into the nose of a runaway blimp. The milk-white blimp, caught in a tree, sank to the ground as helium whistled from the shotgun holes. As the helium leaked, a team from the United States Army rolled up the blimp's tail, which had separated when it crashed. From the tail a 6,700-foot Kevlar tether snaked across the rugged, wooded terrain. A team cut the tether with carbon-steel-bladed scissors—Kevlar is used for bulletproof vests—into small sections, which another team loaded onto a truck.

Four hours earlier, the blimp had broken free of its mooring at the Army's Aberdeen Proving Ground near Baltimore, Maryland. Although designed to always be crewless and tethered to the ground, the 242-foot-long blimp had traveled 160 miles north, crossed into neighboring Pennsylvania, and dragged its mile-long tether along the ground, terrifying local residents. Fortunately, no one was injured or killed. The whip-like cable, however, destroyed two million dollars' worth of power lines—a pittance compared to the now-destroyed blimp's $175 million cost.

The escaped blimp was part of the $2.7 billion Joint Land Attack Cruise Missile Defense Elevated Netted Sensor System (JLENS). It held aloft a radar high enough above the horizon to detect cruise missiles, drones, and other low-flying weapons. Despite its high price tag, the Pentagon rated JLENS as "poor" in reliability, unable to provide twenty-four-hour surveillance. It was labeled as "fragile," Pentagon-speak for "did not demonstrate the ability to survive in its intended operational environment." Critics called it a "zombie" government program: one that feeds on cash and is impossible to kill. It survived with the same justification used by proponents of lighter-than-air craft who aspired to create more than a novelty like the Goodyear blimp or the mere utilitarian and humble weather balloon. The wayward military blimp's promoters promised that this newest version of a lighter-than-air craft would solve one of the most pressing problems of our time. The JLENS blimp would watch the skies and sound the alert at the first hint of an aerial attack from a rogue group or nation.

The front-page news of the runaway JLENS blimp was just that: news to almost all Americans and others around the world. Who knew we used lighter-than-air craft for anything besides covering the Super Bowl or golf tournaments? To several generations, an airship means a zeppelin, and their image is of the *Hindenburg* burning in the sky. Yet airships have a rich history beyond that of the iconic zeppelin.

The story of lighter-than-air craft is one of empire and national pride, of technological advances and human perseverance, of ego and bravery. While the story of winged flight is prominently part of every history textbook, that of lighter-than-air craft, though more glorious and tragic, is largely untold in the modern day. In their heyday—between the First and Second World Wars and before transcontinental airplane flight—airships the size of the *Titanic* were the preferred method of travel between continents.

The allure of lighter-than-air craft to solve pressing problems can be traced back for decades. In 1997, six years after the first web page was posted, a company called Sky Station solicited $4.2 billion to built 250 antenna-equipped blimps to deliver Internet service. In May 1985, the British Antarctic Survey revealed a hole in the ozone layer over the South Pole, and a few years later a professor suggested sending blimps that dangled electrical wires to zap ozone-eating chemicals. In the 1970s, the Aereon Corporation proposed a hybrid lighter-than-air craft that would take off like a jet, then float like a blimp. This aerial workhorse would inexpensively usher all nations into the twentieth century—no need for costly infrastructure such as roads, railroads, tunnels, bridges, airports, warehouses, or harbors. In the 1950s and 60s, when nuclear fuels promised unlimited energy, a Boston University professor proposed a nuclear-powered version of the airship.

The airship—the largest version of any lighter-than-air craft—carried the heaviest payload and traveled at the highest speed of any lighter-than-air craft. This superior performance occurred because an airship's construction differed dramatically from that of a free balloon or a blimp. The latter two are both pressure vessels: their shape is maintained by the pressure of the lifting gas. In contrast, an airship's shape is formed by a metal framework. The metal skeleton houses gas bags that lift the ship, and a cloth cover stretched across the framework protects the gas bags from weather. This structure enables an airship to travel faster than a blimp: the force of the wind generated deforms the nose of a blimp, while the framework of an airship keeps its nose rigid when cutting through the sky.

The greatest advantage of the airship's more complex structure is the larger payload it can carry. For example, the proposed nuclear-powered airship was to be 980 feet long and would haul 400 passengers and ninety tons of cargo. "For freight," explained the ship's designer, like "motor cars and other bulky manufactured equipment, the airship would offer the lowest per ton-mile costs between factory and destination." These characteristics of an airship appealed not only to commercial interests, but also to governments with imperial ambitions.

In 1898, the U.S. annexed the Philippines as part of the spoils of the Spanish-American War. President McKinley promised to "educate the Filipinos, and uplift and civilize and Christianize them," though he worried his "civilizing" of the Filipinos might be impeded by Japan, the rising power in the region. American fears increased in 1905 when Japan surprised the world with its victory over Russia. If war occurred in the region, Japan could seize the Philippines: they were just 2,000 miles from Japan; the U.S. was 8,000 miles away. It would require sixty days for an American fleet to reach them. To create an early-warning system, the U.S. Navy commissioned three large airships for long-range strategic reconnaissance of the Pacific Ocean. Only an airship had the range and endurance to traverse the Pacific quickly and warn of approaching Japanese ships.

Not having the technology in hand, the U.S. military built, in the 1920s, an airship based on a zeppelin captured in the First World War; they also bought an airship from Germany's Zeppelin Company and one from the British government. Although two of these ships crashed, their performance so impressed the military that they decided to build two airships twice the size of the test ships. Construction of the first ship, the USS *Akron*, began in 1929, and of the second, the USS *Macon*, in 1931. Almost 800 feet long, they were dubbed flying aircraft carriers.

Airships revitalized Germany's national psyche after the First World War. When the *Graf Zeppelin* flew over the country in the 1920s, it soothed the sting of defeat by evoking, for Germans, their prewar imperial glory, and the airship hinted at the nation's return to the world stage. Because zeppelin-style airships originated long before the First World War, their appearance in the skies awakened memories of Germany's proud, industrial past. Count Zeppelin designed his first airship in 1874, fourteen years before the militant Wilhelm II became Kaiser. The first zeppelin flew in 1900. This twenty-six-year gestation of a German airship, from design to flight, coincided with Germany's rise as Europe's foremost industrial power. Its production of steel, chemicals, and coal increased by factors of ten until Germany rivaled the output of the United States.

A zeppelin, in size and symbolism, recalled pride in a bygone imperial era when the nation's authoritarian government ran the country with efficiency: the trains ran on time, the streets were clean, and its superb schools drove the literacy rate to over 90 percent. Germany's public universities were models for the world. German scientists won a third of the Nobel Prizes for science awarded from the first one in 1901 until the outbreak of war in 1914.

"What a paradise this land is!" said Mark Twain after a visit to imperial Germany. "What clean clothes, what good faces, what tranquil contentment, what prosperity, what genuine freedom, what superb government!"

After the war, this imperial culture, its institutions, traditions, and values, were shattered beyond repair. The stability of the prewar era was replaced by an intellectual free-for-all in the Weimar Republic: expressionism in arts and literature, exotic Bauhaus architecture, atonal music, and, in science, the revolutions of relativity and quantum theory. In this disconcerting flux, the return to the air of a German airship, an icon of the imperial era, comforted the German public, and it signaled to the world that Germany would overcome the impediments of the Treaty of Versailles. Small wonder that spectators broke into tears of joy when they saw a zeppelin, or that one teacher required his students to salute it and sing the national anthem.

For Britain in the 1920s, there was no nostalgic view of airships; they were of current and immediate political importance for maintaining global dominance over disparate lands and continents. "Distance," said a British official, is the "enemy of Imperial solidarity" and only advances in flight—like a giant airship—could bring "closer and more constant the unity of Imperial thought, Imperial intercourse, and Imperial ideals." Airships "will knit together," said another official, "the scattered peoples of the British Commonwealth."

At that time, Britain's Empire covered a quarter of the world and encompassed a fifth of its population. This great sweep included India, Canada, Australia, New Zealand, the Pacific islands, and a swath through the center of Africa—from South Africa through Rhodesia (today Zimbabwe) to Egypt. Communication across this vast area was, to many, the most significant existential threat to the Empire after the defeat of Germany and its allies in the First World War.

These postwar years were characterized by George Orwell as "the golden afternoon of the capitalist age." In that era, "almost every European," Orwell explained, "lived in the tacit belief that civilization would last forever … nothing would ever fundamentally change." For the politicians who sought to sustain and strengthen the Empire, the problems were, as one historian said, "a temporary and curable disorder."

Indeed, in 1924, as Britain planned a fleet of imperial airships, threats to the British Empire seemed feeble. In India, Gandhi was serving a six-year sentence for civil disobedience. In Germany, Hitler, guilty of high treason, also sat in a prison. The U.S.S.R. sputtered as Lenin lay ill and dying. To preserve the Empire, then, the British developed aviation to control the movement of mail, cargo, and people. It was a job for a grand airship instead of a feeble airplane. "An airplane," wrote one advocate for airships, "is little more than a very high-powered automobile with the mudguards extended laterally to provide surfaces for lifting itself off of the ground."

Airships far surpassed the planes of the day in range and lift. An airship could travel 2,500 miles before refueling, ten times as far as an airplane, and an airship lifted thirty or forty tons, while an airplane carried a single ton payload. With their great range and lift, airships could crisscross the Empire and move vast amounts of commodities, deliver tons of mail and parcels, and transport hundreds of citizens.

To serve the needs of Empire, the British began construction in 1927 on two airships. One, R.100, was built by private enterprise, although partly funded by the government; the other, R.101, was built directly by the government at their Royal Airship Works. The "R" in these names was short for "rigid" to indicate an airship rather than a blimp. These British ships surpassed in luxury the *Graf Zeppelin* and the American airship, *Akron*. Each featured a spacious lounge, a dining room that seated fifty, sleeping accommodations for about fifty passengers (although the original plans had called for one hundred), glass-walled promenade decks, and, in R.101, a smoking room. After the test flights each ship was assigned a long-distance demonstration flight to prove the prowess of airships: R.100 was to fly to Canada and R.101 to India, the latter the politically more important route.

India, said Prime Minister Disraeli in the late nineteenth century, was the "Jewel in the Crown." This alluded to the deep financial ties between Britain and India, ties which grew stronger in the twentieth century—£800 million invested in India from trade in rubber, coffee, indigo, tea, coal, and jute. Beyond the tangible financial links and the geopolitical importance of India,

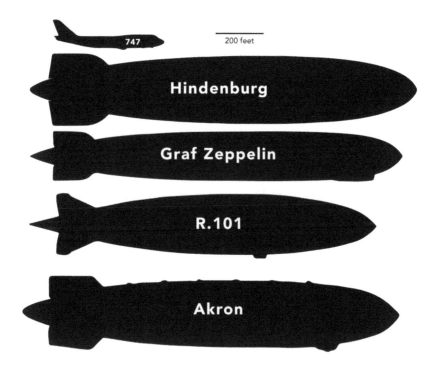

Relative Sizes of the Hindenburg, Graf Zeppelin,
HMA R.101, and USS Akron

In 1929 R.101 was the largest airship in the world. The Graf Zeppelin *(LZ 127), a contemporary of R.101, was forty feet longer but R.101 had a larger cross section and so held 30 percent more hydrogen — 4,893,740 cubic feet for R.101 versus 3,707,550 cubic feet for the* Graf Zeppelin. *The U.S. finished construction of the* Akron *after R.101 crashed. The* Akron *had a volume of 6,850,000 cubic feet, so was larger than R.101 and the* Graf Zeppelin. *The* Hindenburg *was larger than all of these ships, but was not built until 1938.*

the emotional bonds between the two cultures ran deep. By the 1920s, Indians were Members of Parliament, one even a Peer of the Realm, and the British public thrilled to the exploits of Indian cricket stars. And India permeated the psyche of Britain's upper class: the prominent Anglo-Indian families thought of themselves as having dual nationality. To sustain the bonds between the two countries, the British government assigned the India air route to R.101, considered to be more innovative than R.100.

R.100 was "no more than a rehash of the German [zeppelin] methods," said Britain's most prominent airship captain, Major G. H. Scott, "and therefore the last of an outdated form of construction." He celebrated R.101 as "of entirely novel design, embodying the latest and most up-to-date materials and engineering methods, and we regard it as the first of an entirely new series, and decided to use the number R.101, that is the first of a new series." The British expected R.101 to spearhead a fleet of imperial airships that would dominate the skies as British naval ships, a century earlier, had ruled the seas. Germany owned the commercial skies from Germany to the Americas—Berlin-to-Rio by zeppelin was de rigueur for any German of wealth and stature— but Britain had grand plans of maintaining its Empire around the globe, and the airship was central to those.

The interplay of engineering and commerce, of the careful methodology of the ship's builders and the reckless vision of politicians, of money, power, and global influence led to the tragedy of R.101. Although, in the end, the ingenuity and bravery of one person brought the dream of R.101 close to realization: Noel Atherstone the ship's First Officer.

The diaries of Atherstone, found after his death, illuminate the history of R.101 and enrich the pages of this book. Without his bravery, the ship may never have flown, and without his words we would not have as complete a record of the day-to-day struggles in creating R.101.

A colleague of R.101's officers and crew said of their work: it is "an example of admirable corporate courage which those who write airship history should appreciate and recognize and those who write for popular interest should respect."

I hope this book meets this standard.

His Majesty's Airship R.101

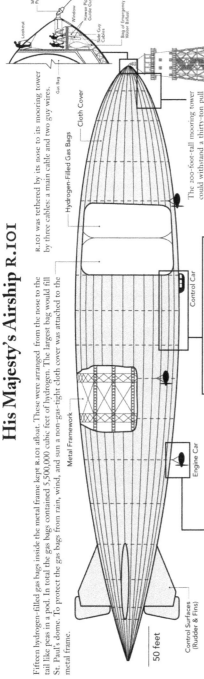

Fifteen hydrogen-filled gas bags inside the metal frame kept R.101 afloat. These were arranged from the nose to the tail like peas in a pod. In total the gas bags contained 5,500,000 cubic feet of hydrogen. The largest bag would fill St. Paul's dome. To protect the gas bags from rain, wind, and sun a non-gas-tight cloth cover was attached to the metal frame.

Five 650-horsepower engines in external cars powered R.101. They burned oil instead of gasoline because of fears that the high tropical temperatures along R.101's route to India would ignite the volatile gasoline. An engine operator was in the car at all times awaiting orders sent from the control car by telegraph. To enter the cars the operators used an open-air ladder.

R.101 was tethered by its nose to its mooring tower by three cables: a main cable and two guy wires.

The 200-foot-tall mooring tower could withstand a thirty-ton pull from the airship. The use of this tower by the British was a sharp contrast to the German zeppelins, which always landed on the ground.

A small control car and five engine cars were outside the ship's metal framework and cloth cover. The crew and passenger decks were inside the framework nestled under a gas bag. (*See facing page for details of these decks.*)

At the mooring tower the crew lowered a ventral hatch under R.101's nose and connected tower and airship by a flexible bridge with stairs. This bridge was on wheels so the airship could swing with the wind around the tower as passengers boarded. To reach the passenger deck, passengers walked along the bottom of the airship until they reached stairs just above the control car.

Lookout · Mooring Pendant · Main Cable · Hawser Pipes to Guide Guy Cables · Window · Side Guy Cables · Bag of Emergency Water Ballast

Gas Bag · Cloth Cover · Hydrogen-Filled Gas Bags · Control Car · Metal Framework · Engine Car · Control Surfaces (Rudder & Fins)

Passenger Deck · Crew Deck · Stairs

50 feet

Passenger Deck
Port
Viewing Windows

Sleeping Quarters

Forward

Promenade Deck

Lounge

Toilets

Dining Room

Promenade Deck

Viewing Windows
Starboard

Aft

The quarters were spartan: bunk beds, a small luggage stool for cabin bags, a small rug, and a note on the protocols of airship life that described how to summon a steward. The cabins were decorated in white and gold. They had no doors and only a Cambridge blue curtain, which saved weight but decreased privacy, already minimal because of the thin cloth walls. No exact layout exists for the cabins, but from an internal memo we know that there were twenty-six double-berth cabins, so sleeping accommodations for fifty-two passengers.

Crew Deck
Port

Stairs connecting decks

Officers' Cabins

Switch Room

Crew Wash

Officers' Cabins

Chart Room

Control Car

Forward

Radio

Galley

Pantry

Crew Cabins

Toilets

Crew Room

Crew Cabins

Aft

Starboard

The only section of the lower deck accessible to passengers was the smoking room. To keep it away from the hydrogen-filled gas bags, the smoking room was built in the lower deck, instead of the upper passenger deck. A ventilator on the ceiling created a higher pressure inside than outside, ensuring that no hydrogen could leak into the room. Its wood walls were layered with asbestos and covered with aluminum. No matches were allowed; only the electric lighters built into the furniture.

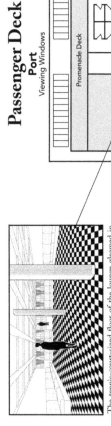

The tennis-court-sized floor of the lounge gleamed in the sunlight that poured in through giant windows port and starboard. Passengers could dance as a band played, or enjoy a drink while sitting on the built-in green-cushioned benches that lined the walls. Or, they could recline in one of the deep-blue wicker chairs scattered throughout. At the center of this drawing a small figure can be seen standing on one of the promenade decks.

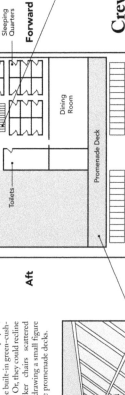

The promenade decks were hidden behind the built-in benches of the lounge both port and starboard. Through an opening at the center passengers entered the decks. On the deck they could lean against a waist-high railing and enjoy a stunning bird's-eye view of the ground through a wall of glass tilted at forty-five degrees.

PART I: THE AIRSHIP RISES

CHAPTER ONE

THE DEBUT OF THE
GREAT BRITISH AIRSHIP

OCTOBER 12, 1929

ALONG THE ROAD LEADING TO THE Royal Airship Works, forty-five miles north of London on the farmlands of the Bedfordshire Plain, 15,000 cars were jammed into 3,000 temporary spots earmarked for spectators. They arrived to watch Britain's huge new airship, R.101, emerge for the first time from its protective shed—a 4,000-ton building so immense that Westminster Abbey could be tucked into a corner, with room next to it for a football field. Between the cars threaded thousands of locals on motorcycles and bicycles, and hundreds more on foot.

Most had arrived long before sunrise; a few lit fires along the roadside and grilled bacon for breakfast as they waited for the debut of R.101. Latecomers were moved along by the local police stationed every hundred yards along the four miles of road closest to the Royal Airship Works, often referred to as the "Works" for short. Officers from nearby counties had been drafted in to help because the crowds arriving to view R.101 surpassed those at Britain's most popular horse races, the Derby and the Grand National, and exceeded the attendances at royal events. Spectators flocked from as far north as Newcastle and as far west as Swansea. They arrived in thousands of cars and hundreds of buses, weaving for miles through the gentle hills of Bedfordshire, forming a segmented black line that looked like a worm crawling along the countryside.

The fascination with R.101 reflected the people's love of machines, especially of those that tested the extremes of size and speed. They were eager to win the "triple crown" of land, sea, and air speed records. They rooted for Malcolm Campbell as he roared across the Pendine Sands in Wales at 146 miles per hour in his car, *Sunbeam*. They cheered on J. G. Parry-Thomas as he broke that record by reaching 178 miles per hour across the Sands, then gasped when his car's chain flew loose and it careened out of control, killing him. Britons celebrated when Henry Segrave set the world's water-speed record in his 1,000-horsepower *Golden Arrow*. Only a few years later, he died doing a hundred miles per hour in the *Miss England II*. When his boat crashed, he hung onto life long enough to ask his crew, "Did we do it?"

No machine fascinated the public as much, though, as anything that flew, and this enthusiasm for aviation was spurred by the press, especially the sensational *Daily Mail*. It declared that flying "was a new faculty, a new power … a fresh revolution—the greatest conceivable—in human transit …." The newspaper championed flight by offering cash to entice Britain's pilots to set world records. Their £10,000 prize in 1919 for the first transatlantic flight motivated Henry Hawker of the Sopwith Company to try the crossing—Lindbergh wouldn't achieve that feat solo until 1927. On a clear day in May 1919, Hawker and his copilot prepared their Sopwith plane by straining its oil six times, then packed two sandwiches and a thermos of coffee. As they took off from Newfoundland for the Irish coast, *Daily Mail* readers waited with anticipation for news of their arrival. When Hawker and his copilot disappeared, the newspaper bombarded readers with daily headlines: "Still No News, Gravest Fears Entertained," followed by "Small Hopes for Hawker." A few days later, the paper screamed in a banner headline, "HAWKER SAFE!" The plane had crashed five hours into its flight, and a steamer without radio had rescued Hawker and his copilot. This sensational news bumped off the front page the recently signed Treaty of Versailles.

The latest aviation sensation was R.101, the largest craft in the world—almost a third larger than its rival, Germany's *Graf Zeppelin*, which had launched in 1928. The British read in the press of the certain triumph of R.101. *The World Today*—"An Illustrated Magazine of National Efficiency and Social Progress"—proclaimed in a headline that "His Majesty's Airship R.101" was a "Triumph of Aeronautical Design." The airship was, the magazine declared, "a modern magic carpet of tangible and progressive reality," which "easily eclipses everything of this kind that has been attempted." The *Illustrated London News* printed lavish two-page spreads about R.101, often featuring an overwrought "artist's impression" of the mighty airship.

No detail was too recondite to be celebrated. The *Illustrated News* called it "a marvel of engineering skill and a beautiful example of British craftsmanship." The popular magazine *Flight* remarked on the "simplicity of the joints" that held together "His Majesty's Airship." And now, after five years of planning and construction, the public would finally see, this autumn morning in 1929, the new wonder of aviation.

Inside the mammoth shed, First Officer Noel Atherstone leaned out of a hatch above the nose of R.101. The ship floated only a few feet above the floor of its shed, but Atherstone's perch was eighty feet above the ground. To brace himself for the imminent movement of the airship, he pressed his hips against the hatch's rim, then grasped the edge of the opening. His fingers slipped on the plasticized cloth comprising the outer surface of the airship, so he tightened his grip. The fresh coating on the cover emitted a slightly acidic odor, almost like banana oil, although to Atherstone it smelled of vinegar and burned in his nose. No matter; he had to concentrate on the task at hand—the safe departure of R.101 from its giant shed.

When the 470-ton fortress-like hangar doors opened, Atherstone felt a slight breeze. He worried that as R.101 exited, a wind gust would smash the ship into the shed's door frame and destroy the airship even before its first flight—the fate, eight years earlier, in 1921, of one of R.101's five predecessors. (See Appendix A.) He and the builders of R.101 had worked furiously for five years to get to this day, and the pride of the British Empire relied on this first small step of safe transit from the shed to the mooring tower.

The only sounds in the shed were the rattle of the pull chains from the hand-powered winches used to open the doors and the grunts of the six men operating the winches. As the doors parted, light spilled from the brightly lit shed into the predawn darkness. Inside, the 732-foot-long airship floated lightly, a few feet off the ground. Its new coating, infused with aluminum particles, gleamed silver, the hull a shiny contrast with the dark floor of the shed. R.101's immensity, when viewed from the floor of the shed, nearly the largest building in the British Empire, often induced dizziness in first-time visitors. The graceful lines of the cigar-shaped ship guided everyone's gaze to its rounded nose, exposed through the opened doors. Up front and high up, Atherstone prepared himself for the ship's movement as the echo of the door winch chains faded. The ship was now ready to emerge and the shed fell silent.

A shrill whistle broke the silence. From the floor of the shed, Major George Scott, a senior official at the Royal Airship Works, lifted his megaphone and commanded in a calm voice: "Walk the ship forward." Four hundred men began to tug the floating ship into the dawn. Two hundred of them had spent the last four years building the ship, a full three years longer than expected; the ship's completion had been promised, in the words of a frustrated observer, "between 1926 and the Day of Judgment." The rest of the men were soldiers from a nearby Royal Air Force base or locals from a labor exchange—the latter earned one shilling and sixpence an hour, about thirty-five cents. One cluster of men gripped a metal lattice on the control car, the lowest part of the ship, which was protected by a temporary wicker-basket "bumper." Another group held grips on each of the five exterior engine cars; most, though, tugged on ropes tied to the ship from nose to tail.

R.101, powered only by the men walking it forward, moved through the doorway at a brisk 200 feet a minute—more than two miles an hour. The doorframe was only twenty-five feet wider than the ship on each side, so R.101 had to pass straight through the center of the opening. As the men hauled the floating ship toward the shed's doors, Atherstone gazed at the white guidelines painted on the grass outside the doorway. From his perch atop the ship, he sighted down the nose and watched its alignment with the centerline; he stood ready to shout orders if the airship deviated from this path. Two lines on the outside marked the edges of the ship and guided the men tugging on the ropes. Those underneath clutching the frame of the control car followed the centerline, while staring at a shot-filled white bag that dangled from the ship's nose. They kept this plumb line dead over the centerline as they walked the ship forward.

Everyone stayed mute, as Atherstone, a former Royal Navy officer and a strict taskmaster, had reminded the crew at every drill over the last eleven days of the cardinal rule for airship-handling crews: silence is golden. In three and a half minutes the ship's giant rudder, ten times taller than the tail fin of a Boeing 747, cleared the doorframe, missing the top of the opening by a mere twenty feet. When the ship's tail left the shed, a crew member at the rear of the craft shouted to Major Scott: "All clear, sir!"

Outside for the first time, R.101 looked in the gray half-light of dawn like a silver cloud hovering near the ground. As the mighty airship floated in the open air just above their heads, the crew roared in unison, releasing their pent-up emotions. This enthusiastic outburst even comforted the stoic Atherstone, enforcer of crew discipline, as this small success brought him closer to his dream of the last ten years: to captain a giant airship. He hoped to take full command of R.101 when its current captain was promoted to the next airship to be built; the Works planned to construct a behemoth with twice the volume of R.101.

These airships would run a regular service from England to India. In only a few months, if all went to plan, R.101 would fly to Karachi, India as its long-distance demonstration flight. First, though, the ship must safely arrive at its mooring tower.

In preparation for R.101's movement to its mooring tower a half-mile away, Atherstone climbed down a fifteen-foot ladder, careful not to bump the delicate gas bag only a foot away. The outer cloth cover protected the gas bags from inclement weather, but inside the bags were exposed and so, from time to time, a careless worker put a foot through one. Atherstone stepped from the ladder onto the winch platform at the ship's nose, glanced to be sure the three crew members there were ready to pay out cable when the ship reached its mooring tower, then scurried down a short ladder to the interior gangway that ran along the bottom of the ship. As he walked, the floor flexed below him; to reduce the ship's weight, the floors were three-ply wood stiffened with spruce, although visitors walking on them for the first time often feared they would break through and plummet to the ground. When Atherstone reached the middle of the ship, he shot down another short ladder into the control car, slung under the ship.

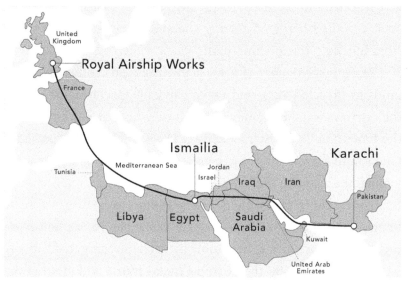

R.101's Proposed Route to India

R.101 was assigned the politically important route from Great Britain to India. It was to fly this route in two legs. The first leg was from the Royal Airship Works, forty-five miles north of London, to Ismailia, Egypt, where the ship would moor at a British-built mooring tower. This leg was about 2,600 statute miles and took forty to fifty hours depending on the wind. After refueling and refilling the gas bags with hydrogen, R.101 would then fly over Iraq and near Iran to land at Karachi. At the time Karachi was part of India, but today it is in Pakistan. This leg was about 2,800 statute miles and would take fifty-five to sixty hours. Karachi was chosen over Bombay (modern day Mumbai) because Karachi was near sea level, where increased atmospheric pressure would allow for more lift. At Karachi the British had built another mooring tower and a shed. This shed was the largest building in the British Empire. This map shows current country names.

He took his place next to his superior officer, R.101's captain, H. Carmichael Irwin.

Still powered only by the handling party, the whale-like ship moved crabwise at a stately one mile per hour across the flat 300-acre field next to the shed. At the field's edge, a farmer on horseback corralled herds of grazing sheep and cattle to keep them from blocking the airship's path.

The eerie movement of R.101 across the field caused the thousands of bicycles, cars, and buses carrying spectators to halt as their drivers watched spellbound. Those who had gathered along the fence since predawn looked on in awe. They all expected a loud sound from an object so large—next to it the handling party looked like a swarm of busy ants—yet the ship emitted no noise. Its vastness contrasted with its weightlessness to create a dissonant image—the ship floated, as one observer put it, "as lightly as thistledown." R.101 was held aloft by fifteen hydrogen-filled gas bags, arranged inside the airship's metal frame and cloth cover like peas in a pod, running from bow to stern. (See figure, page 12.) The largest bag would fill St. Paul's dome; the smallest a tenth the volume, yet could still lift a ton. The bags contained enough hydrogen that a single spark could ignite the gas and destroy the ship and its shed.

Flammable hydrogen seems a poor choice for an airship, compared to inert helium, yet for a commercial airship, hydrogen is the *only* choice. The lighter hydrogen lifts more weight than helium. Substituting helium for hydrogen in R.101 would cut the payload by nearly 50 percent: the airship could lift its crew, but not fuel, passengers, or baggage. Beyond the loss of lift, helium's cost prohibited its use on a large scale. For Britain to buy the five million cubic feet of helium needed to inflate R.101 would cost about £180,000, a huge sum in 1929. To extract helium from natural gas required expensive distillation plants near the gas wells.

The largest gas fields, and so the largest supply of helium, were in Kansas, Oklahoma, and Texas. So, not only would the Works have to buy the helium from the U.S., they would have to pay to have it shipped to Britain. In contrast, hydrogen was manufactured cheaply and on-site at the Works from steam. Five million cubic feet cost £2,500.

Although today we fixate on the dangers of hydrogen, to those building and flying airships in the 1920s, the dangers were over-rated. "To the uninstructed mind," said one of the engineers designing R.101, "danger of fire in airships is generally thought to be due to the presence of hydrogen." The fuel on board was more deadly, he went on: "If the fate of an airship carrying from twenty to fifty tons of briskly burning petrol, whether inflated with hydrogen or helium, is contemplated, it will be readily real-ized that the advantages in the use of helium are not so obvious as would at first sight appear." An officer of R.100 noted that:

> The thought of potential danger [from hydrogen] never entered my head, nor, I think that of any other airship pilots or crews. If it had, I doubt if any of us would have ventured to fly. Of course in the back of our minds we were aware of its presence and took all precautions against risk of fire. Does anyone nowadays think of the potential danger from fire in the petrol in the tank of their motor car—one does not, of course, light a match to see if there is any in the tank.

Atherstone had earlier that day enforced all the proper precau-tions: no hobnailed boots, only rubber-soled shoes that could not spark; no smoking, although he craved a cigarette; and no mo-torized vehicles within four miles of the field.

As the airship traversed the field, Atherstone, still riding in the glass-paneled control car, watched the ground a few feet below. He remained at full alert because, in transit, a single gust of wind against the five and a half acres of R.101's cloth cover—a surface area more than one hundred times that of a 737's wings—could smash the ship into the ground and destroy its metal framework.

Suddenly the ship plunged, its nose descending toward the ground. Captain Irwin glanced above his head at the gauges that reported the pressures in the ship's fifteen gas bags. A rear gas bag contained more hydrogen than those near the front, so Irwin actuated a valve on the errant gas bag to release its excess hydrogen. In seconds, the ship righted itself. Irwin's rapid response impressed Atherstone, even though he had observed Irwin's skill as a pilot many times in the First World War.

In the war, the two men had patrolled the Channel in an airship about a fifth the size of R.101, on the lookout for U-boats. Irwin had served, like now, as captain and Atherstone as first officer. They worked well together despite their contrasting temperaments: Irwin was sensitive, warm, his emotions rising quickly to the surface, but always with a ready smile; Atherstone, introspective and often tough on his men. They contrasted also in appearance: Carmichael "Bird" Irwin was a tall, athletic Irishman with the reddest of hair and pinkest of skin, less than a year older than the thirty-four-year-old Atherstone; Noel "Grabby" Atherstone was a smaller man with rounded shoulders and Slavic complexion. (The nickname Grabby was derived from his original last name— Grabowsky; when he married he had taken his wife's last name.) Now, eleven years later, these two singularly talented wartime pilots worked in peacetime as a team to test and pilot this giant airship that would connect the far-flung dominions, mandates, and states of the British Empire.

Twenty minutes after leaving its shed, the airship neared the dome-capped mooring tower built in the middle of the field far from any buildings. At the top of this 200-foot tower, R.101 would be tethered by its nose, free to rotate with the wind around the tower head. The ship halted a few feet from the tower's base and crew members on the ground removed the wicker basket protecting the control car. To prepare for mooring, the spry Atherstone returned to the ship's nose, climbing from the control car to the ship's walkway and back up a ladder.

Major Scott, who had walked along the ground on the airship's low journey across the field, opened the door to the control car, the wicker basket now gone, and tried to haul himself in to join Captain Irwin. The door's threshold was just a few feet off the ground, but Scott, a small, pudgy man, struggled to get in. Only a few years earlier, he had been a boisterous boyish-looking man—he threw the best parties at the Works—but now, age forty-one, he had a paunch, pasty white skin, and dark circles under his eyes.

When Atherstone arrived in the nose cone, he was pleased that his crew had already paid out the ship's mooring cables: one main cable to hook to the top of the tower and two guy wires to pass through large eyelets on the ground. He leaned over the forward-most winch and looked at the ground through a window under the ship's nose. Outside, two members of the ground crew joined the ship's main cable to the twenty-five-ton tower cable, while others connected the guy wires. Once the cable was secured, Atherstone drew a voice pipe in close and told Irwin, in the control car, that R.101 was ready to ascend. Atherstone pressed the voice pipe close to his ear and waited for an acknowledgment in Irwin's Irish lilt. He heard, instead, the soft voice of Major Scott—he often sounded almost embarrassed to be speaking. Atherstone abhorred this interference. Irwin, the ship's captain, should be in charge.

The First World War had drilled into Atherstone the necessity of a proper chain of command. Before teaming up with Captain Irwin in a larger patrol airship, he had flown a small military blimp, a hundredth the size of R.101. He had searched the English Channel for subtle signs of German U-boats: the distinctive feather wake of a periscope, traces of oil, or a gathering of gulls. One of his fellow pilots described the work as "utter boredom"; yet the monotonous patrols, often conducted in foul weather, hardened Atherstone mentally and physically. They molded him into "a calm, cool, analytical man," as one of his colleagues at the Works observed, "much respected by his fellows, but a bit tough," and taught him the need for order, routine, and a clear chain of command. Major Scott had violated this code by pulling rank on Captain Irwin.

Soon after his message was acknowledged, Atherstone felt the ship jerk as water ballast poured from a vent two or three feet below him. Thus lightened, the ship inched up, its rate of ascent increasing as it rose. Atherstone wanted the airship to float high above the tower's top so the main cable would not entangle itself with the tower.

There was a problem: at the tower's top, 200 feet above the ground, R.101 halted. To continue its rise, Scott or Irwin in the control car—Atherstone couldn't be sure—discharged more ballast. The water spread into a fine mist; it sparkled in the early morning light. As he listened to the rush of the draining water, Atherstone timed its rate of discharge—too slow for an emergency. The first blast of ballast having been discharged, he waited for the ship to rise. It didn't budge. Another half-ton burst. Still, no motion. A half-ton more, then another half-ton of water, which, by then, had drenched the crew below. Finally, the nose slowly rose and the main cable between ship and tower lifted from the ground. R.101 crept to 600 feet above the ground—400 feet above the tower head.

Atherstone relaxed momentarily, the most perilous stage of the ship's journey complete. A crucial step in the mooring was done, but another vital maneuver remained to be completed successfully.

The British Empire's newest airship was now in its element, safely floating high in the scarlet morning sky, flecked with clouds of pale gold. In that light, the airship's metallic egg-shaped engine cars glittered as if on fire; its shiny cover refracted the early morning sunlight into a rainbow of colors.

From this height, Atherstone surveyed the entire grounds of the Royal Airship Works. A half-mile away sat shed NO. 1, which R.101 had just left, and next to it the slightly larger shed NO. 2. A quarter-mile farther on, on a small hill, stood the red-brick buildings that housed the drawing office, the paint shop that created the plastic coating for the ship's cover, and the fabric shop where hundreds of women constructed the ship's gas bags. He gazed at the horizon, marveling at the size of the crowds who had come out to see this magnificent creation.

Atherstone's reverie was cut short by the roar of the starboard forward engine.

To carry passengers, the airship had to be winched in closer to the tower and attached, so that passengers and crew could walk along a gangway from near the top of the tower into the airship; unlike German zeppelins, the British didn't load their giant airships from the ground.

First, R.101 had to pull the cable taut. The force from the propeller drew the airship away from the tower, which could withstand a thirty-ton pull: each of the tower's four legs was embedded in a piece of concrete twelve feet square buried six feet into the ground. As the ship backed up, Atherstone inspected, through the nose cone window, a metal bowl-shaped pendant threaded on the main cable. It dangled from the ship's nose and rattled as it knocked against the ship's underside. When the cable between the ship and the tower became taut, the pendant hung a few feet from the ship's nose. Atherstone sighted along the taut cable to a telescopic arm at the tower head. Attached to this arm was a cup, the female counterpart of the cone. Through the center of this cup the main cable was threaded; when the tower's cup mated with the ship's cone—separated now by 400 feet—R.101 would be moored.

To begin this step of the mooring, the tower crew ran up a white signal flag to alert Atherstone in the nose and Irwin in the control car that they would soon haul in the ship. On the tower a gong clanged. At the tower's base, three steam-powered winches, one for each cable, pulled the ship toward the tower. Every twenty seconds, the winch drew R.101 fifteen feet closer. In about ten minutes, when the pendant on R.101's main cable was fifty feet from the tower head's cup, the winches pulling on the yaw guy wires were stopped and the main winch slowed to a crawl. The steel pendant inched toward the cup on the telescopic arm, until the pendant pushed back spring-loaded latches in the cup with a crisp snap—a sound Atherstone thought "most gratifying."

Finally, three men, clinging like flies to the telescopic arm, inserted heavy locking pins to secure the airship. Once it was locked in, a small motor shortened the arm to a length of eight feet and righted it to vertical. Atherstone and his crew in the cone stood motionless and quiet. Atherstone pressed his ear to the voice pipe.

"Ship secured," Irwin said.

Atherstone ordered his crew to drop the ventral hatch under R.101's nose. This transformed the airship into a silver sky-whale with its mouth agape, ready to bite the tower a few feet away. To close this gap, the tower crew extended a flexible bridge to the airship, which connected it to the passenger platform, a large disk forty feet in diameter, covered in thick steel plate, textured to keep passengers from slipping during inclement weather. As passengers boarded the airship across the narrow bridge, they had a chill-inducing view of the ground 170 feet below. Yet their boarding could be even more thrilling: wheels on the bottom of the bridge allowed it to revolve around the tower as the ship swung with the wind.

For the rest of the day Atherstone supervised the final steps of mooring. He kept careful watch as his crew connected the water main, fuel, and hydrogen lines. He reminded them to ground the ship before plugging in the electrical cables and stringing the leads to the control car for the portable telephone—one could dial Bedford 2255 and ring R.101.

Atherstone followed the telephone leads through the corridor that ran along the ship's belly until he arrived at the control car. From there he watched workers connect the four "garden roller" ballasts that lay on the field below—cylindrical tubes with an axle along their long axis. As the ship moved around the tower, these ballasts rolled on the field below, stabilizing it against updrafts.

In the evening, Atherstone turned R.101 over to a small crew of half a dozen or so, the minimum needed to maintain the ship when locked at the tower. His work done for the day, he headed home to his wife, two children, and his German shepherd, "Tim."

As Atherstone left the Works, he glanced back at R.101. It gleamed silver in the setting sun. At the tower the ship would safely swing, roll, rise and fall with the wind. To him the ship rode "beautifully" at the mast, yet he knew much hard work lay ahead—just that day he had learned that the NO. 3 gas bag leaked, the cloth covering on the fins fluttered too much, and the water ballast discharged too slowly. Yet he felt everything was coming together: the mooring gear worked well, the ship's cloth cover stayed intact and even his crew "was beginning to shake down very quickly"—he always feared what he called a "secondhand" crew."

That night he jotted in his journal: "Very tired but happy about the ship as she promises well."

The Mooring Tower at the Royal Airship Works

Major Scott's invention of the mooring tower, shortly after the First World War, paved the way for the giant commercial airships Britain planned to build. As airships grew to the size of R.101, ground landing became more difficult, although Germany always used ground landings for its zeppelins. Scott's mooring tower solved all of the problems of landing an airship. First, it reduced the number of people required to land the airship to around twenty. Second, it enable the airship to land or depart in almost any weather, thus eliminating the need for expensive revolving sheds. Third, the tower provided an easy way to supply the airship with water, fuel, and gas. The Cardington mooring tower could withstand a thirty-ton pull at its top. Each of its four legs was embedded in a piece of concrete about twelve feet square that extended six feet into the ground. This anchored the tower with a force of sixty tons. At the base were three large winches, one for each of the cables used to haul in the airship. With drums five feet in diameter, oil-fired and steam-driven, they could pull in a fifteen-ton load at fifty feet per minute. The ground crew controlled them from the top of the tower, but there were duplicate controls at the base in case of failure at the top. Up the center core of the tower ran pipes up to a foot in diameter to deliver hydrogen, water, and fuel. Huge pumps at the base could lift 5,000 gallons of water per hour and pump fuel at 2,000 gallons per minute from the 10,000-gallon tank buried in the ground near the tower. At the tower's top a circular dome-capped steel turret, twenty-five feet in diameter and a little over twelve feet high enclosed an arm, which attached to the airship. The arm telescoped, from sixteen to twenty-four feet in length, could swing thirty degrees from vertical and rotate a full 360 degrees around the tower. This motion allowed the ground crew to position the arm as the winches hauled in the airship. The ship could spin around the arm's vertical axis, enabling the ship to ride with the wind.

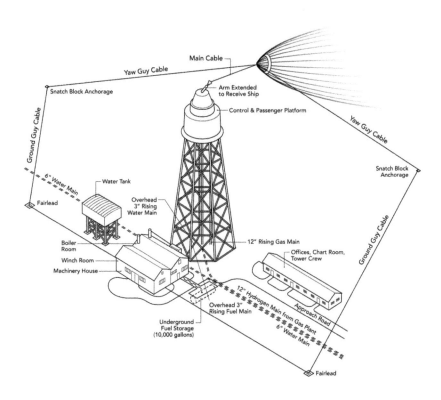

Main Cable

Yaw Guy Cable

Snatch Block Anchorage

Arm Extended
to Receive Ship

Control & Passenger Platform

Ground Guy Cable

Yaw Guy Cable

Snatch Block
Anchorage

6" Water Main

Water Tank

Overhead
3" Rising
Water Main

Fairlead

Ground Guy Cable

12" Rising Gas Main

Boiler
Room

Offices, Chart Room,
Tower Crew

Winch Room

Machinery House

12" Hydrogen Main from Gas Plant

Approach Road

Underground
Fuel Storage
(10,000 gallons)

Overhead 3"
Rising Fuel Main

6" Water Main

Fairlead

AIRBORNE AT LAST

OCTOBER 14–15, 1929

TWO DAYS LATER, RELEASED FROM ITS tight bond to the tower, R.101 tugged on its mooring cable as it floated 600 feet above its tower at the Royal Airship Works. In the ship's nose cone, First Officer Atherstone pressed his ear close to the voice pipe waiting for orders from the control car. The voice pipe's sound quality vexed him—"rotten," he called it; he wished the ship used internal telephones instead. When Major Scott's muffled command of "slip" echoed from the voice pipe, Atherstone nodded at his crew and they released the mooring cable.

At 11:17 a.m., R.101 began its first flight. As the ship rose, the ground crew waved their hats and cried, "Good luck to you boys!" Many reporters yelled, "Good luck Scottie!" in honor of Major Scott. The airship drifted in the wind for a moment before a midship engine roared to life. Powered by this single engine, the majestic R.101 circled at a speed of thirty knots around the Works. From the nose cone, Atherstone watched R.101's shadow flicker on the ground, then swell to full size as the departing ship passed over a cloud; the shadow's edges shimmered with miniature rainbows. How different this ride was from one in an airplane, where the scenery zipped by, a blur vignetted in a tiny window; in a slow-moving, low-flying airship one had time to see the details.

The airship expanded its circular path, passing over a forest. Atherstone could see treetops and hear the rustling of the trees because R.101 produced so little noise—another sharp contrast with an airplane ride. The ship rose to 1,200 feet as it flew over nearby Bedford, where schoolchildren waved their handkerchiefs in greeting. A second engine started up and the ship inched its way higher. At a height of 2,000 feet, Atherstone heard the metallic click of a valve, and a hiss as hydrogen vented from the gas bag behind him. R.101 had reached its maximum altitude.

This maximum, called the "pressure height," was set by the size of R.101's gas bags and how full they were at ground level. An airship's gas bags expand as the ship rises because the atmospheric pressure drops. At a particular altitude, the pressure height, the thin bags will burst. To prevent this catastrophe, each gas bag on R.101 was fit with a valve that automatically vented hydrogen at 2,000 feet. An airship could fly higher, but at the expense of payload. For every additional 1,000 feet of altitude designed into R.101, the airship lost five tons of lift—lift to haul the Empire's citizens and goods around the globe. So R.101's gas bags were filled at ground level to 90 percent of their total volume and sized to expand to 100 percent volume at about 3,500 feet. The valves triggered at 2,000 feet to add a safety margin; if turbulent weather forced the ship to rise, the valves had time to vent.

The ship, now at its pressure height, continued widening its circular path with each circuit. On this first flight, Scott and Irwin were flying the ship to London, then Atherstone would pilot the return trip. So, for the first hour of flight, he investigated every inch of R.101. From the nose cone, he worked his way to the back of the ship along the bottom walkway, inspecting crew members at their stations to ensure they didn't become "secondhand." The crew wore the regulation rubber-soled shoes, white sweaters, and dark-brown overalls—another source of frustration for Atherstone. Months earlier he had requested uniforms to raise crew morale, but the senior staff of the Works had turned this suggestion "down flat."

He also examined the parachutes stowed along the corridor; he was proud of their quick-release hangers, which he'd improvised from a piece of metal tubing and some string. He looked above him at the bottom of the giant gas bags that lined the top of the walkway and watched for a moment their gentle rocking. Between two of the bags he noticed the small, gaunt figure of Michael Rope, the Works' engineering genius, who had designed the wire netting that tethered the bags to the ship's framework. Not a soul at the Works "knew more" than Rope, said one of his colleagues, "about R.101 and about the mechanics of handling an airship than anyone else in Britain." He now observed the wire netting in flight for the first time.

As Atherstone continued his tour, R.101's engine expert, Harry Leech, rushed past; Atherstone glimpsed only Leech's hallmark round-rimmed glasses—the jovial engineer resembled silent comedian Harold Lloyd. Leech shuttled among R.101's five engine cars as he tended to the ship's temperamental engines. The newly developed 650-horsepower engines burned oil instead of gasoline because of fears that the high tropical temperatures along R.101's route to India would ignite the volatile gasoline. The oil, in contrast, combusted only when heated to the temperature of boiling water. These predecessors of today's diesel engines were finicky, so Leech had to nurse them throughout the flights, although this was nothing new to him. He had maintained airship engines since he joined the Airship Section of the Royal Naval Air Service in 1916. He had begun by servicing the engines on the small military blimps Atherstone employed for sea patrols and graduated to the larger airships used at the end of the First World War. He survived two crashes in those larger ships. Although keeping the engines running was a high-pressure job, he sought more demanding assignments; he often asked for leave to work with Malcolm Campbell, a British driver who set land-speed records. On and off from 1921 to 1925, Leech was Campbell's mechanic, alongside Leo Villa. The two men installed and maintained an aircraft engine in Campbell's car *Sunbeam*—"the most pampered car in the world," declared the *Daily Mail*—and stood by like faithful valets ready to attend to the car's needs. With pride, Leech listened to the finely tuned engine as Campbell, in 1924, roared at a record 146.16 miles per hour across the Pendine Sands in South Wales. "I owe more," declared Campbell, "than it is possible to express to the loyal work of Villa and Leech."

On the day of R.101's first flight, the shuttling Leech headed to one of the engine cars and left Atherstone alone on the walkway, standing still and listening to the ship and feeling its motion. The lack of vibration or creaking of the framework impressed him. He continued to the rear, tucked his hat under his arm, climbed a short ladder and shimmied into the rear observation post at the tail of the ship. The post was a vertical tube, barely larger than Atherstone's shoulders. With the wind whipping past him at forty miles per hour, he rested his arms on the tube and gazed at the horizon, the giant airship hidden from view behind him: he felt as if he were on a small platform in space. He turned around, looked past the sixty-seven-foot-tall rudder and over the rear fins, and watched the ship's cloth cover. It never budged—no flapping, fluttering, or, God forbid, ripping—so he declared the cover "wonderfully good." He returned to the walkway and headed to the control car. The ship, he concluded, was "immensely strong"; he felt "security, even confidence" in it. Perhaps, Atherstone thought, the knives he had issued each crew member—by his orders they dangled from each man's waist—had been overcautious. In an emergency, they were to cut R.101's fabric cover, grab the nearest parachute, and jump.

As Atherstone arrived in the control car, Major Scott ordered a third engine powered up. R.101 now cruised at fifty-eight miles per hour. In a half-hour the airship approached the distinctive white clock tower of the glass-covered Metropolitan Cattle Market, a favorite landmark north of London among airship pilots: no one could miss the thirty-acre complex of merchants, pubs, and banks. Ten minutes later, R.101 arrived over London, where Scott ordered the stern engine shut off to slow the airship. He intended to "give them [Londoners] one good look."

Scott started his journey over the West End. The traffic noise drowned the sound of the airship's engines—if all were quiet on the ground one could hear a rhythmic clanking from the slow-moving propellers, rather than a hum as from a rapidly rotating airplane propeller—yet word of the airship's arrival spread and soon the shops of Soho emptied and rooftops filled with people. Three airplanes carrying reporters buzzed around the airship. Their pilots had to dive, climb, and turn to travel slowly enough to keep pace with the airship, which moved at only forty miles per hour. Even the Prince of Wales zipped by in his sporty De Havilland Gypsy Moth.

Like a huge silver fish soaring through the sky, R.101 glided over Buckingham Palace, flew over Piccadilly Circus, and then over Trafalgar Square and Nelson's Column—Atherstone could even make out the details of the *chelengk*, the Turkish military decoration, on Nelson's hat. Scott then steered R.101 past the Houses of Parliament and over Gwydyr House, where Lord Thomson, the Air Minister, abandoned the bureaucratic papers piled on his desk, ascended the stairs to the roof and watched R.101 fly above. At six foot five—even taller today with his

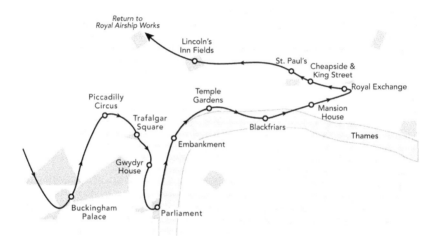

Route of R.101 on its First Flight over London

R.101's London route was carefully chosen for political reasons. It flew over Parliament, the Air Ministry, and Mansion House, the Mayor of London's residence. Scott and Irwin together commanded the ship over London; as it left the city to return to the Royal Airship Works, Atherstone took the helm.

Homburg hat—and dressed in a perfectly tailored suit, Thomson was as stately as the airship itself. He carried himself with an aristocratic bearing that, noted an observer, "lent a grace and distinction to everything he touched." This aura, he hoped, would be transferred to R.101.

Thomson staked his political career on an "all-red girdle of air transport" that reached "more than halfway round the earth"—red was the striking color of Empire territories on official maps. His chance to carry out this vision occurred when the left-leaning Labour Party came to power in 1924. When he became Air Minister in the new government, Thomson extended Labour's election slogan of "nationalization of railways, mines, shipping and electric power" to airship construction, and tried to shut down a scheme approved a month before the election by the outgoing Conservative government. They planned to build an airship, called R.100, by subsidizing a private manufacturer. This arrangement violated Labour's principles, yet their coalition partners refused to stop R.100. Undeterred, Thomson devised a hybrid scheme: the government would supervise the building of the "capitalist" R.100, but would also build a "government" ship, named R.101.

To prove their worth, each sibling ship was to fly a demonstration flight: R.100 to Canada and R.101 to India, the latter the politically more important route. The two ships were planned and built simultaneously, but R.101 took to the air first, while R.100 waited in a shed at the Howden Airship Works for its turn at the Royal Airship Works' tower, the only tower in Britain.

Thomson promoted these airships, which he called "my children," in florid speeches. "I can foresee," he said when introducing his airship scheme in the House of Lords,

> the time when noble Lords will leave this House and the terrace in gliders with light engines, winging their way westward along the valley of the Thames, northward to Scotland, and southwards

to Hampshire, Berkshire and Kent. On their way—and this is my main point—they will need to rest, perhaps in some great caravanserai in order to take a rest or greet a friend, and that great caravanserai may be one of the giant airships floating serene and safe high up and far removed from terrestrial dirt and noise.

Thomson spoke so often like this that *The Aeroplane*, an aviation magazine, wryly called his after-dinner speeches the "outstanding success" of his work as Air Minister. This sly comment hinted at Thomson's lack of aeronautical knowledge or training. This deficiency resulted in extravagant claims for R.101: he suggested often, for example, that it could fly in any weather. And this weakness also displayed itself in his sense of how fast airships could be built and how little they had to be tested.

He shocked Atherstone with an accelerated timeline for R.101's demonstration flight to India. On a tour of the airship four months before this first flight, Thomson had told Atherstone and his crew: "Before so very long, I look forward to the day when we shall fly together down the old route of Marco Polo to India." This was typical Thomson grandiloquence. By the time his visit ended, Atherstone learned that "before so very long" meant December 1929—four months from this first flight, a rapid timeline for a never flown, never tested R.101 to be ready for a transcontinental journey.

From Britain's capital, R.101 flew up the Thames, passing over large crowds at Embankment and Temple Gardens. At Blackfriars, ships and tugs tooted their horns and, from the nearby railway yards, engineers blew the whistles of their locomotives. Then R.101 turned north at Mansion House, and west once over the Royal Exchange. The ship stopped traffic on King Street and Cheapside, then dwarfed the mighty dome of St. Paul's as it hovered there for a moment, where a blood-red ray broke through the gray clouds and reflected off the ship's specular nose. At two in the afternoon, soon after R.101 passed over St. Paul's, Scott pointed its nose north toward the Royal Airship Works. He headed to lunch in the ship's dining room—a meal of mutton, potatoes, cabbage, fruit salad, cheese and coffee—and turned over command to Atherstone. Atherstone had waited eleven years to command a giant airship.

When the First World War ended in 1918, Atherstone longed to pilot a commercial airship, to use the skills he'd honed in flying small military blimps and airships. His dream faded as British efforts to pioneer airships foundered. Between 1919 and 1921 Britain spent two million pounds to build six airships for commercial, instead of military, air service—a large sum in a time when a laborer earned about £230 a year. Three of these airships were destroyed in accidents, another showed metal fatigue so was scrapped, and the final two were too small for commercial use and were also scrapped. (These attempts are briefly described in Appendix A.)

By 1921, the British government mothballed the Royal Airship Works and stopped all airship production. So, with no airships planned, Atherstone emigrated to Australia. For a year he worked in Gippsland for a farmer, then, soon after his first child, a son, was born, Atherstone farmed on his own for two years. Next he moved to Melbourne, where his second child, a daughter, was born. He worked as the assistant sales manager of Corbett, Derham & Company and sold radios until the firm failed. Unable to find work, he served a month as a radio operator on an expedition to central Australia. When he returned to Melbourne, he sold telephones, and, when he was laid off from that job, he sold bonds to plant forests in New Zealand.

And then, in 1927, Britain concluded that, after all, airships were *the* way to link the territory of its colossal Empire. In anticipation of the rise of British airships, Atherstone was hired by the

Civil Aviation Branch, Australian Defence Department as "Inspector (for duties with Airship Mission)." He was to assist this mission—a British delegation—when they visited Australia in late June. They had already toured Gambia, Kenya, Sierra Leone, Singapore, Ceylon (today Sri Lanka), and South Africa and were to spend four or five weeks in Australia, before heading to New Zealand. In each country they surveyed sites for mooring towers, documented meteorological conditions, and, most importantly, they proselytized for airships, hoping to excite the public and entice governments to finance the construction of towers. To generate interest prior to the mission's arrival in Australia, Atherstone lectured at the Constitutional Club of Melbourne. Airships, he told his audience, would connect Melbourne to London in a mere ten days via a base in India. The cost would be no more than that of a first-class steamer: only ten pounds. He described how the airships would haul ten tons of mail, and house one hundred passengers in luxury—large dining rooms, lounges, smoking rooms and baths. The new airships, he said, could travel 4,000 miles without a stop and zip along at an astonishing seventy miles per hour.

In late June, Atherstone met the mission in Albany and accompanied them to Perth, Melbourne, Hobart, and Sydney. The members of the mission, led by the aptly named Peregrine Fellowes, promoted airships at every stop. In Sydney they threw a "Flying Ball" for the New South Wales section of the Australian Aero Club, where they sold miniature airships to raise money for the club. At the ball the members of the Airship Mission were treated like celebrities: the society pages celebrated "the apple-green charmante" of Lady de Chair, a prominent arts patron in Sydney, with its "cascade of green ostrich feathers," and they noted the beauty of the "orchid-pink" dress of Mrs. Fellowes. At the Royal Society in Victoria, Peregrine Fellowes dazzled audiences with lantern slides of the construction of the giant R.100 and R.101, explained that danger from fire "was practically nonexistent," claimed the ships' dance floors would be "of unsurpassed quality," and described riding in an airship—"a complete absence of any motion likely to upset the most squeamish traveler." The first airships, he said, would travel from England to Australia by the end of 1927 or in early 1928.

So, by late 1927, as construction of R.100 and R.101 progressed, the British needed skilled pilots like Atherstone to fly the new ships. Atherstone seized this chance to return to the air, with the possibility of commanding his own airship. After nine years away from his homeland and from airships, he happily swapped his view of the Dandenong Mountain Range near Melbourne for the flat, featureless Bedfordshire Plain, home of the Royal Airship Works.

Now, in the early afternoon, Atherstone took command of R.101. He stepped to the center of the control car and surveyed the horizon through the semicircular plate-glass windows that lined the car. A few feet from these windows, directly in front of Atherstone, a coxswain gripped the ship's wheel that controlled R.101's sixty-seven-foot-tall rudder. Atherstone ignored the magnificent view of London as it passed under the ship; instead, he gazed at the waist-high binnacle compass in front of him. To his right, another coxswain operated the ship's elevators, looking over his left shoulder at an altimeter hung from the ceiling; its dial rotated counterclockwise for easy reading. Next to the altimeter, arranged for viewing by Atherstone at the middle of the cabin, were a speedometer and a set of gauges that reported the pressure in the gas bags. At Atherstone's left, three voice pipes dangled from the ceiling; they rocked back and forth with a gentle pendulous motion, their lightweight funnel-shaped ends making a soft metallic clang in rhythm with the airship's slight pitching.

Suddenly the voice pipes rattled loudly; R.101 pitched up then down three degrees. Turbulent air rocked the ship.

"Three degrees up," said Atherstone, "neutral, four degrees down."

In response, the height coxswain adjusted R.101's elevators, the horizontal fins at the airship's rear, to drive the ship up or down. The coxswain had to hold the airship, in all conditions, within five degrees of horizontal—an eight-degree tilt would cause glasses to slide across a table, while at ten degrees wine bottles would tip over. Veteran airship commanders joked that the height coxswain should "feel in his boots" if the ship were tilted and what direction it was about to tilt. The height coxswain's job was the hardest as an airship was rarely stable in the air.

We think of an airship as a simple thing to fly, picturing it, perhaps, like a hot-air balloon with a propeller attached. The pilot, we imagine, lets the airship float or hover, then starts an engine to waft the ship through the sky. Yet an airship, although a lighter-than-air craft, requires as much use of dynamic lift as an airplane's wing. An airship relies on its elevators for holding it at the proper altitude.

Flying an airship is "radically different both in kind and degree" from flying a plane, noted Ralph Upson, a pioneer in flying balloons and airships, who was among the first to earn balloon and airship pilot's certificates in Britain. He won the 1913 International Balloon Race, and was the second person to win the Wright Brothers Medal in 1929.

The pilot must first compensate, Upson explained, for the ship being out of static equilibrium and out of trim. A ship at equilibrium will hover, its lift balanced by its payload; a ship in trim is balanced from front to back. The static equilibrium is controlled by the amount of gas in the bags, the gas temperature, and the amount of ballast. Rarely is an airship in this state during its journey.

As it flies, an airship's buoyancy changes. First, it uses up fuel, thus changing the ship's weight. Second, gas can leak from the bags or the temperature of the gas in the bags can change, even varying across the gas bags, which also alters the amount of lift. A ship flown light will appear nose-heavy when it moves, while a heavy ship will be tail-heavy in motion. To compensate for these deviations from equilibrium, the height coxswain uses the elevators to correct the airship's pitch and achieve horizontal flight. In turbulent conditions the airship will pitch and, because it's not in equilibrium, will not return to its previous position. This means that a sinking ship continues to sink and a rising ship continues to rise. So, flying in rough weather at low altitude required precision by the height coxswain and excellent judgment and supervision by the pilot.

As Upson explained, "the pilot has to be constantly on the alert to catch the smallest deviation from course, or a serious change in gas pressure will develop."

While the height coxswain labored to maintain the proper height, the rudder coxswain made scores of small adjustments to the rudder position. If the coxswain did not continually adjust the rudder, R.101 would tend to circle. If the coxswain corrected the path with large changes of the rudder, the airship would shake or rock. Upson explained that an airship "is fundamentally unstable on course. No matter in what direction it is headed, it always wants to go in some other direction."

An airship's ovoid shape tends to turn broadside to the direction of motion. "A large airship," Upson continued, "deflects much more slowly, so much so that passengers might not notice it, but which, because of the huge mass of the airship, requires quick and determined action to counteract it."

The rudder at the ship's rear diminished this tendency to divert. A large rudder would stabilize the airship, but then it would be like a weathercock, its nose swinging to meet every gust of wind it encountered. Also, such an airship would have a low useful or disposable lift because of its large, heavy fins and would be fuel-inefficient because of drag. It would also be sluggish in response—even with the undersized fins of R.101 it took thirty or forty seconds to respond to changes of the rudder's position. So, an airship is designed with undersized fins that trade off stability for maneuverability. Atherstone preferred a strongly unstable ship as did most airship pilots of R.101's era.

As R.101 moved away from London, Atherstone took a turn at the rudder. He was impressed by how little effort was required to steer the ship.

Leaving the outskirts of London behind, Atherstone increased the ship's speed. He thought of using one of the three speaking tubes on his left to give orders to the engine cars. He knew, though, that, in flight, the roar of the engines made it impossible for the crew to hear, especially if they wore their standard-issue earplugs. Instead, Atherstone signaled the rear engine car using the telegraph system mounted on the wall just beyond the speaking tubes. Each of its five dials corresponded to one of the five engines. He positioned its central arrow toward an action—choosing full throttle, rather than standby, slow, or half throttle—and turned a crank. This rang a bell in the rear engine car, and alerted the crew—operated by the cheery Yorkshireman, the lantern-jawed Joe Binks, and the dour Arthur Bell—to look at an identical dial, its arrow pointing now to full throttle. From the control car Atherstone could not feel the change; instead he watched the speedometer—

no more than fifty miles per hour on this return trip.

In the late afternoon, as the airship approached the Royal Airship Works, Atherstone turned control to Irwin, and returned to the nose cone to prepare for mooring. The team of "Bird" and "Grabby" gracefully landed R.101. At 4:57 p.m., after five hours and forty minutes of flight covering 108 miles, R.101 locked itself into the tower's gimbaled arm. The crisp snap was broadcast to the nation by the BBC microphones stationed at the top of the tower near the nose of the airship. As the crew connected the ship to the tower with a walkway, cries of "Well done!" rose from the ground.

Atherstone supervised his crew in finalizing the mooring, while the pudgy Scott departed the airship. Elated and confident, he headed to the BBC microphones within earshot of Atherstone, and announced, "We had a very satisfactory flight." He added that "the ship handled very well, and was largely controlled with ease." To create a contrast between the comforts of airships and the tiny quarters and noise of its competitor the airplane, Scott reported: "The noise of the engines was very slight in the passengers' car. You could not hear very much, and it was very comfortable indeed." Ever mindful that many thought airships too lumbering to be of much commercial value, he added, "We did not run it at full speed or anything approaching it."

———————————◄■■►———————————

Indeed the airship's raison d'être was to connect London to Karachi, India in five days—ten days faster than by sea. The airship's air rival, the plane, linked London to Karachi in sixteen days—but with frequent stops to refuel. The journey could be shortened to nine days via a grueling combination of rail, flying boat and airplane. As one India-bound airplane traveler explained, "the only discomfort is the noise of the engine"; he recommended "the use of cotton-wool or India rubber plugs in the ears."

In addition to refueling stops every two to three hours, plane travellers endured overnight ground stays—the plane's navigational systems restricted flights to daylight. A traveler en route to India might find him or herself in a location like Rubar Wells; a desolate place in the desert, its only occupants the Bedouin, their camels, and the Iraqi soldiers who kept at bay desert raiders. And nine days was the best-case scenario to travel by airplane from London to Karachi; fog or high winds could delay flights significantly.

An airship, though, could hopscotch over the obstacles and hazards that made India so remote from Britain. At an altitude of about 2,000 feet it could pass through the fog of London, over France, into Asia Minor, and fly over the dreaded Sinai Desert. For hundreds of years this desert impeded empire builders, but now it was easily traversed with an airship. In air so clear that you could see for forty miles, passengers could contemplate the sun-baked sands of the Sinai in safety. The airship would continue its journey to India by gliding over the grandest scenery of southern Persia, its jagged, precipitous, but cool mountains delighting the eye until near Basra, the ground's green color faded and the gold of the desert shone through again as the water supply failed. From there the airship could travel in a straight shot to Karachi, a British oasis in an Asian land, offering the Hotels Bristol and Carlton, the Imperial Bank, a St. Paul's, a St. Andrews, a Polo Club, and a statue of Queen-Empress Victoria.

And every inch of that journey would be enjoyed in an airship as comfortable as an ocean liner.

Atherstone worried that the scheduling for R.101's flight to India might follow Lord Thomson's unrealistic and politically motivated timeline of departing in December, a mere three months away. The Works' senior staff, which included Major Scott, had already tended to rush ahead. Only a month earlier, Atherstone had considered the date for this first flight "unduly optimistic." And indeed the preparation for that simple 108-mile flight with only, he thought, the "bare necessities" aboard, required "a mad rush and panic." This involved only a fraction of the work that must be done to prepare for flying 5,000 plus miles to India. To Atherstone an accelerated schedule for this and future flights was "grossly unfair" to him and Irwin, and his crew. He needed time to be sure "each crew member understands his duties." Beyond that, Atherstone, the ace First World War pilot, had to master the controls and understand the aerodynamic behavior of R.101. So, he hoped this flight would highlight the need for careful, thorough preparation and systematic testing of the ship.

Yet a day after R.101's first flight, Thomson made a surprise announcement in a speech at the Twenty-Fifth Annual Banquet of that most earthbound organization, the Commercial Motor Users' Association. Thomson began by extolling the pleasures of riding in an airship. "Compared to the airplane," he said,

> the airship is, or will be, a sober and even dilatory conveyance. Travelers will journey tranquilly in airliners to the earth's remotest parts, visit the archipelagos in Southern Seas, cruise round the coasts of continents, strike inland, surmount lofty mountain ranges, and follow rivers as yet half explored from mouth to source."

Airship travel, he told his audience, will be "high up above mosquitoes and miasmas, and mud and dust and noise." He ended his speech with a shocking surprise: "Shortly after Parliament opens," he announced, "I hope to invite one hundred Members of all parties to take a flight in R.101," adding with a hint of gallows humor: "and I trust there will not be one hundred by-elections."

He even hoped for poor weather: that the MPs would fly with a "fresh breeze" of forty to fifty miles per hour and show that "the ship does not roll much." This flight, on an aircraft so far flown only once, would transport the largest number of people ever carried on a flight except those on Germany's flying boat, the Dornier DOX—a plane with a wingspan of 157 feet. It had flown 169 people for forty minutes, but only as a stunt—passengers crowded together on one side or the other to help the plane turn; usually it carried only sixty-six passengers.

Atherstone railed against this proposed flight, declaring it "cheap and vulgar," and an "absolutely unjustifiable risk." Atherstone, who believed in order and authority, hoped Scott would realize that the flight would be illegal. "The ship has not finished her trials," he told Scott, "has not got her Certificate of Airworthiness, and has not got enough lift to cart twelve tons of humans about with any degree of safety."

Yet Scott, the senior Works' staff person in charge of scheduling all flights, refused to cancel it. Atherstone's suggestion was turned "down flat," just like his request for uniforms. He hoped the Aeronautical Inspection Directorate, which must issue the Permit to Fly, would halt the flight.

They had time to act because R.101 was scheduled for five more test flights before the MPs' joyride was due to happen.

PART II: TROUBLES

AN INEPT COMMANDER TAKES CHARGE

OCTOBER 18–NOVEMBER 10, 1929

ALTHOUGH R.101 SOARED THROUGH the air on its first flight, the airship was nearly destroyed only three days later.

In the clear, still afternoon air of October 18th, R.101 approached the mooring tower on its return from its second flight. Clang, clang—the gong in the nose cone alerted Atherstone to an incoming message from Captain Irwin in the control car. Atherstone pressed the voice pipe to his ear.

"Pay out main wire 600 feet," said Irwin.

"Pay out main wire 600 feet," repeated Atherstone to a crew member. He opened a trapdoor below the largest of the three winches in the nose and shoved out a 150-foot loop of cable—a length that weighed enough to overcome the friction of the winch. As the winch drum spun, its cable clattered in a ring that prevented the cable from moving sideways. When 600 feet of cable dangled below the airship, Atherstone commanded, "Stop winch."

"Stop main, brake on," said the winch operator.

"Main wire out 600 feet, sir," said Atherstone into his voice pipe.

"Main wire out 600 feet, thank you," said Irwin, then added, "short pause." As Atherstone awaited orders, he peered out the small window in the nose. On the ground 800 feet leeward of the tower lay the tower's main cable and two guy wires arranged in a T-shape. Near the T on the ground, a small cluster of men readied the tower cables to attach to the cables lowered from R.101.

Clang, clang. "Stand by to pay out port yaw guy," echoed through the voice pipe. Atherstone repeated the order and his men started the "evolution" of the first guy wire, the crew's term for lowering a smaller cable, which had to creep earthward and swing freely so it wouldn't twine itself around the other cable. Then, on orders from the control car, the crew "evolved" the starboard guy wire.

With the ship's mooring cables now ready, R.101 moved forward so the ground crew could "catch hold of the beast"—Scott's colorful phrase for connecting the ground and ship cables. R.101's nose tilted toward the earth, driven down by its elevators against the ship's natural buoyancy, until a few feet of the ship's main cable lay slack on the airfield. The ship dragged it toward the men on the ground, who prepared to latch it to the tower's twenty-five-ton cable. Atherstone braced himself for the moment the cables were joined because, once they were connected, R.101 would ascend as it dumped water ballast to draw the main cable taut and prevent it from tangling with the guy wires.

That was the plan, at least.

Instead, as its cable neared the ground crew, the airship dumped ballast, jerked up, and lifted the ship's cable beyond the reach of the ground crew. The dangling cable was carried by the gliding ship past the tower and into a small grove of trees. The snap of a branch echoed through the nose cone as the cable snagged on a limb.

Although R.101 yanked the cable free when it revved its engines and circled for a second pass at landing, this movement spun the guy wires, wrapping them around the main cable. The gong clanged in the nose cone. Atherstone listened for orders from the control car: instead of Irwin's voice, he now heard Scott's. Scott had taken command from Irwin.

R.101 circled the tower and returned to try to "catch the beast" again. As it approached the T landing, the ship's engines roared and its elevators tilted to bring it and the cables lower to the ground. Instead, the ship remained level; it was too light. The release of ballast on the first pass had been too early; it had happened before the ground and ship cables had latched.

The ship circled to bide time while the air cooled enough to decrease the ship's lift. The hydrogen in the gas bags was warmed by the sun throughout the day's flight; the "superheating" of the hydrogen above the temperature of the surrounding air increased R.101's lift by 3 or 4 percent. This "false lift," would dissipate as the evening cooled. Meanwhile, Atherstone and his crew worked to untangle the snarl of cables. They hauled in a few feet until they reached a matted section, untwisted it, and then drew in another foot or so. Repeating this tedious task, they rushed to finish before sunset; otherwise they would need to use flashlights—a great inconvenience.

Near six o'clock, three and a half hours after R.101 arrived at the airfield, the airship dipped low enough for the ground crew to connect to the ship's cable. The tower then hauled R.101 in until the spring-loaded latches on the tower's arm clicked. Scott, still in the control car, issued the command "ship secured." Atherstone's crew dropped the nose cone hatch and shoved the bridge into position to connect ship and tower.

Moments later, Major Scott lumbered across the bridge, shadowed by the graceful Lord Thomson, R.101's advocate and the sole non-crew member aboard that day. The appearance of the two men contrasted sharply: Thomson, tall with ramrod straight posture, Scott, squat with a slouch; Thomson's chiseled features radiated health, while Scott's pasty skin and black rings under his eyes conveyed sickness. Few would guess that Thomson was thirteen years older than the forty-two-year-old Scott. When Scott arrived at the base of the tower, the reporters greeted him as a vigorous hero returning from a long voyage. "Well done Scottie!" they cried. They still lionized him for his crossing of the Atlantic ten years earlier.

In 1919, Scott had commanded the airship R.34, a third the size of R.101, from Scotland to New York. With his hallmark "press on regardless" attitude, he had flown the ship through thunderstorms, overcome unreliable engines that threatened to strand the airship over the ocean, and arrived in New York with enough fuel left for only forty more minutes of flight. The voyage was so unsettling that Scott's crew demanded rum to calm their frazzled nerves, despite prohibition in the United States.

After his Atlantic crossing, Great Britain celebrated Scott as a national hero; he achieved fame similar to that enjoyed by Lindbergh when he crossed the Atlantic eight years later—the sixty-fifth human to do so, but, the first to fly solo. Scott's display of nerve on the Atlantic crossing earned him a reputation for bravery; even now, ten years later, newspapers still extolled his "press on regardless" attitude. And the president of the Royal Aeronautical Society claimed "no one" had "greater knowledge of the handling of such great airships" than Scott. Indeed, Scott had invented the mooring tower, shortly after the First World War, which led to the giant commercial airships Britain planned to build.

Before the tower's invention, airship landings required a large, well-trained ground crew with precision timing. As the airship approached, the men arranged themselves in a v, with the tip pointing toward the wind. The airship pilot flew into the open part of their V, dangling a rope from the bow. When it hit the tip of the V, the ground crew grabbed the airship's rope. This step was the most treacherous because the pilot lost control as the airship slowed, and he could no longer use dynamic lift to position the craft. It became a balloon that either ascended or sank because of its buoyancy. Next, the pilot slowly released gas while the ground crew hauled in the bow rope. The airship slowly neared the ground until the crew could grab the control car and guy ropes. If the ship sank too fast, the pilot released ballast. If all went well, the airship gently touched the earth.

However, as airships grew to the size of R.101, ground landing became difficult and expensive. The ground crew blossomed from one hundred to nearly 500, and the wind had greater leverage on the ship; even a slight breeze could prevent an airship from landing or could trap it in its shed. If the ships couldn't land safely, or couldn't even leave their sheds in high winds, Britain could not run a commercial airship service.

Scott's mooring tower solved all the problems of landing a large airship. First, it reduced the number of people required to land the airship to around twenty. Second, it enabled the airship to land or depart in almost any weather. Third, the tower offered an easy way to supply the airship with water, fuel, and gas without, as a technical journal put it, the "incidence of risks which must always be entailed in" transferring a ship to its shed.

At the base of the tower, reporters awaited Major Scott's expert account of the delayed landing of R.101. They leaned in as he began his briefing. His authoritative yet soft voice competed with the echo of clanking chains and shouted orders from the hollow metal dome atop the mooring tower. Scott explained that, although it seemed "a perfect day, with little wind, a bright October sun, and clear air," in reality "the air was full of disturbed currents, rising and falling with varying temperatures." For this reason he decided to "lay off for better conditions just as a ship lies off the harbor for the tide." Scott added that when he had "more experience of the ship and the extent to which she responds to various conditions" he would have "no difficulty in coming into the mooring tower." He also noted that the airship had returned early and the tower crew was not yet ready for it. Lord Thomson then chimed in, claiming that the delayed landing was caused by "overzeal and a desire to be slick," adding that "the ship was a bit light, and the conditions for the mooring operations were unstable." No harm was caused and the delayed landing "gives experience to the crew." The reporters distilled these comments into two words: Scott was in "supreme command."

Atherstone, though, knew the truth: Scott botched the landing.

R.101 encountered no "disturbed currents," nor did it need to wait for "better conditions," nor did its arrival "surprise" the tower crew. Instead, Scott caused the accident with the mere twist of a stopcock that jettisoned water ballast.

Fourteen tons of water were distributed throughout the airship and stored either in tanks or in bags—smaller in size and number than the huge gas bags, but no less critical to smooth flight. The captain used the water as ballast to adjust the overall lift of the ship or finetune its trim. An airship might become light at its nose or its tail, either due to a gas bag leak or due to gas bags having heated unevenly by the sun. To redress this imbalance the captain could, from the control car, use compressed air to shift water between tanks distributed throughout the ship. Or, he could adjust the trim, and the overall lift of the ship, by selectively jettisoning water.

The two water storage systems, the bags and tanks, were controlled in different ways. The water bags were under "local control." To release this ballast the captain sent a messenger to a rigger stationed at the bags, each shaped like a pair of trousers. The rigger would open each leg to rapidly empty them. The draining of the storage tanks, in contrast, was triggered directly from the control car. The tanks were connected to a pipe running bow to stern. At the control car a T-fitting connected a vertical pipe that passed into the control car and through its floor. Near the floor a stopcock released the ballast from the tanks: one twist and ballast was released during landing. Although this centralized control simplified flying the airship, it also let Scott err in mooring it on its second flight.

Earlier that day, as Irwin aligned the airship to drag its main cable over the T of tower cables on the ground, Scott announced in his quiet, authoritative way that he would now land the ship. As R.101 neared the ground cables, Scott spun the stopcock to release water ballast. His goal was to raise the airship and pull the wire taut, but he discharged the ballast too early, causing the ship to pass too high over the ground cables. He told reporters that inclement weather fouled the landing.

This was a serious error by an experienced flier, which caused a three-hour delay, but could also have destroyed the airship and killed those aboard, yet Scott would not acknowledge his mistake. His actions and his dissembling afterward angered Atherstone and Irwin, but it did not surprise them. They both had firsthand knowledge that Scott had destroyed airships.

Eight years earlier, on June 21, 1921, Irwin was preparing to land R.36, Britain's first passenger airship—a ship half the size of R.101. Although no passengers were aboard on this test flight, when it did go into service passengers would ride in a cabin slung under the ship. This cabin would be a sitting room by day, but be converted at night by curtains to bedrooms. *The Times* best captured R.36's passenger experience with a left-handed compliment: "R.36's saloon," the paper wrote, was "almost luxuriously comfortable."

As Irwin brought R.36 close to the tower, Scott took over the landing. He miscalculated the ship's speed; and it rushed toward the tower, fouling the cable at the bottom of it. It jerked the airship and ruptured two forward ballast bags. R.36's nose rose and yanked on the mooring cable, which collapsed the ship's nose. The airship hung canted from the tower; no longer could it ride safely there. The ground crew toiled for five hours to untangle the damaged airship, but as they released it and lowered it to the ground, the wind rose. To protect R.36, the current glory of the empire, the crew prepared to move it into a shed, but the shed was already occupied by two zeppelins, forfeits from Germany under the terms of the Treaty of Versailles. To create space for the damaged airship, crews sawed one of the zeppelins into pieces. It took another five hours, until, finally, by 2 a.m. space was available. But as the ground crew attempted to move R.36 into the shed, a gust of wind rammed the airship into the shed doors, destroying the middle of the ship. When the sensitive Irwin saw the damage, he broke down because he knew that R.36 would never fly again. An inquiry exonerated Scott and blamed the accident on equipment failure.

Despite this accident and others—under Scott's command two more British airships were destroyed when they struck their shed doors—Scott's public reputation as an airship pilot soared. Privately, however, many at the Works knew Scott was, in the words of one of his colleagues "a sick man," a euphemism for an alcoholic. If he were invited to dinner, Scott would drink two whiskey and sodas beforehand, three cocktails, a stiff whiskey at dinner, a liqueur after the meal, and then, if the partygoers attended the movies, he drank another whiskey there. Scott's visits "cost us," complained one of the Works' wives, "a small fortune in drinks."

Atherstone himself saw the lunchtime gin that Scott often drank. It impaired Scott's judgment, stripping caution from his natural inclination to "press on regardless." His risk-taking extended to his personal life: although married and the father of three children, he engaged in affairs. So public where these affairs that many at the Works avoided a pub frequented by both Scott's wife and his current mistress. Scott's domestic troubles were intensified by his worries about the success, or possible failure, of R.101.

"I am probably," he told a gathering of airship experts, "more interested in this airship than anybody else present." And indeed for Scott to maintain his public acclaim as a hero and his status as a powerful figure in aviation, R.101 must succeed. R.101 must show that giant airships were destined to heft the Empire's bureaucrats, workers, tourists, and troops around the globe; otherwise it would become a footnote in aviation history, a sterile attempt to connect all regions of the Empire. And he knew that if R.101 failed, Britain would abandon airships, as the nation had done once before.

In 1921, the Air Ministry had halted all airship work and shuttered the Royal Airship Works. Airships were revived because of the immense efforts by Scott and others, with support from Lord Thomson when, in 1924, he became Secretary of State for Air. When this airship renaissance occurred, Scott hoped to be R.101's captain, but was assigned a larger role at the Works: he scheduled the airship flights and set policies for flight procedures. His title was Assistant Director of Airship Development (Flying and Training), often abbreviated as Assistant Director (Flying). He was number two in the Works' power structure, only the Director was above him, but Scott controlled R.101 because his opinions on flying were unchallenged by the Director. Scott decided when and where R.101 would fly, which enabled him to take command of the airship whenever he wished from Irwin, the ship's captain.

Scott commanded R.101 on its third flight when the ship circled over Sandringham, the British Royal Family's country house in

Norfolk. As the sun shone through the last wisps of fog on a crisp November morning, R.101 circled the royal estate three times, while the King, Queen and their young granddaughter Elizabeth—the future Elizabeth 11—watched from a gravel path. The King acknowledged the airship crew with a simple tip of his hat, while little Elizabeth, her eyes bright with excitement, furiously waved.

A few hours later, in the bright afternoon, R.101 approached the mooring tower at the Works. The ship dragged its main cable toward the T of cables on the ground, when Scott, unknown to Irwin, released ballast from the rear of the ship. R.101 plunged nose first toward the earth. The alert Irwin ordered ballast released from the front and righted the ship. The ground crew captured the ship's cable and the tower crew safely towed in R.101.

Atherstone fumed. He said the ship would "have dived on to the ground, if she had not been so light."

Scott again caused problems on the ship's next flight. As R.101 returned from a long night flight, Irwin guided it and its tired crew to a smooth landing. The tower crew hauled in the airship, Irwin adjusted the rudder to meet the tower head on and ordered the reverse engine to power up; R.101 pulled the cable taut. At this moment Scott took over. The wind changed direction and the ship moved crabwise from the tower, slacking one of the guy wires and drawing the other taut, causing the ship to twist as it neared the tower. Irwin watched for the touch of rudder needed to right the ship, but Scott did nothing.

Suddenly, a loud metallic crack. Only six feet from the tower's arm, the giant ship lunged forward and broke a spring on the arm and the ship's motion wound a guy wire around the ship, crushing a small girder that held the cloth cover taut. Quick work by the tower crew secured the airship to the arm.

Afterward Scott explained the accident to reporters. "The ship is still perfectly airworthy," he said, "but we think slight repairs necessary before we attempt another mooring."

Scott's errors disturbed Atherstone. The deteriorating Scott had become aloof, rarely communicating with Atherstone and Irwin, the ship's captain. "It would be rather more helpful," Atherstone said of Scott, "if opinions and recommendations of ships' officers were given rather more consideration." When Atherstone insisted that Scott issue changes in flying procedures and policies to increase efficiency or to enhance safety, "it was never done unless" Atherstone did "much cagging." Scott's scheduling of flights, his sole responsibility, irritated Atherstone. Scott announced a flight with little notice. This caused Atherstone to "crash right into full flight within a few hours of taking over." Although this late notice upset him, even more unsettling was the type of flights Scott allowed.

Atherstone advocated for careful, systematic testing of the airship, but what he got, he said, was "window-dressing stunts and joy rides." The precedent had been set when Scott had allowed Lord Thomson to ride a few weeks earlier on R.101's second flight. This photo-op diverted the crew from what Atherstone called work "that really matters," like calibrating the bow strain gauges at the tower head, and forced them to engage in "titivation."

"The passenger accommodation," Atherstone said, "got its face washed and hair brushed, all cabins, lounge, smoke-room, dining-room, frantically furnished." This "titivation" included converting two berths into a private office for Lord Thomson, who arrived with his secretary and a large suitcase of state papers. All so the reporters could "swarm like earwigs"—Atherstone despised the press—around Thomson to hear his florid rhetoric. He enjoyed eating "breakfast, lunch and tea entirely free from all outside disturbance high up above all terrestrial dirt and noise." Thomson revealed to reporters that R.101 would not soon travel to India: "I am told," he said, "that my hopes of making the journey at Christmas-time will not be fulfilled. That does not matter, as I wish to make it quite clear that the men in charge of these experiments are not going to be rattled while I sit where I do."

The delay, claimed Thomson, occurred because of the "time required to build spare engines." In truth, R.101 could not be tested and ready in only two months for a long-distance flight. Although Atherstone appreciated that Thomson's timeframe for departing to India had become more realistic, he worried about the Air Minister's reckless thoughts on airship operation. Thomson had told reporters that he regretted that "the weather conditions were so fair" because he "wished to see the behavior of the airship in rough weather." In every meeting with the press, he stated that airships were all-weather crafts and he chided the officers if they protected R.101 from the weather. He was annoyed when R.101 was transferred from tower to shed because of gale force winds, calling this action "unnecessarily cautious."

Thomson's interference diverted Atherstone from important tasks. He should be testing the ship, instead of hosting teas on board; he should be drilling his crew, instead of playing nursemaid to visiting bureaucrats. And his crew should be running drills instead of cleaning up lunch splattered across the dining room— at one of the many PR luncheons a gust of wind had jostled R.101 and sent dishes flying.

Of most immediate distress to Atherstone was the imminent flight with one hundred MPs: the airship would be taking a good portion of the Empire's government up into the skies, with Scott in charge again.

In his diary, written late at night aboard R.101, Atherstone railed against the flight. He thought it "damned unfair of the Air Ministry" to insist on flying one hundred MPs on the untested ship. He worried whether the ship could even lift these twelve tons of MPs. "How on Earth it's going to be done?" he wondered, and then despaired: "I simply don't know." "I hope," Atherstone wrote, "that something will happen to prevent this stupid flight, because it is really stretching things too far and only asking for trouble."

"It will be taking an absolutely unjustifiable risk with practically nothing to gain and everything to lose."

CHAPTER FOUR

INSIDE THE GREAT AIRSHIP

NOVEMBER–DECEMBER 1929

O N SATURDAY, NOVEMBER 23, 1929, Atherstone surveyed, from the control car, the horde gathered at the base of the mooring tower. "Quite a crowd of Lords and Commoners," he thought. Sixty-five Members of Parliament, eighteen peers and their six guests braved high winds and pelting rain as they waited for a chance to ride on R.101. To the queued parliamentarians the rain was merely a nuisance, but to Atherstone it signaled danger.

Heavy rain added to the weight that the soon to be overloaded R.101 must lift because the cloth cover absorbed the rain. The eighty-nine people below, once boarded, would constitute the heaviest load ever borne by R.101, and nearly the largest number ever aloft in any craft. To accommodate this load, Atherstone had struggled for the last twenty-four hours to shave weight from the airship.

On Friday, the night before the Members arrived, Atherstone checked R.101's lift and trim indicators at the mooring tower: the ship was three and a half tons short of the lift necessary to carry eighty-nine passengers, crew, and a prudent amount of ballast and fuel. So, to increase lift, Atherstone gassed the bags to 97 percent of capacity, which risked bursting them if the ship accidentally rose too high. To lighten the ship's load, he drained all except five and a half tons of fuel, enough for eighteen hours of flying in calm conditions. And he removed loose articles not essential for the ship to get off the ground; for example, he moved from the ship to the tower all parachutes. His last stop of the day was at the Works' meteorological tower to check the weather for Saturday. The forecast was for dropping barometric pressure, rising temperature, and heavy rain, conditions which might drop R.101's lift five tons by midmorning.

With a record number of passengers prepared to board and the wind rising and the rain increasing, Atherstone was shocked that Scott had not canceled the flight.

"It was obvious," Atherstone thought, "that the flight was impossible." He resented this diversion from the more important task of testing the ship in preparation for its flight to India. To Atherstone this unnecessary flight "doesn't say much for the brains up at the Air House"—Lord Thomson's Air Ministry—"if this is the only way they can think of getting Parliamentary support for airships."

Few in Parliament raved about Thomson's plans for a fleet of airships; more often Members, including those in his own Labour Party, dismissed the idea as a pipe dream. His toughest critics were in the House of Commons, where, as Air Minister, Thomson defended his government's yearly request for funding.

In 1928, the Scottish Labour MP Frank Rose protested the idea of using "gas bladders" to connect the Empire, pronouncing Thomson mentally ill. "Of all the phases of aeronautical dementia," Rose told the House, "that known to the faculty as gasbagomania is the most virulent and the most malignant."

Since Rose's diagnosis, the objections increased as R.101, and its sibling R.100, missed deadlines and struggled to meet their benchmarks of speed and lift. "Anyone," declared an MP from Thomson's Labour Party, "who has been following the construction and the development of R.100 and R.101 [knows] that these two airships are failures. They can never be run on regular services. They can never be used for commercial purposes." He continued:

> It is easy to tie a football up to a mast and to get it to remain there for twelve months. That is not the test. The real test is whether the airship can fly regularly and efficiently during a large proportion of the weeks of the year. Neither of these airships can do that. They are too slow to fight against the average wind that they will have to meet, and they cannot carry a load which will make them commercial propositions.

This Labour MP advocated that the government, run by his party, "cut our losses before more money is spent and more lives are needlessly risked." This was the most extreme criticism of R.101, but there were many MPs who were lukewarm about continuing funding for airships. Thomson hoped to convert them to enthusiastic supporters with a ride in the luxurious R.101.

The only luxury, though, seen by W. P. Brown, MP for Wolverhampton West, was glimpses of the teak-lined interior of the tower's elevator as its door snapped open to admit twelve of his colleagues. With a soft whir of its electric motor, the elevator zipped to the tower head in ninety seconds, although passengers had to wait there fifteen or twenty minutes before boarding R.101. The crew allowed one passenger at a time to enter the ship, then waited until Irwin, in the control car, trimmed the ship by redistributing fuel with blasts of compressed air. This time-consuming process was slowed by an error with the first group of MPs. Because signaling between the ground crew and the control car broke down, thirty Members boarded before Irwin knew of their arrival, upsetting the airship's trim. After an angry phone call from Irwin to the tower, the rate of boarding slowed as the gun-shy tower crew double-checked with Irwin whether to allow the next passenger to cross into the ship.

As Brown approached his third hour waiting in the driving rain, he reflected how warm he and his colleagues had started off, when, as a "happy band of pilgrims," they had boarded a bus at Westminster's Old Palace Yard. Now, he thought, they looked more like arctic explorers than Members of Parliament. Dr. Ethel Bentham wore a thick coat, her utilitarian hat pulled low to defy the wind; the tiny Miss Wilkinson—her colorful dresses a welcome contrast in the Commons to the black-and-white clothing of most women MPs—disappeared into the folds of her enormous coat, her violently red hair hidden by a hat. The Bishop of Southwark, who joined the MPs as a guest, had "his coat buttoned as tightly as his Episcopal gaiters," and William Allen, an MP from Belfast, snuggled his small dog to keep it warm. Among the gray overcoats on this overcast day the only spot of color was the irrepressible Jack Hayes' trademark red carnation: it shone brightly from the buttonhole of his mackintosh.

As they waited, the MPs chatted about riding in R.101. Brown wondered whether the ship's movement induced motion sickness. Another MP revealed that two of their colleagues feared R.101 would crash: one had his will witnessed before boarding, and the other reviewed his life insurance policies for coverage of aviation accidents.

Soon the elevator returned. The tower crew pushed the Conservative MP Jack Cohen to the elevator in a wheelchair at the base of the tower. He had lost both legs in the Third Battle of Ypres in the First World War. As he neared the elevator a loud snap rang through the air, followed by an indistinct warning shout, and then, a few seconds later, by an ear-shattering crash. The elevator cable had snapped and its counterweight plummeted to the ground. An MP broke the stunned silence with a hoarse whisper of "ominous." With the elevator broken, Brown and his fellow guests of honor left a disappointed Jack Cohen, and slogged up the 300 steps of the tower as the wind and rain lashed them. Led by Jack Hayes and his red carnation, they arrived at the top breathless, but still eager to fly in R.101.

When instructed by the tower crew, the MPs clutched their embarkation tickets and climbed six short steps from the tower's platform to the three-foot-wide bridge that connected the tower to the airship. As they reached the bridge, a gust of wind swung R.101 around the tower—an "insecure and swaying monster," thought one MP.

No one tarried once on the bridge: over the thin metal railing was a 170-foot drop to the ground.

Inside the ship they climbed down a short set of steps to a walkway along the ship's bottom edge. Its three-ply spruce floor bent with each step so the MPs trod with caution. Lining the walkway were canvas walls that flapped as the wind buffeted R.101. Gaps in the fluttering canvas exposed the metal girders of the framework and revealed the ship's thin cotton-linen outer cover. To one MP, the outer cover looked so "transparent" and "frail" that he feared "a gently dropped small stone might go clean through," which created "a despairing feeling that a false step might plunge me into eternity."

About 350 feet along the walkway they arrived at the ship's center above the control car. The crew directed the Members to a utilitarian metal staircase—none of Thomson's promised luxury yet—from which they rose into the interior of the airship.

In R.101, in contrast to all other airships, including the *Graf Zeppelin*, crew and passengers rode inside the ship's metal framework instead of in a gondola slung under it. The conventional gondola limited the number of passengers—the *Graf Zeppelin* carried twenty—and restricted the size and opulence of the passenger accommodations. A car slung under the ship had to be narrow to prevent passengers from congregating at one end or the other because that would alter the ship's center of gravity.

"This movement of passengers," said R.101 designers about the narrow gondola, "is more likely to take place when an airship is maneuvering to land and is traveling at slow speed when the effect of any alteration of the center of gravity affects control more seriously than at higher speeds."

Equally important to R.101's designers were the limitations of a narrow car given that they planned to ferry one hundred passengers to the remote corners of the Empire. In addition, they wanted passengers to move freely as on an ocean liner. And they intended to emphasize passenger comfort, something decreased by a car slung under the airship: "in the event of the airship pitching or flying at a slight angle to the horizontal, a long, narrow car accentuates the angle in the eye of the passengers." And finally, an external car increased the aerodynamic resistance of the airship and decreased fuel economy.

So, in R.101, the passenger quarters were built inside the airship's ovoid framework, nestled below the center of buoyancy under a gas bag. And on a deck below the passengers, but still inside the framework, were the crew quarters. In this arrangement of decks the front and back trim was not affected by the number of passengers carried. More importantly for the passengers, this placement inside the airship also allowed the quarters to be as wide as the airship itself. With this innovation the designers hoped that R.101 would feel like a flying ocean liner.

As the Members climbed the stairs of R.101 they passed through the lower deck, which housed the crew quarters, the chart room, and the smoking room, then up another short flight of stairs to the passenger deck. The juxtaposition of the utilitarian walkway and stairs with the passenger quarters stunned the Members: the undecorated stairwells contrasted with the brilliant white walls trimmed in gold. One MP thought they "might be in the lobby of our hotel."

Mr. Albert Savidge, R.101's steward, enhanced this impression. A dapper man with a trim, pencil-line mustache and ram-rod-straight posture, he lent legitimacy and elegance to R.101's claim to be as luxurious as an ocean liner. Indeed, he had honed his skills as a steward aboard the White Star's RMS *Majestic*, a luxury ocean liner later replaced by the *Titanic*.

The "airship bug" had bitten him after he served, in 1921, as Britain's first airship steward on R.36—the ship destroyed by Scott's errors. Although the change from ocean liner to airship lowered Savidge's salary—one crew member estimated Savidge's income dropped by £400 a year—Savidge preferred, he said, the "comforts of the air" to the "perils of the sea."

He also relished the bit of fame accorded to an airship steward: he appeared in a print advertisement as the airship's "food expert," who uses "Chase and Sanborn's Fresh Coffee." Beyond the thrill of riding in an airship, Savidge enjoyed the comradery among the crew; he often amused his crew members by drawing caricatures of them in his spare time.

Now Savidge collected the Members' tickets, checked their coats, and directed them past the toilets and into the lounge. After they had walked through the dim, utilitarian stairwell lit by low-wattage bulbs in glass globes, the lounge's grandeur and scale delighted the Members. The lounge was the size of a tennis court and spanned the width of the airship. Its polished wood floor gleamed in the sunlight that spilled through giant triplex glass windows port and starboard. The light reflected from the lounge's bright-white walls and illuminated every corner of the room, in contrast to the windowless deck below. Framed photographs of clouds on the walls shimmered and the walls' gold inlay glittered.

The gold was complemented by the royal blue trim on the thin, white pillars that supported the ceiling. Garlands of flowers in silver buckets at the base of every pillar provided dramatic bursts of color.

The vast floor dazzled one MP, who exclaimed that "it would make an admirable dance hall." And indeed R.101's designers planned for passengers to fox trot all night as the airship, to quote Lord Thomson, passed "tranquilly" over "archipelagos in Southern Seas." When not dancing, passengers could enjoy a drink, sitting on the built-in green-cushioned benches that lined the walls. Or, they could recline in one of the deep-blue wicker chairs scattered throughout. Once settled they could pull up a small table, write letters on note paper imprinted with "R.101," and slip them into special envelopes marked "On His Majesty's Service, Posted on R.101 in flight."

Those passengers not engaged in dancing, writing, or reclining could examine Lord Thomson's "archipelagos" from the lounge's masterstroke: the promenades, hidden behind the built-in benches both port and starboard. To the first-time visitor, the benches on either side seemed to form a half-wall topped by small windows, dressed with Cambridge blue curtains, but behind this half-wall, accessible through a two-foot-wide opening at the center of the benches, was a promenade deck. On this ten-foot-long deck passengers could lean against a waist-high railing and almost press their noses against a wall of glass ten feet by twelve feet.

The glass was tilted at forty-five degrees so passengers could enjoy a stunning bird's-eye view of the ground, the horizon, and the clouds. The windows were so large that the glass could not be made uniform so in places the view was blurred and distorted. Yet it still delighted passengers: "From these windows," noted an MP, "one surveys the world with a confidence strangely absent from a similar height on the tower." Another imagined "no experience more delightful than an afternoon spent in a deck chair on one of those promenades gazing down upon Mediterranean islands or the deserts of Egypt and the Canal."

Although the promenades captivated most visitors, one MP worried about the placement of the passenger accommodations deep inside the airship. He had an "awful shut-in feeling" and questioned how, in an accident, a passenger would exit the ship. Could, he wondered, a passenger "make his way with an ax or a hammer" through the giant glass windows? He need not have worried because the solidity of the passenger quarters was an illusion.

The ceiling was "like a piece of stage scenery," observed one MP who climbed on a chair to touch it. It was fabric, as were the walls. The pillars in the lounge were constructed from balsa covered with metal. The tables and shelves were also of balsa, although, to increase their durability, covered with a one-millimeter thick veneer. And the chairs were made of the lightest cane.

As the MPs explored the rest of the passenger deck, they noted that the grandeur diminished. On their way to the sleeping quarters, they passed the toilets, where—as an internal report phrased it—"the smells in the Ladies and Gentlemen's Toilet Rooms were frequently in evidence." The toilets were not up to the standard necessary for paying passengers in other ways: the doors had no locks and the flushing was so complex that instructions had to be posted on the walls, otherwise passengers might unscrew the septic tank plugs—labeled for this MPs' flight "DO NOT TOUCH." More of the luster wore off as the Members toured the sleeping quarters.

Just beyond the toilets and aft of the lounge were twenty-six cabins, all double berths, which meant sleeping accommodations for fifty-two passengers. Although tastefully decorated in white and gold, the berths had no doors and only a Cambridge blue curtain. This saved weight but decreased privacy, already minimal because of the thin cloth walls. And the quarters were spartan: bunk beds, a small luggage stool for cabin bags, a small rug, and a note on the protocols of airship life that described how to summon a steward. The most ostentatious furnishing in the room was the porthole-shaped electric light on the wall, an homage to the ocean liners that R.101's passenger quarters sought to emulate. Yet even that flourish had a practical side: the housing was a double-bulkhead with ten thick bolts to deter passengers from changing a light bulb, which might create a spark and explode the airship.

As the weather outside deteriorated and R.101's departure was delayed, the senior staff of the Royal Airship Works and the ship's crew distracted the MPs with tours of the deck below the passenger quarters. The passengers reached this lower deck via the same set of stairs used to access the lounge. At the bottom were two doors: one leading to the smoking room and the other, usually off limits to passengers, was the entrance to the lower deck. As the MPs entered the lower deck, Irwin greeted them.

Irwin began their tour with a visit to the chart room, only a few steps away. The chart room, sometimes called the captain's bridge, was command central for the airship. Here the officer of the watch was only a few steps from the stairs to the control car gondola, the radio cabin, and the captain's sleeping quarters.

On the chart room's table, Irwin unfolded a forty-by-thirty-inch map annotated by M. A. Giblett, Superintendent for Airship Services in the Meteorological Office and Chief Meteorologist, RAW. This map was from a set that constituted the pinnacle of Giblett's meteorological work. He devoted his career to forecasting the weather in every inch of British Empire airspace where an imperial airship might fly. From 1925 to 1927 he gathered data to create this set of "synoptic" maps that showed the day-to-day variations in weather from April 1, 1924 to March 31, 1925 along all imperial airship routes: Britain to North America, the Middle East, South Africa, India, Australia and New Zealand. To create these maps Giblett traveled to Egypt, Italy, France, India, New Zealand, Ceylon (present day Sri Lanka), South Africa, Australia, and Malta. At every stop he measured the wind speed and temperature and noted the frequency of thunderstorms. "Electrical storms," Giblett had learned from Scott, "are the airship's greatest danger." Not from lightning, but because of "the very serious bumps and eddies that accompany them; these can be extremely violent and very seriously stress the structure of the airship." An airship's best course of action would be to fly around a thunderstorm. The crew could not drop ballast and rise high above the storm because the ship was designed to fly at a maximum altitude of 2,000 feet or so. Therefore an airship crew needed detailed knowledge of the weather along its route so they could fly around storms.

Giblett's measurements were listed on the maps Irwin shared with the MPs. Marked along R.101's various routes were the typical atmospheric temperatures and winds; these would be only a rough guide for planning routes and were updated during R.101's flights through forecasts sent to the ship by radio.

The radio cabin, only six feet from the chart room, was crammed full with the latest communications equipment: on the wall the circuit box for the ship—radio operators doubled as electricians— and wedged into a corner, a cot. On this lay the latest copy of *Wireless World* for the operator on duty to flip through as he listened for the faint dots and dashes directed to GFAAW, R.101's published call sign, although the frequencies used were secret to prevent the public from sending messages to the ship. Messages were sent by Morse code rather than by voice because voice signals disintegrated into a garbled mishmash once the airship was 200 miles from the tower, while Morse signals carried 2,000 miles. To get the most up-to-date reports, the operators sent R.101's position, often every hour, to the Royal Airship Works.

The officer of the watch frequently determined the positions by observing landmarks—like the Metropolitan Cattle Market or St. Paul's Cathedral—but when flying over stretches of featureless terrain, he calculated the ship's position using bearings reported from a nearby radio ground station. The radio operator asked the station to prepare to take a bearing. Once acknowledged, he would again contact the station, which used its antenna to measure the bearing of the ship's signal within two degrees. The operator repeated this twice and then shared the three bearings and the times with the officer of the watch. These three pieces of information on a map revealed the ship's position. If R.101 were near two ground stations, the officer of the watch could use a single bearing from each to establish the ship's position.

During R.101's journey, officers at the Royal Airship Works marked the ship's position with green flags on a large wall map and then combed through weather reports from stations near R.101's location. They sent these to the ship's radio operators, who rushed them to the officer of the watch.

From the radio cabin, Irwin guided the Members in parties of two or three down a short flight of steps to the control car. At the controls, coxswains operated the rudder and elevators. Even though the ship was at the tower, it required a crew in the control car. If the winds became violent, they would slip from the tower and fly to calmer weather.

When the Members returned from the control car to the chart room, the aroma of chicken filled the air—the meal to be served to them after they finished their tour.

The smells wafted from the kitchen, tucked into a corner near the radio room. To view the kitchen, Members squeezed through a narrow hallway and entered a room fourteen feet by six and a half feet—a thirtieth the area of the passenger lounge above. The kitchen was stuffed with an astonishing amount of equipment: for preparation, a sink and a small table; for cooking, an electric oven with four hot plates, a forty-gallon water tank with three immersion heaters, and a vegetable or pudding steamer; and for serving, a hot cupboard to warm plates and cabinets jam-packed with service for fifty-plus passengers.

The electrical equipment was powered by a small windmill that dropped from one of the midship engine cars. It generated electricity for the kitchen whenever R.101 traveled faster than forty miles per hour. And, for safety, the electrical apparatus met the standard used in coal mines: in mines, as in a hydrogen-filled airship, open flames were prohibited so the heating elements used "black heat," low-resistance thick wires that do not glow red.

Once prepared, the plated food was lifted by a dumbwaiter to the dining room above the kitchen. With this minimal equipment, Savidge, the steward, intended to surprise R.101's paying passengers with meals that were, he said, "as well cooked and as well served as in any West End Hotel." To achieve this standard he had hired a prominent London-based chef to prepare menus for seven-course dinners.

From the kitchen, a few intrepid and hungry Members returned to the walkway where they could view the engine cars slung under the ship. Crew stationed there guided them to openings in the hull above the two midship engine cars. Five engines powered R.101: two toward the front, a slight distance apart; two, also similarly spaced, just aft of midship—where the Members now stood—and the fifth on the centerline near the tail. Each engine was housed in an egg-shaped, brightly polished metal engine car about twelve and a half feet long and just over ten and a half feet in diameter. From the hull opening, the Members looked down a short, open-air ladder used by engineers to access the cars. "Utterly perilous," muttered one of them. Inside the engine car, easily seen by the Members through the car's open door, an engineer worked only a few feet from a running engine. In the chilly weather, excess heat from the two midship engines was blown into the passenger quarters because only the thin fabric cover separated passengers from the outside.

When they had finished their tour, the Members returned to the lounge in the passenger quarters. Savidge, the steward, guided them fifty at a time into the dining room next to the lounge and sleeping quarters. The dining room, "as roomy as a big yacht," was brightly lit by large glass windows that diffused and softened the sunlight. Elegant white tablecloths with a damask square pattern graced each table; on them Savidge had laid, with precision, cutlery and tableware blazoned with the Royal Airship Works crest—white china trimmed with royal blue. Silver salt shakers, crystal glasses, and small butter dishes complemented the table setting.

Savidge stood against a wall with his back straight and his chin raised—his appearance was "spick and span," said a crew member. He signaled his staff to begin service. White-clad waiters served the Members a feast: thirty chickens, twenty-five quarts of soup, twenty-five quarts of tea, seventy pounds of potatoes, 400 dinner rolls, and five gallons each of milk, port, whiskey and beer.

At lunch, R.101's officers mixed with the guests. Atherstone told the Members near him a few "home truths about the short-handed way this ship is being run." Irwin noticed that in the bumpy weather the tableware bounced off the table because beading along the edge was not deep enough. Also, he noted, the tables needed a batten or wood strip along the center to keep plates in place. And Scott detailed the ship's operation and extolled the virtues of an Empire-wide airship service.

As the Members feasted, heavy rain and hail beat on the dining room's windows. The wind rose to sixty miles per hour and swung R.101 thirty degrees around the tower in less than a minute. As the squall rocked the ship, Scott reassured the MPs. Only two or three weeks before, he said, he would have prevented passengers from boarding if the winds exceeded thirty miles per hour, but now that the ship was tested—after only seven flights—winds of double this speed posed no danger. Once the squall had passed, Savidge ordered the waiters to bring dessert.

With the Members in high spirits, the staff of R.101 delivered a message from Lord Thomson, absent because of pressing Air Ministry business. "The weather conditions," Thomson had written, "have proved to be much more unsuitable than was foreseen as late as eight o'clock this morning." Because of this the flight was canceled. "The ability of R.101 to stand up to conditions is not in question," only whether passengers would "be exposed to discomfort and delay in disembarkation." He explained that "the wind is nearly a mile a minute" which "might render her return to the tower a slow and difficult operation." No mention of decreased lift from heavy rain, or of the record load on the airship.

Disappointed but sated after lunch, the Members gazed from the windows of the promenade deck as hail and rain continued to hammer against the windows. Across the haze-covered fields of the Works the wind thrashed the nearby trees. Those sitting in the wicker chairs were rocked to sleep by the ship's gentle rolling, but those on the bench fidgeted because the ninety-degree angle between seat and back was too severe for comfort. One drunk Member heard an engine come to life—more heat was needed in the passenger quarters—and was convinced he'd taken a "longish" flight on R.101. Those not inclined to a rest after their meal raided the stacks of stationery, clearing out the supply in minutes.

Several descended to the lower deck to enjoy the smoking room. The room was small—thirty people could squeeze into the built-in benches and wicker chairs—yet had a high ceiling, which an MP thought created "an odd, cell-like effect." A ventilator on the ceiling drew in air, ensuring a higher pressure in the room than outside, so that no hydrogen could leak into it. The room itself was, of course, fireproof, its wood walls layered with asbestos and covered with aluminum. Still, no matches were allowed; only the electric lighters built into the furniture. As further protection against an explosion, it was built into the lower deck, instead of the passenger deck above, "so as to have," said the ship's designers, "at least one complete deck" between the smoking room and a hydrogen-filled gas bag that rested on top of the passenger quarters.

As the Members smoked, conversation turned from the features of R.101 to a discussion of its larger role in the empire's aviation plans. The Conservatives, Thomson's political opponents, thought little of the ship. "Not a commercial proposition," said the Irish MP William Allen as he petted his small dog. Lord Askwith praised the Royal Airship Works for the ship's design, but needed "much more proof before I believe they can be a successful commercial proposition." And the die-hard capitalist Lord Monkswell called R.101 "an enormous amount of space" for a "comparatively small accommodation."

More worrisome, Members of Thomson's own Labour Party thought dim the prospects of R.101's success. MP Fielding West, from Kennington North, announced himself "against the R.101 from a commercial point of view." And Robert Young, Islington North, doubted "whether this type or any type of airship will ever be successful as a freight-carrier," although he hoped it might compete against planes as purely a passenger ship.

By evening the Members departed in groups of ten, with a short interval between each group as the ship was trimmed. After all had exited, Atherstone was glad to be "rid of the last of them." He saw no "useful purpose" in the flight. "The whole show," he said, "was merely stupid." And the questionable measures he used to lighten the ship bothered him: "taking all the emergency and tinned rations and parachutes out of the ship!" With the MPs gone, he assessed R.101's performance to date.

Although Atherstone thought some features of the ship a success—the cloth cover, the automatic venting of hydrogen, and the "undoubted strength of the hull"—he groused about everything else. "We have never had any confidence in the machinery," he wrote in his diary, "and we have not made a single flight [where] something or other has not broken down." The engines, especially, disappointed him.

The engines had impressed Atherstone when they were first tested in the shed. Their terrifying roar echoed through the metal shed—a shout a few inches from an ear could not be heard. The engines shook the ship and pulled on the cables tethering it to the shed floor. Static electricity generated by the engines created blue halos that rose from the floor like electrified smoke rings. To prevent the discharge from igniting the hydrogen-filled ship, workers sprayed the floor with water. The propellers, just a few feet off the floor, swirled the water and created miniature tornadoes that skidded across the floor.

Although the engines impressed in the shed, they disappointed in the air.

The nearly two-and-a-half-ton engines propelled the ship too slowly. Designed originally for bolting to a one-hundred-ton locomotive chassis, they vibrated violently when run at full power in R.101's engine cars—housings tethered to the airship by two slender posts. The vibrations split open the aluminum cooling pipes for the engines and cracked the hollow metal propellers. To solve the problem, the engines were run at 80 percent of full power and wood propellers had to be installed instead of metal.

But, as often is the case, in solving one design flaw—the cracking of the hollow metal propeller—other significant adjustments had to be made. Unlike the metal propeller, a wood prop, due to stress, could not change from a forward to a reverse pitch, and so one of the engines had to be dedicated to reversing—leaving four of the five engines to move the ship forward. The result was that, without wind, R.101 traveled at sixty-three miles per hour at best when cruising, and, because the typical headwind was about fifteen miles per hour, more often than not the ship traveled at just forty-five miles per hour.

"The speed," Atherstone noted with deliberate understatement, "is nothing wonderful." But then his anger showed as he wrote that the engines were a "joke" and the shed tests a "barefaced wrangle."

Yet he worried less about the engines than about the weight R.101 could lift.

Earlier the ship had struggled to stay horizontal at the tower when overloaded with Members; it would have dropped to the ground if it weren't for the stiff wind of forty-five miles per hour. Yet even with only crew, Atherstone was sure the ship could not haul enough fuel to travel to India.

"I investigated the question of lift in England, Egypt, and India about a year ago," he noted, and concluded that "unless there is at least an extra fifteen tons there is no use in talking of flying to India with only one stop for refueling." He had sent his calculations to the Works' technical staff, but heard nothing in the year that followed. However, soon after the canceled MP flight, Atherstone heard rumors of changes to the ship, a "refit" in Works terminology. At first he could not confirm the rumors: "Neither

Irwin nor I," he complained,

> have received any information as to what the refit is to consist of,
> that is a very peculiar state of affairs but typical of the manner in
> that the whole of this place is run. We have not even been supplied
> with an official lift and trim statement although this has been
> repeatedly asked for.

By early December, though, he learned that the Royal Airship
Works' technical staff had spent November studying data from
the airship's test flights. They flipped through the ship's logbooks
and tallied every ounce of ballast water used, each puff of hydrogen added to the gas bags, and every drop of fuel consumed. And
they perused detailed studies of the weather along R.101's route
from Britain to India.

The data revealed a startling truth: "It would be impossible,"
the Works' engineers wrote in an internal report, "to attempt to
operate the ship [R.101] on the India route even for demonstration
flights." On the return trip from India, R.101 could not haul
enough fuel to travel more than half the first leg. In the searing
heat along the 2,800-mile leg from Karachi, India to Ismailia,
Egypt, R.101's fuel would run out over the Arabian Desert; the
ship would float with its engines stalled a thousand miles from
the mooring tower in Egypt. The lift that should have been used
for fuel was taken up by R.101's overweight metal framework and
engines. The ship needed at least six more tons of lift to have the
slimmest margin of safety when leaving India. And even with
this amount, "R.101 can hardly be expected to operate with any
degree of regularity on the Indian route."

R.101 would be a mere ghost ship, a metal carcass with a skeleton crew.

To rescue the airship from failure, the technical staff devised
an audacious two-step plan to modify it. The first part of the plan
meant moving R.101 to its shed and stripping excess weight from

it and enlarging its gas bags to increase its lift. To test the changes wrought by this "intensive effort," R.101 would fly, in late June, in the Royal Air Force Display, a great pageant of British air-craft—an "imperialist orgy" to its critics. Then back to the shed from July to September for workers to implement a second stage of the modification.

This second modification was so brazen that Atherstone wondered how it would be done. "How this miracle is going to be accomplished," he wrote, "is entirely beyond me."

The plan was to add a gas bag to R.101 by cutting the ship in half and inserting a new center section. The scope of the change was so complex that Atherstone felt sure the burden of readying R.101 for a late September 1930 flight to India would fall on him. "I suppose it will be another flap and panic," he wrote in his diary, and "the flying staff will again be called upon to save the faces of the 'heads' by taking over the ship in a semiready and nearly totally unairworthy condition."

CHAPTER FIVE

PROBLEMS WITH THE CLOTH COVER

JUNE 1930

SIX MONTHS AFTER R.101 RETURNED to the shed for the first stage of its refit, Michael Rope, the Works' engineering genius, crawled along the top of the airship and scrutinized its cloth cover. Once a specular, reflective silver, it was now a dull gray, its smooth surface crenulated. At regular intervals, the lean, gaunt Rope knelt and pressed his fingers against the plasticized cloth cover palpating it to test for tautness and strength. When it flexed, he cut out a section two by eight inches, which he handed in silence to a colleague. The reserved Rope usually broke his silences with wry jokes, but today he was grim.

Rope returned to his workshop, picked out one of the small cloth sections he'd gathered, clamped each end to a stand, let the middle sag, and hung a small weight from the cloth to draw it taut. He increased the weight until, at eighty-five pounds, the cloth ripped. This failure point was far lower than the typical forces on R.101's cover: at the ship's highest speed the wind battered the cover with 140 pounds of force, even higher in turbulent weather. A storm would rip open the cover and expose the gas bags to pelting rain and piercing wind.

89

Rope, always methodical, repeated this test on each strip he'd gathered from the ship. All failed the test. He drew a conclusion, which he summarized in a memo to his superior, Vincent Richmond, R.101's chief designer: "There is no margin of safety for flight in rough atmosphere."

The cloth cover's protection may seem mundane when compared to the strength of the ship's metal framework, the forceful lift of its gas bags, or the roar of its powerful engines—yet the thin cotton-linen cover was as essential as the framework, engines, or gas bags. It kept at bay water that might corrode the framework, protected the gas bags from the elements, and guided air over the ship in a smooth slipstream so the engines' full power could propel R.101 forward.

To protect the airship the cloth cover must possess three key properties. First, it must be taut; if it flaps, the cover weakens until it fails. Once it is breached, disaster strikes: the now un-streamlined ship bucks in the air, rain and wind punch holes in the gas bags, the airship loses lift and crashes into the ground in an inferno. Second, the cover must be waterproof otherwise the ship's metal framework could corrode over time. The framework was constructed from stainless steel and duralumin, an early form of aluminum. Both materials resisted corrosion—for additional protection, the steel was coated with lacquer, and the duralumin was anodized—but over years of exposure to water, they could weaken. And third, the cover must be opaque and reflect as much light as possible. This kept the gas bags cool and prevented heating that could cause the bags to expand and burst.

No textile displayed all three of these characteristics, so the Works' technical staff spent months searching for a material to replace the low-tech cloth used on most airships. To create a strong cover, they looked into thin sheets of the same material as the frame—stainless steel and duralumin—but each weighed too much; a stainless steel cover weighed thirty-six tons more than a cloth cover and a duralumin cover exceeded cloth by six tons. They thinned the sheets until they weighed no more than cloth, but the metal then tore. They corrugated the thin sheets to increase strength, but soon realized that was impractical for R.101's five and a half acres of cover. The staff evaluated phosphor-bronze, a metal gauze that blended the properties of metal and cloth, but it snapped when pulled taut. In the end, they settled for the material used by Germany's zeppelins: chemically treated cloth.

The cloth used for R.101's cover was impregnated with cellulose nitrate—known as "dope" at the Works. A predecessor of today's plastics, the dope conferred on the cloth all three of its crucial properties: the weather-tight seal, reflectivity, and, at least in the past, tautness. On previous airships, workers always laced the cloth cover to the airship's framework—then coated it with dope. To apply the dope, workers hung from the shed's rafters and used sprayers. This slow, hazardous task impeded the rapid production of airships; mass manufacturing a fleet of airships, a goal of the Royal Airship Works, was a necessity.

The Works' team decided on an alternative method: workers applied a less rigid dope and then attached the cloth to the ship's frame, cranking the cover taut. This mechanically induced tension was reinforced by internal pressure created by circulating air allowed in by vents. Although this new method saved time, it weakened the cloth—as proved by Michael Rope's tests. Cranking on the rigid precoated fabric created thousands of small cracks that let water seep into the weft. The rains in October and November and the humid air in the shed soaked R.101's cover, which absorbed three tons of water. This rotted the fabric until, as Rope noted, there was "no margin of safety."

This was a damning indictment from Rope, who had, according to a colleague, "the best mathematical brain amongst the staff" at the Works. Another said he was "an outstanding and practical design genius." Rope applied his superb technical skills to carry out the sometimes unorthodox ideas of Richmond, the ship's chief designer. Richmond had little airship design experience and no engineering training, so he relied on Rope to put his ideas into practice.

For example, when Richmond's design called for a hydraulic system to control the ship's rudders and elevators, Rope dutifully installed it—but designed solid control linkages to eliminate posts, cables, and pulleys throughout the ship. It worked so well that the ship responded to the lightest touch with the hydraulics turned off. Or, when Richmond's design for R.101's framework deviated from established zeppelin principles and eliminated the structures that restrained the gas bags, Rope devised a clever wire netting to keep the gas bags in place. Richmond, a good manager and picker of people, embraced Rope's help. "He's got two loves," Richmond joked, "R.101 and Doreen"—Rope's wife, four months pregnant—"but I say it's almost bigamy: Michael's married to R.101 already."

Although Richmond celebrated Rope's acumen, the engineer's natural reserve and modesty prevented his opinions from reaching beyond Richmond. Rope was "so modest and retiring," said a colleague, "that he tended to efface himself and to discount the credit which was really his due. Few realized how gifted and valuable he really was."

In his memo warning of "no margin of safety," Rope asked Richmond to consider whether "the risk involved" in sending R.101 "on a long overseas flight is—or is not—greater than is justified by the need to fulfill public expectations." And he ended his memo with the most stunning suggestion. "Is it not conceivable," he wrote, "that a public statement could be made which would satisfy the people who matter—to the effect that overseas flights have been postponed for, say, six months on account of improvements which have been undertaken with the reliability required of convincing demonstrations ...." By "people who matter" Rope was alluding to R.101's patron, Lord Thomson.

At around the same time that Michael Rope was writing his memo outlining the deficiencies of R.101's cover, the grandiloquent Lord Thomson hurried across the Tudor rose that graced the floor of the Peers' Lobby, eager to promote the airship in the House of Lords. When the Air Minister entered the chamber, a Peer rose from his crimson leather bench and asked: "Does civil aviation pay?" He continued: "How much is it going to benefit the Empire as a whole? What is civil aviation worth to the Empire? What is it worth to the political life of the Empire?"

Lord Thomson rose to defend his government's aviation program and its flagship R.101. "Civil aviation," he began, "is a fertile field and needs constant weeding because of its fertility." Airships, he said, "would link up our Empire in a way that, so far as I can see, no other means of transport can approach. I am aware that there has been a great deal of disappointment in regard to the airship program." Thomson's stunt with the MPs' flight had fueled that disappointment. It led Members to think, he said, that R.101 was ready to "take one hundred MPs all over the country." Thomson now called the proposed flight "the greatest error of all my life," although he refused to admit that weather caused the flight's cancellation.

"It was not because," he had told the chamber earlier, "of the weather condition in the least from the point of view of safety of the airship, that we postponed the [MPs] flight." He claimed R.101 could "have easily flown that day," but that the cloudy day would have made for poor "entertainment." Members would have seen only "a sea of cloud" below them or "nothing but driving rain." The canceled flight, though, epitomized the slow development of British airships.

The airship program had started in 1924 and ships were to be flying by 1927, but none did so until 1929. In front of his peers, Thomson cast the delays in building R.101 and its postponed flight to India as blips on the path to a fleet of imperial airships. "In spite of many setbacks," he said, "and some disappointments, my faith is absolutely undimmed, and I am sure the people of this country will be right in continuing these experiments." Many Members wondered why British airships were still experimental, while Germany's *Graf Zeppelin* soared around the world.

As Thomson spoke, the *Graf Zeppelin* flew over the Azores at eighty miles per hour on its way to a triumphant return to Germany from a twenty-three-day, 13,400-nautical-mile Pan-American tour. How puny seemed R.101's seventy-three hours of flight compared to the *Graf Zeppelin* voyages: its approach to Lisbon marked its eighth ocean crossing and 100,000th mile of travel.

The *Graf Zeppelin* would continue on to Germany, stay for a few days and then start its summer European tour—to Switzerland, Denmark, Sweden, and, gallingly, Scotland, Ireland and England. These whirlwind world tours astonished the Peers. They remembered well the terror of wartime zeppelin raids and recalled the provisions of the Treaty of Versailles to dismantle the Zeppelin Company.

The treaty mandated the destruction or surrender of all German airships, the demolition of hangars, hydrogen gas plants, and airship factories. As their first act under the treaty, the Principal Allied Powers—Britain, France, Italy, and Japan—seized all Zeppelin Company airships and moved them to their countries. With no airships to sell, and no lucrative military contracts, the Zeppelin Company neared bankruptcy. Undeterred, Hugo

Eckener, the force behind zeppelin, ordered his workers to use wartime surplus parts to build two small passenger airships. Once they were built, the allies confiscated them—one airship was sent to France, the other to Italy. But Eckener fought back.

To combat the mandates of the Treaty of Versailles, Eckener cut a deal with the American military: the Zeppelin Company would build an airship for the U.S. as a reparation. America now had a stake in keeping the zeppelin factories intact. U.S. influence helped persuade the allies to leave zeppelin facilities untouched and to lift the treaty's restrictions on German airship construction. With the threat of extinction lifted, Eckener, in the mid-1920s, dreamed of creating a transatlantic airship, the *Graf Zeppelin*, but "after seven years of depression," he said, the Zeppelin Company "is at the end of its tether." Eckener approached the Weimar government for funding, but they refused to support his dream. The cash-strapped government had just conquered hyperinflation, returned Germany to the gold standard, and secured their first international loan. They worried that a zeppelin in the sky would evoke memories of bombing raids and offend Germany's hard-won international partners.

"I've just got one solution left," said Eckener, "that's to take our problem to the German people." To him zeppelin-brand airships were an "eminent national and cultural achievement" and a "national treasure" of the German nation. To raise money through donations to build the *Graf Zeppelin*, he formed the *Zeppelin-Eckener-Spende des deutschen Volkes* (the Zeppelin-Eckener-Fund of the German People). To drum up support, he and other senior zeppelin executives tirelessly traveled across Germany. They attended lunches and teas during the day; in the evenings they addressed civic organizations, clubs and formal dinners.

They brought with them zeppelin kitsch: campaign buttons, postage stamps, pictures, and postcards. On the postcards they printed appeals to German patriotism: "No genuine German," read one, "will fail to contribute to save the Luftschiffbau Zeppelin, no matter how small his gift. Everyone must give something, so that the unity of our entire nation may be seen to hover in the skies above us! Be Sure to Give! Immediately!"

Eckener urged the German public to sustain "its spiritual and technological strength, lest it lose confidence in itself and its future." The *Spende* raised two and half million marks, far short of the seven million needed to build the *Graf Zeppelin*. The Weimar government eventually contributed a million marks, but the rest came from the Zeppelin Company. After the First World War, they had retooled their factories and facilities to manufacture consumer goods: engine crankcases for the automobile manufacturer Opel, heavy engines for railcars, and aluminum containers for gas, milk, and beer. Their hydrogen plants synthesized industrial gases. The factory that wove the cloth for the zeppelin's outer cover created consumer textiles. And they leased one for their giant airship hangars to a movie studio. All of these facilities could be used again for zeppelins.

From donations, government funds, and contract work the Zeppelin Company cobbled together enough funding to create a single airship—the *Graf Zeppelin*—although the company continued to manufacture consumer goods.

The partial return of the Zeppelin Company to building airships and the *Graf Zeppelin*'s freewheeling around the globe cast doubts on the competence of the Royal Airship Works and on the soundness of R.101's design.

In his speech to the House of Lords Thomson addressed the matter of the German success.

> You may well ask why it is that the *Graf Zeppelin* can go round the world and make enormous flights while our two ships spend their time mainly in their sheds. That is a very easy question to answer. The Germans have thirty years' experience of building airships. They ran commercial ships from Lake Constance before the War. I do not wish to decry the virtues of our own people, but in view of that experience I think it is only natural that we should accept the fact that there are very few Dr. Eckeners [the great intellectual force behind zeppelins] in this world. We have not had time to produce our Dr. Eckener—one of the most remarkable men I have ever met. They are not found in every generation.

Zealous, though, for the "British" approach to airships, Thomson defended R.101's design: "We have started out on the design of these two ships [R.100 and R.101] on a basis of first principles. We have not copied any well-known model, but we have produced two ships that are the strongest in the world." He proclaimed them "almost unbreakable." Thomson declared R.101 and R.100 "capable of flying in any foreseeable weather provided they are properly navigated." Yet, as he spoke, the cover of R.101 rotted in its shed to the point, in Michael Rope's words, that it had "no margin of safety for flight in a rough atmosphere."

Unwilling to back down from his vision of airships as the standard bearers for British aviation, Thomson asked the Peers to "proceed forthwith" with approval for the construction of a 7,500,000-cubic-foot ship—a third larger than R.101. He characterized this proposed ship, in a telling phrase, as a "commercial proposition," a phrase inappropriate for the overweight R.101. And he closed his speech with praise for R.101: "It combines speed, safety, and indeed amenities, because to travel in an airship is by far the most delightful form of travel that I personally have ever experienced." Yet as Thomson spoke, those amenities were being stripped from R.101.

At the Royal Airship Works, fifty miles north of London, workers executed the first stage of R.101's two-stage refit to gain lift. They treated the airship like a critically ill patient; as ordered by the Works' technical staff, they triaged three tons from R.101. They lopped off more than a half-ton of girders shown by the test flights to be unnecessary for supporting the cloth cover. They stripped the 400-pound hydraulic power steering for the rudder and fins, redundant because of Rope's clever linkages. They replaced the wavy triplex glass of the promenade deck with cellon windows, and swapped the cast aluminum cylinder covers on the engines with sheet metal ones. They axed now useless fuel tanks— R.101's capacity for fuel far exceeded the amount it could lift—to pare 1,000 pounds. They demolished twelve of the fifty-two double-berth compartments and barricaded the empty space. And, because R.101 would for now haul no paying passengers, only enthusiastic guests, they removed amenities. No longer was hot water piped to the rooms. "Supplies of hot water," reported the technical staff, "could be obtained in lieu from the galley." This simple change cut 630 pounds from the ship. They snipped 350 pounds from the ventilation and heating systems of the passenger cabins. "For the flight to India," they reasoned, "any question of passenger car heating should be abolished." They removed two passenger bathrooms to shed 130 pounds, and stripped the kitchen of its vegetable steamer and hot cupboard. Desperate to shave every bit of weight possible they whittled thirty pounds by dismantling the engine telegraph in the room above the control car. And they even trimmed three pounds by building the bow voice pipe into the passengers' handrail along the ship's corridor. To gain three more tons of lift, they enlarged each gas bag by three or four inches by letting out the netting designed by Michael Rope to keep the gas bags in place.

These changes increased R.101's lift by five tons, enough to add 650 nautical miles of range when cruising at fifty-five miles per hour. Not enough to cross the Arabian Desert when flying from Egypt to India. To cross the desert required lift gained in the second stage of the refit, which would add 1,500 or so miles to the range.

To test R.101's changes, Major Scott scheduled a flight to the Hendon Airfield in North London, where the airship would, he hoped, stun audiences at the upcoming RAF Display—an annual air show that showcased Britain's aviation prowess.

A few days beforehand, at 3:30 a.m. on June 23rd—twenty days after Thomson had told his colleagues in the House of Lords that R.101 could fly "in any foreseeable weather"—Scott, megaphone in hand, barked orders to a few hundred men as they walked the greatly modified airship from the shed to the mooring tower.

Exiting the shed without incident was the last thing that would go well that day.

Soon after the ship was attached to the tower's arm, the wind picked up. The cover rippled from bow to stern. As the wind increased, ripples from the ship's bow collided with those originating aft. A crew member watched the violent action and thought: "No cover can stand that sort of treatment for long." He was correct: a 140-foot-long tear opened along the top of the ship.

The next day, newspapers followed the Air Ministry press guidance: "Slight damage to the fabric near the top of the airship was noticed yesterday afternoon but it was learned that it was nothing to worry about." The Works' nimble and efficient riggers scrambled across the ship's cover and glued shut the split with strips of cloth, like a bandage over a wound, to allow R.101's star turn at the RAF Display to go ahead later that month, but everyone at the Works knew that the cloth cover's failure imperiled its demonstration flight to India in October.

CHAPTER SIX

THE AIRSHIP FLIES AGAIN

JUNE–JULY 1930

THE TWO PLANES DOVE AND ASCENDED, twinning their smoke trails—orange and white, respectively—until they created an ephemeral Prince of Wales feather, the heraldic badge of the heir apparent. As the feather dissipated, R.101 circled the Hendon Airfield in North London while Irwin awaited the cue for the ship to rehearse its role in the RAF Display scheduled for the next day. He flew a revitalized ship, its lift increased by five tons—two tons from shaving more weight, three tons from enlarging the gas bags further—and with a patched together outer cloth cover.

As R.101 circled at an altitude of 1,500 feet on this late June afternoon, the august tones of the RAF Central Band in the stands below occasionally wafted into the control car, but the music was often obscured by the growl of planes. First, Interceptor fighters zoomed by at an astonishing 200 miles per hour, then nine aerobatic biplanes swooped over the airfield. They split into groups of three, each group linked by elastic ropes. The planes came astonishingly close while flying at 150 miles per hour, crisscrossing to create with the ropes a colossal pendant in the sky. Their nimble maneuvers highlighted R.101's stately majesty as it hovered in the blue summer sky. Once the biplanes departed, Irwin received the cue for R.101 to fly over the airfield.

Irwin ordered the rudder coxswain to swing R.101 around until its nose pointed toward the airfield. R.101's engines roared and the mighty airship surged forward. Today, Irwin commanded R.101 without his friend and trusted First Officer, Noel Atherstone. Atherstone was detailed to Canada to lead the relief crew for the soon-to-depart R.100, the sibling airship assigned to pioneer Atlantic crossings. Although Irwin missed Atherstone, he was relieved to be without the meddlesome Major Scott; he was on the Canada flight as well.

Irwin ordered the elevator coxswain to execute a shallow dive to imitate a bow to the royal box. The viewing stands were empty today, but would be full tomorrow. The coxswain nudged his wheel to start a gentle dive, but the ship dove sharply toward the ground. The quick-thinking coxswain spun the elevator control wheel to reverse the direction of the elevators, but R.101 continued its descent. The ship dropped, in a few seconds, 1,000 feet, until about 500 feet from the ground its nose rose, and the ship glided over the back of the stands as it climbed to 1,500 feet. The dive shocked the control car crew, alert now for further unusual motions of the ship.

On its return to the Works, R.101 chopped through the air, its nose again and again descending then rising and Irwin struggled to keep the ship above 1,000 feet. He knew, of course, that the lift changed based on fuel consumption and the air temperature, which caused the hydrogen to expand or contract, but still the ship's erratic flight was unusual.

Although R.101 guzzled two tons of fuel on its flight, Irwin had to drop nine tons of ballast before landing. He attributed the ship's "heavy" flying to the weather. The day of the RAF Display temperatures reached 70°F and, through the sparse clouds, the sun baked R.101's outer cover for more than twelve hours—the pale, redheaded Irwin was always aware of the sun. He knew it heated the hydrogen in the gas bags and caused them to swell, which increased the lift by as much as five tons.

This was not an uncommon problem for airships. The *Graf Zeppelin* had overheated only a week earlier. It had landed on the ground in Hamburg—the Germans preferred ground landings to mooring towers—and the captain and first officer had stepped off the ship to greet the crowd of 25,000, which included the Senate of the Free State of Hamburg, all wearing formal dress. As the town's mayor presented the captain with an engraved cup to commemorate the first landing of a zeppelin in Hamburg, the stern of the airship rose, the ship almost standing on its nose. The second officer, still in the ship, ordered ballast dropped and the engines started. He righted the ship, but its buoyancy increased by the heating of its gas bags, it could not land again. He returned the ship to Berlin, where the cooler night air decreased the ship's lift and allowed it to land.

To Irwin, this phenomenon explained not only R.101's rapid rises, but also its abrupt descents. The heat enlarged the gas bags so much that the automatic valves purged hydrogen to prevent the bags from bursting. This cycle of expanding and purging repeated throughout the flight.

The next day, R.101 returned to Hendon Airfield and awed 150,000 spectators with a spectacular entrance. The ship hid behind a cloud, and on cue flew low and slow over the airfield. On Irwin's orders it executed the rehearsed "bow" to Prince George, the future Duke of Kent, who sat with Prince and Princess Takamatsu of Japan.

En route, R.101 had behaved well but, on the return to the Works, the ship repeatedly dove sharply. After each dive the coxswain angled the elevators to force R.101 to creep back to its proper altitude. "It is as much as I can do to hold her up, sir," said the exhausted coxswain, his face streaming with sweat—"sweating blood," recalled an observer. The moment the coxswain leveled the ship, it dipped again. The crew suggested to Irwin that it was "bent," their term for a heavy airship. They recommended that he drop ballast. Irwin rejected this. Better, he said, to keep the ballast for landing. Turbulent air, he thought, caused R.101's instability. When R.101 arrived at the tower, Irwin jettisoned more than eight tons of ballast to lighten the ship enough for mooring. He now worried that R.101 leaked hydrogen. Perhaps the seals around the automatic valves had loosened. When the ship was moored he planned to investigate the gas bags and the valves.

The ship's gas bags are "the least satisfactory part" of R.101, declared the ship's chief designer, adding that "development and improvement" of the bags "is badly needed." In their five years of planning R.101, he and his staff searched for the perfect gas bag material: something impermeable to hydrogen, lightweight, flexible, yet durable. They considered the varnished silk or cambric used in balloons, but these fabrics weighed too much. So, they investigated rubber, gelatin and glycerin, and viscose, a synthetic fabric, coated with latex. All failed. When crumpled then inflated, each of these materials cracked and leaked.

So they settled for the traditional material used to construct airship gas bags: the intestines of oxen.

The outside of an ox's intestine is lined with a fine membrane, called the cecum, which is thin and flexible, and through which hydrogen seeps only slowly. It's an ideal material for a gas bag, except for its size. The cecum of an ox is about thirty inches by six inches, a little over a square foot, yet one of R.101's gas bags when spread flat covers 30,000 square feet—a square about 175 feet on a side—so to create a gas bag constructed from a double layer of cecum calls for 50,000 entrails. In total, over a million and a half oxen intestines were needed to create R.101's fifteen gas bags.

The grisly work of fabricating the gas bags was done by the women of the Royal Airship Works. Almost all the labor at the Works was local, what one aviation expert called "Bedfordshire yokels," although he noted, "they are extraordinarily good workers and well disciplined." To start construction of a gas bag, the women first unpacked oxen entrails shipped in barrels from Argentinian slaughterhouses. In a room reeking of offal, they soaked the intestines to remove the salt crystals used as preservative in transit, scraped away lumps of fat with blunt knives, soaked the skins overnight, and then scraped again.

Next, they placed the skins on a huge roll of canvas stretched top and bottom between two rollers, tilted at fifty degrees like an easel. Twenty women standing a shoulder's width apart each laid down two layers of skins on the canvas in front of them and then, on cue, they rolled the canvas to flatten the skins and expose a new, blank section of canvas to work on. They repeated this until they fused about 25,000 skins into a single, continuous sheet with the weight and texture of parchment.

Next, they moved the giant rolls to the gluing room. In the oppressive mothball-like odor of the creosote-based glue, they unfurled the canvas, peeled off the thin skins, smoothed them like tablecloths over large tables, and clamped them taut. On the taut skins they glued cotton fabric. The gluing room then filled with the odor of formaldehyde as the women coated the cotton-skin composite with a waterproofing varnish.

After this the skins were moved to the large floor of the humid assembly room—maintained at 80 percent humidity to keep the skins pliable—where the women laid out the cotton-skin layers on the floor to create the vast surface of a gas bag. They used two of the rolled sheets' worth of skins for the smallest bags, but eight or so for the largest bag, which covered nearly three acres.

Once the delicate sheets were laid out, the women sandpapered the edges of each sheet and glued them together to form a flayed and flattened gas bag. After cutting a hole for the gas valve, they wrapped this vast sheet around a cotton form in the shape of a gas bag, its shape maintained by an air blower. They glued shut the remaining seams, deflated the cotton form and removed it through the valve hole. The glue improved on the sewing technique used to construct zeppelin gas bags because gluing left no needle holes that could leak.

After construction the deflated gas bag lay on the floor, a mass of folds, large enough to hold 37,500 cubic feet of hydrogen—a sphere with a radius of twenty feet—yet weighing only thirty pounds. Soon it would be transported to R.101, inserted into the metal framework and inflated with care because the bag cost over £8,000, or ten times the price of a house in a London suburb in 1930.

After R.101 returned from the RAF Display, Irwin investigated the gas bags and their embedded automatic gas valve. To do this he climbed from the walkway into the bag area. The gas bags formed an off-white ceiling ten feet or so above the walkway. His inspection of the seals on the first three gas bags uncovered no problems. When he reached the fourth, he climbed a small ladder, then grabbed the wire netting that tethered the gas bag to the ship's stainless steel and duralumin framework. He lifted himself onto the bag. A small flashlight dangled from his neck. Although electrical lights illuminated the walkway, the gas bags above were always dark, even dank. The odor of mold permeated the air; after months in the dark the animal intestine bags often rotted. Irwin used the netting like a jungle gym to climb across the gas bag's vast surface, the tall man so insignificant on the bag that he looked like a fly in an enormous spider's net. The delicate gas bags were fragile—less than a year earlier a rigger had slipped and punctured one with his foot—so as he climbed Irwin gently parted the area where the neighboring gas bags touched.

The giant bags muffled all sound, yet in that echo-less atmosphere he sang, talked, and whistled as he climbed, hoping that, if he reached a pocket of escaped hydrogen, his voice would become high-pitched or his whistle shrill. Hydrogen is odorless, colorless, and tasteless so it asphyxiates without warning; more than one unconscious worker had plunged to his death while working inside an airship. When Irwin reached the valve, he ran his hand along its seating, where a fabric patch covered with rubber solution secured the valves to the gas bag. The seal was intact; it had no ruptures. Then he placed his ear close to the seal and listened for escaping hydrogen. He heard no hissing. To test for smaller leaks Irwin held up a bit of tissue paper. He saw no fluttering.

Then, casting his light around the gas bag, he noticed holes. He climbed to the top: more holes. He returned to the walkway and continued his inspection, discovering holes in gas bags five, nine, ten, eleven, twelve, thirteen, and fourteen. He found holes in seven of R.101's fifteen gas bags. They were tiny, a mere three-eighths of an inch in diameter, yet they worried him.

Irwin was troubled by the holes' origin. The quest for increased lift by letting out the wire netting restraining the gas bags had defeated itself: the newly enlarged gas bags chafed on the sharp edges of the framework bolts, which sliced the bags in many places, and, Irwin noticed, indented them in thousands of locations. If the rattling of the gas bags caused this much damage on a short flight, then the motion of the gas bags could cripple the ship on the long flight to India.

Although alarmed by the holes, Irwin was sure they were not the cause of R.101's dives as it flew to and from the Hendon Airfield. "Even allowing," he reported to his superiors at the Works, "for the numerous holes which are now being found in the gas bags where they have rubbed" on the framework, "the loss of gas would not have accounted for the heaviness of the ship during flights."

Irwin suspected that the automatic gas valves were leaking hydrogen; perhaps too much. He had three concerns. First, the valves were easily triggered intentionally to avoid gas bags bursting on R.101's trip to India. En route the airship might encounter a tropical thunderstorm, where turbulent air could force it high into the sky and burst a gas bag unless rapidly vented. So the valves were calibrated to expel large quantities of hydrogen. Second, in shed tests, the gas valves leaked when tilted to five degrees. And third, on the last Hendon flight a rigger heard chattering of the valve on gas bag eight. So Irwin hypothesized that in the turbulence on the flights to Hendon the gas bags surged and the ultrasensitive valves opened. Although he suspected the gas valves were the chief culprit in R.101's instability, he knew that the holes created by the chafing on the framework poised an equally grave danger. He ordered his crew to do a "thorough inspection of each gas bag," followed by "padding of [the framework's] longitudinals, radial struts, and reefing booms."

As crew men glued patches over the holes in the gas bags and padded the framework as a consequence of Irwin's findings, Mr. Frederick McWade inspected their work. The Royal Airship Works had, like every large British aircraft manufacturer, a resident inspector assigned by the government's Aeronautical Inspection Directorate (AID). An aviation inspector was regarded by "the average person," wrote *Flight* magazine, "as a sort of back-stair detective, who, disguised in a bowler hat and a false beard and armed with a micrometer, lurks behind machinery in airplane factories." In truth, the magazine's writer clarified, the inspector is "an extremely human and hardworking civil servant."

Indeed, McWade coordinated his inspections with the Works' Drawing Office, which issued all orders for construction and maintenance—an office so important that McWade joked that "if it was necessary to move a table from here to there, I should get the Drawing Office Instructions." The Office drew up orders for construction or for changes, McWade reviewed them and issued a small white chit if he approved, then the work was done. He repeated the inspection and issued a pink chit to certify he approved of the final result.

Despite McWade's intimate role in the daily routine of creating and maintaining R.101, AID regulations required that he form opinions independently of the Works' staff about the ship's deficiencies and the efficacy of any corrections. His regular reviews of the ship deepened the brain trust creating R.101 because he could draw on nearly thirty-five years of experience with lighter-than-air craft. He had begun with balloons when most of the Works' staff were still in diapers, then headed the construction of *Nulli Secundus*, Britain's first military airship. He spent twenty-seven years building and inspecting airships and knew the joys and difficulties of building them, and the terrors of flying them: he rode in *Nulli Secundus* when, on its second flight the ship plunged to the ground and shattered its metal framework.

His opinions were paramount because he recommended monthly whether the Director of Civil Aviation should issue a Permit to Fly. This legal document allowed experimental aircraft like R.101 "to be flown without having been certified as airworthy." It restricted R.101's test flights to no farther than 250 miles from the Royal Airship Works, forbade it from "carrying passengers for hire or reward," and noted it "may be withdrawn at any time." The current permit expired in less than a month, at the end of July 1930. McWade now had to recommend a new one, but the holes in the gas bags concerned him.

Only a few weeks before, McWade reflected, the bags were reconditioned—removed from the ship, examined, repaired, reinstalled, then reinflated—yet now the framework was punching holes in the bags. To investigate the condition of the bags himself, McWade climbed into the airship and repeated Irwin's inspection. At nearly sixty, climbing on the gas bags was harder for him than for Irwin, who was twenty-two years younger and a former Olympic athlete. Once in the gas bags, McWade aimed his lamp onto the padded framework; he leaned forward and rubbed the padding. To his surprise it easily moved. How, he wondered, could this padding protect the gas bags if the ship flew in rough weather? He parted the padding and studied the framework: he ran his fingers along the sharp nut and the end of the bolt. He realized that there could be thousands of puncture points in the gas bags. The padding worried him for another reason: how could he, or anyone else, tell whether the metal framework underneath was sound—it could well corrode and no one would know.

McWade's observations compelled him to alert his superiors.

Though he always addressed his report to his immediate superior, this time, anxious that it should be read by the highest-ranking official, McWade blazoned, "For the attention of DAI (AID)" in red letters across the top. The DAI, the Director of Aeronautical Inspection, ran the Directorate, and was two ranks above McWade. He headed his report "Confidential HMA R.101," then added a subheading: "Airworthiness of the above ship." In crisp prose he detailed the problems. "Padding," he reported, "is, in my opinion, very unsatisfactory, because the bags move when the ship is in flight and the padding becomes loose and the projection [i.e., the bolts] complained of is again exposed." He alerted his superiors to the possible lethal consequences of the padding: "The fabric will become damp and in many cases wet when the ship is in flight, therefore, there will be alternate processes of wetting and drying of the fabric which must be detrimental to the metal underneath."

He closed with a stunning conclusion: "Until this matter is seriously taken in hand and remedied I cannot recommend to you the extension of the present permit to fly or the issue of any further permits or certificates."

In McWade's opinion, the remedy required "a change of construction" in the gas bag wiring and framework—a rethinking of two miles of girders, eight miles of tubing, fifteen miles of rods, and eleven miles of cables that composed R.101's framework. As an experienced airship builder he knew this "would be a large undertaking," but he saw no other course; never in his years of experience with airships had a systematic structural defect been fixed by padding the framework.

So, in early July 1930, R.101 floated in its shed, banned from flying. The Works' staff prepared to execute the second stage of the refit—the "miracle," as Atherstone described it—to increase R.101's lift in time for a demonstration flight to India, three months away, but years behind schedule.

RADICAL SURGERY

W E PLAN," VINCENT RICHMOND, R.101's chief designer, explained in a letter to a friend, "to cut the ship in the middle and add an additional bay, which should give an additional eight or nine tons of disposable lift."

On July 29, 1930, workers began the second stage of R.101's refit, the "miracle" as Atherstone called it, to gain enough lift for safe travel to India. They circumscribed R.101's cover between the eighth and ninth gas bags and then sliced the cloth along that line. With the cover severed, the workers unbolted the exposed metal framework as clusters of men under R.101 counterbalanced the lift of its gas bags. Some men gripped handles on the control and engine cars; most, though, clutched ropes tied to the ship. As the ship parted, half the men walked the nose section toward the shed's 470-ton doors, and the others inched the sixty-seven-foot-tall rudder to the shed's rear wall.

The stench created in the shed was putrid. The cutting of the cloth cover released the vinegar-like smell of the "dope," the fluid used to treat the cloth. And with the oxen-and-glue gas bags open to the air for the first time in months, mold and mildew joined the odoriferous mix.

Still, the work had to be done; the new lift of an extra gas bag added to the five tons gained by shaving weight from the ship in the first step of the refit meant that R.101 could fly, in the searing heat, from Karachi, India to Ismailia, Egypt without refueling. The ship would carry enough fuel to cross the Arabian Desert plus a small reserve as a contingency. This modification of the ship, the splitting in two, was possible because of its revolutionary modular framework designed by Richmond.

Nothing in Vincent Richmond's manner suggested a revolutionary of any stripe. "That quiet, dark little man," as a journalist characterized him, adding that Richmond preached lucid and straightforward sermons as a lay preacher, nursed his invalid mother, and played a solid game of tennis. His colleagues at the Works described him as "stolid," "solid," "reliable," and "able" in his professional work. While none called him "gifted" as an engineer, they appreciated his tenacity: nothing interfered with Richmond's work designing airships for an Empire airship service.

When he took time off to attend a concert in London, he made up the lost hours by working late into the night. This was no burden to him: "I am one of the most fortunate of men," Richmond said of himself, "for I earn my livelihood doing what I love the most in the world." What he loved was his "baby," his nickname for R.101, which was to be the first in a fleet of airships that were the most comfortable form of transport in the history of humankind. These ships would feature, he once said, an "absence of motion, noise, dirt and smell"—and so would meet "British ideas" of comfort. The contrast he had in mind was with the comfort of the *Graf Zeppelin*, which Richmond experienced firsthand.

Earlier that spring, on April 26, 1930, the *Graf Zeppelin* had flown to the Royal Airship Works. As it neared a large white T painted on the ground, the ship's nose tilted down and it dove four times to descend in steps from 1,000 to 300 feet. The captain shut off the engines and the zeppelin came down to 200 feet. Two ropes dropped from the ship and a landing party seized them to restrain the zeppelin from swinging while it landed. A few moments later the German airship skidded across the ground.

Zeppelins were not designed to attach to a mooring tower, so the Germans had mastered this form of landing. It was so simple, said an observer, "that the mooring tower to the south might have appeared a superfluity." Minutes after the landing, the doors opened, a ladder was dropped, and the captain stepped out, apologizing for arriving fourteen minutes early.

The *Graf Zeppelin* had come to pick up Hugo Eckener, the unstoppable force behind the Zeppelin Company's resurgence after the war. He was visiting the Works following several meetings in London, where he had advocated standardizing mooring methods so German airships could begin regular transatlantic service by 1933.

Within an hour of the *Graf Zeppelin*'s landing, Richmond boarded it with Eckener to fly to the zeppelin factories in Friedrichshafen, Germany. As the ship departed, Richmond noticed a fuel smell in the passenger cabin and, although the odor disappeared once the flight was under way, he caught whiffs of it throughout the twelve-hour journey to Germany. Sitting in the passenger section of the car he noted that an "appreciable draught was felt from the windows" when the doors of the control cabin at the front of the car were open. The sound of the engine was "most noticeable" when the "beats of the two wing engines were nearly in step." And the bathroom sinks were "somewhat inadequate."

To best the Zeppelin Company and meet the British idea of comfort, Richmond devised what he described as a novel and radical metal framework for R.101 that deviated from the time-tested design used in zeppelins. Zeppelin engineers built strong yet light frameworks from thin, flexible circular rings, stiffened by radial wires drawn taut—the wires functioned like the spokes of a bicycle wheel. This design, to Richmond, hindered the creation of a commercial airship. The wires blocked crew members' transit during flights from bow to stern, preventing them from servicing the ship. The thin zeppelin rings had no stowage for fuel, ballast, equipment, or luggage—a low priority, of course, for those wartime airships. And even if a zeppelin had stowage, it lacked the lift to haul a significant payload. Payload was traded off in a wartime zeppelin for altitude. A zeppelin soared to 10,000 feet to escape enemy fire and detection; a commercial airship like R.101 rose no higher than 2,500 feet.

This inverse relationship between altitude and payload occurs because an airship's gas bags expand as the ship rises. To reach high altitudes the gas bags of a wartime zeppelin were partly inflated at ground level, which resulted in lower lift than if the bags were fully inflated. In contrast, a commercial ship like R.101 was designed for large payloads not for avoiding discovery. The gas bags of R.101 were inflated at ground level to over 90 percent of their full volume so they traded altitude for payload. Although these were all significant considerations for Richmond in his design of R.101, the zeppelin frameworks also limited his plans to build a fleet: the zeppelin design precluded mass manufacturing an airship.

To build zeppelins, workers first riveted metal sections to create flexible, unwieldy rings. They then hoisted the flimsy rings into the air and tightened the wires to stiffen them, before joining the rings with long bars. To attach these bars required a skilled worker to hand-fit a custom gusset plate—a thick sheet of steel used to connect beams and girders—to each ring.

In Richmond's opinion, this "erection work is costly and slow, especially if much of it has to be carried out at considerable height above the ground." So, with R.101, he changed the manufacture of airships from handcrafted masterpieces assembled by artisans pounding in rivets to mass-manufactured products assembled by semi-skilled workers using nuts and bolts: R.101's metal framework was constructed as if from a giant Erector or Meccano set.

The new bay for R.101 arrived in hundreds of pieces from the construction firm Boulton and Paul, Limited a few days after workers split the ship in two. Each piece was built to Richmond's exacting specifications; a tolerance, for example, of just three thousandths of an inch in a forty-five-foot girder so its holes would align with the other parts. The new girders were piled on the shed floor alongside the space between the halves of the airship. Without haste, though, workers brought order to the shed. Using nuts and bolts, not rivets, they assembled the girders to create the two rings that formed the ends of the new bay. The rings were so rigid—Richmond eliminated wires by thickening the zeppelin rings—that workers could add, he said, "all the fuel and water stowage, branch mains, ladders, gas bag nets, etc." as the rings lay flat on the shed floor. Once outfitted, the rings were hoisted into the air and positioned between the halves of the ship and then bolted to its two ends with long bars; no time-consuming gusset plates needed.

By late September 1930, the refitted R.101 was ready. In only five weeks, the men had bolted the bay into place, inserted and inflated an additional gas bag, and attached a cloth cover to the new framework. This rapid lengthening—it had grown from 735 to 777 feet—of the world's largest craft was a triumph for Richmond's modular framework; such a change would be impossible in a handcrafted zeppelin.

The Times reported that R.101 was now "the biggest and longest airship in the world," noting as an afterthought that it always had been the biggest: "her cubic capacity has always been much greater than that of the *Graf Zeppelin.*" *The Times* focused on the external changes to R.101, but unnoticed by them was the addition of 4,000 pads between the gas bags and the framework. This additional padding was to overcome the recommendation a month earlier of the Works' resident inspector, Frederick McWade, to deny a Permit to Fly for R.101. He was overruled by the Director of the Aeronautical Inspection Directorate (AID).

The AID Director, Colonel H. W. S. Outram, with his inspectors, helped develop Britain as a worldwide power in aviation. The high regard in which the world held "British aircraft," *Flight* magazine wrote, "owes much to him." With superb organizational skill, Outram had grown AID from its start in a room little wider than a table where all the records fit in a single index card box into an organization where hundreds of staff coordinated the inspection of all hangars, tents, machine tools, raw materials, and fabrics used to make airplanes and airships. So thorough was the work of Outram's inspectors that aircraft manufacturers joked that AID stood for "Anything Inferior Detected." Outram's skill as an administrator created the powerful AID, but what sustained it was his personal touch.

Outram had VIP status in the British aviation world. He rarely skipped a chance to judge an air contest, attend the annual de

Havilland Ball, or reunite with his friends from manufacturer Handley Page at Lloyd's Register Cricket Club, while, simultaneously, hobnobbing with officials from Lloyd's, the major insurer of airplanes. And whenever a famous aviation star celebrated, Outram, sporting his AID tie, lifted a glass. When the *Daily Mail* staged a grand luncheon at the Savoy Hotel for Amy Johnson, the first woman to fly solo from England to Australia, Outram was present, brushing shoulders with glitterati such as Noel Coward. When Sam Saunders, builder of flying boats, celebrated his golden wedding anniversary, Outram was among the guests. When Handley Page Limited, Britain's first publicly traded aircraft manufacturer, delivered a new aircraft to Imperial Airways, Frederick Handley Page himself rode on the flight, with Colonel Outram at his side billed as "distinguished cargo."

So when Outram needed to decide on McWade's recommendation to deny a Permit to Fly, he phoned the Royal Airship Works' senior official, Wing Commander Reginald Colmore, and asked him to respond in writing to McWade's memo.

At the Works, Colmore was known as the head of the "Big Three": Colmore, Scott, and Richmond. Colmore, as Director of Airship Development, approved every decision about R.101 and its sibling, R.100, but he relied strongly for advice on Scott and Richmond. Scott, as Assistant Director of Airship Development (Flying and Training), advised on all decisions of when and where either airship flew, while Richmond, Assistant Director of Airship Development (Technical), conferred with Colmore on all technical issues. Outram's request brought into conflict two facets of Colmore's personality: he was a dreamer who wanted to build the largest airship in the world but also a cautious man who often counseled moderation at the Works.

That conflict was the essence of Colmore, a study in contradictions. He was the courageous man who had led an Armored

Car Division into battle at Antwerp and Gallipoli in the First World War, yet feared flying. Although shy, he shone as a leader of men and organizer of matériel. His innovative antisubmarine patrols that combined airships and seaplanes earned him rapid promotion in the Royal Naval Air Service; they also honed the skills of pilots Irwin and Atherstone.

Yet, so far, he ignored Scott's deteriorating ability to fly an airship and his problems managing his flying staff. Colmore believed in the potential of airships to become a useful means of transport, yet was clear-eyed about their limitations. He knew, sooner than any of the true believers above and below him in the chain of command, that R.100 and R.101 could not fly in any weather, that they were mostly useful for travel in the summer, or over the sea where the air was smooth. Still, he dreamed of building a ship larger than R.101.

"I have every hope," Colmore wrote to a friend, that he would "get permission to go ahead [with a supership] after the Imperial Conference." At this conference the leaders of the Commonwealth would decide on the future of airship development.

Although diffident, he boasted, "I could build the ship within two years from the order to go and could turn out a second new ship within eight months after the first." Yet he was a cautious man; "inherently sound" is how an Air Ministry official described him. When the committee organizing the RAF Display at the Hendon Airfield suggested R.101 pass twice over the airfield in ten minutes, diving each time at sixty miles per hour within 500 feet of the ground, Colmore loudly objected.

So, when he responded to Outram's request for comment on McWade's recommendation that a Permit to Fly not be issued, the cautious Colmore, the clear-eyed man who quietly made contingency plans, could have responded; instead, the battlefield commander of armored cars and confident airship developer launched a blunt, head-on assault on McWade's conclusions.

"I am sure you will agree," he opened his letter to Colonel Outram, "that we cannot accept, as a matter of principle, that the gas bags in an airship should be clear of all girders." A blunt negation of McWade's central point. Then Colmore refuted McWade's conclusions about padding: "I expect you will agree that we can accept padding as being a satisfactory method of preventing holes forming in gas bags for this cause." Colmore continued to dismiss McWade's observations: "As far as we can trace at present there have been remarkably few rips in the gas bags of R.101 ...." He asserted that he and his staff at the Royal Airship Works had "little doubt" that padding would be a "permanent remedy," and, doing so was "certainly not a large undertaking," it could be done by the "end of the present week," no later than "the next week." To Colmore the need for lift outweighed all other considerations.

In assessing Wing Commander Colmore's response, Colonel Outram balanced the mission and goals of the Empire's airship program with those of Britain's burgeoning commercial aviation industry, which swamped Outram and his AID staff. He complained of "more and more new problems arising every day" from manufacturing methods that were "advancing rapidly." Every year the number of commercial airplanes, engines, and spare parts that AID must inspect increased: in 1926 it was 807,000, but by 1930 had risen to 1,428,000.

Outram believed that, as the product of an experimental program, R.101 was in a different class from the AID work inspecting mass-produced commercial planes. The expertise in airships lay not with his inspector, however careful and contentious, but with the Royal Airship Works, which had the collective wisdom of the best airship designers in the world. After a phone call to clarify a few points, he wrote to Inspector McWade: "As you yourself realize, it is impossible to alter the hull structure of the ship at this stage." He closed with firm orders for McWade: "It is your duty to see that every point which may lead to damage is padded in a proper manner." So McWade watched and inspected, as workers crawled through the ship and installed 4,000 *more* two-ply fabric patches, most three inches square and fitted with aluminum eyelets to lace to the framework. Some 9,000 patches now filled the interior of R.101.

While the workers installed the padding, Atherstone inspected the rebuilt airship. The soundness of the cover concerned him the most. Back in early July, soon after the flights to the RAF Display, he had walked along the top of the ship from bow to stern to check the cover. To test the strength of the cloth he often stopped and pressed his hand against it. In many places it tore with the lightest touch; no better, it seemed to him, than a piece of paper. Letting the airship fly with this substandard cloth was, in Atherstone's opinion, another of Scott's blunders: his scheduling of R.101's RAF Display flights, said Atherstone, was "a totally unjustified risk."

But, now, workers had replaced most of the cloth, coated it in place with plastic solution, then applied varnish laced with aluminum powder. These aluminum particles embedded in the cover sparkled in the sunlight that streamed through the shed's windows. As Atherstone finished his inspection his confidence in the ship grew: the cover was now "really good" and the refit fixed, he thought, most of the "glaring defects."

Atherstone was most pleased by two new engines. Nine months earlier he had called the engines a "joke" because they could not operate in reverse: one of R.101's engines had to be dedicated to reversing, which diminished the ship's forward speed. Now, though, new engines with forward and backward gearing and reversible metal propellers replaced the two forward engines and their wooden propellers. They "functioned perfectly," he said. And he enjoyed each engine's "most unheard of feature"—"it is actually 150 pounds lighter than the non-reversing engines."

After his inspection, Atherstone met with Irwin to plan R.101's final test flight before India. In May of 1929 Irwin had written a four-page memo outlining what needed to be done before that flight could go ahead. The list included thirty-nine items to be checked, several days of tests in the shed and the tower, followed by five test flights starting with a ten-hour flight and ending with one of forty hours. Now, with departure for India imminent, Irwin said he would like to "fly thirty-six or forty-eight hours at a reasonable cruising speed in bad weather in order to thoroughly test out the ship."

He hoped for at least six hours of continuous flight in turbulent air to test the new cloth cover because, with five forward engines instead of four, R.101's higher speed would apply stresses much greater than on previous flights. With four engines the airship travelled at fifty-seven miles per hour; with all five engines working the ship cut through the air at sixty-three miles per hour, with bursts of up to seventy-one miles per hour. The stress on the cover increased as the square of the ratio of the speeds, so the change from fifty-seven to seventy-one miles per hour would increase the stresses on the cover by 50 percent. To check the effects of these higher speeds, Irwin planned for R.101 to return to its shed for a "complete bow to stern inspection" before flying to India.

That evening, September 23rd, Atherstone summarized the next steps in his diary: after a successful test flight, R.101 "is to start to India about thirty-six hours later. Every effort is to be made to leave for India on or before 4th October."

PART III: A NEW AIRSHIP

DEPARTURE FOR INDIA

OCTOBER 4, 1930

FROM THE BASE OF THE mooring tower, Major Scott surveyed the newly lengthened R.101 above him. Its silvery cloth cover was dove-white against the dull, gray October sky. In the still air the airship floated motionless, but soon, as Scott knew from the dropping barometric pressure, stormy weather would arrive. Because of this he hoped to slip the tower before the scheduled departure of six o'clock, an hour away, but R.101's principal passenger, Lord Thomson, was yet to arrive. Ready to hasten Thomson aboard, Scott waited at the base of the tower, pipe in hand.

Scott was confident of a successful flight to India. A few hours earlier he paraded a visitor by the new bay, explained how it was bolted into place, and, perhaps, thought like Irwin that the lengthened ship handled better than when shorter. Scott believed the whale-like ship's demonstration flight to India would secure his reputation as an aviation pioneer. Historians would celebrate, he thought, his heroic Atlantic crossing as the pivotal event in developing commercial airships, when, in the future the public crossed continents and traversed oceans in larger airships.

Scott turned as a car rattled along the road leading to the tower, but it was only the Works' green Trojan van driven by the boyish second officer Maurice Steff, accompanied by Albert Savidge, the ship's steward. At the tower, the two men unloaded the truck and filled the elevator with fresh food for the flight: meat, vegetables, bread, Bovril and Oxo cubes for soup or a hot drink, and a cask of ale. As he watched, Scott drew in on his pipe, then, when the elevator doors shut, he again turned to the road. In the late afternoon light, his pasty skin contrasted with the crisp blue of his new uniform; his slouch at odds with the straight, sharp crease in his new trousers.

The new uniforms for officers and crew were a response by the Air Ministry to the visit seven months earlier by R.101's rival, the *Graf Zeppelin*. The zeppelin officers had walked off their ship in smart blue uniforms, while British airship officers and crew wore nondescript civilian clothes. Britain's Air Ministry immediately gave an order for R.101's officers to wear a deep-blue reefer—a double-breasted jacket—with gold buttons, a peaked hat with a white dust cover and a gilded badge. At the center of the badge was "R.101," under this "Royal Airship Works" circled, and at the top a crown.

As Scott waited, an old friend and reporter approached and asked him why he wore a uniform instead of civilian clothes. "I am not a passenger," Scott said, his words slightly slurred, "I am the officer in command of the flight." He decided "when the ship would sail, her course, her speed, her altitude."

Scott's firm response was prompted by the events surrounding the flight of R.100 to Canada four months earlier. To eliminate Scott's errors and misjudgments, Sir John Higgins, the civil servant at the Air Ministry overseeing the airship program, in consultation with Colmore, the Director of the Royal Airship Works, had assigned Scott as a "non-executive Admiral." In this role he was not the captain of the ship. He was not to issue any orders to crew members, but could offer advice to the ship's captain—who could accept or refuse the advice.

Scott chafed at this new role, especially because of the implications drawn from the press briefing for the R.100 flight to Canada listing him as one of the "officials from the Royal Airship Works" and not as one of the officers of R.100. Rumors swirled that Scott had been superseded: when R.100 arrived in Canada, he was often introduced as the second in command. This hurt Scott. He wanted it clear that he had authority over the ship.

On the morning of the day of departure for India, Scott had examined the press guidance for R.101's flight: it had the same secondary description of his role. He felt this would once again lead the public to believe that he was a passenger with no responsibility for the flight. He cornered the Air Ministry press officer and complained this was "far from this being the case" because "if anything happens on this flight I will be held responsible." Scott insisted the press brief be changed, but was told it was too late to do so. To appease Scott, however, the Air Ministry press officer consulted with Colmore and others to quickly write a press release to be issued the moment R.101 slipped the tower. It contained the sentence: "The flight has been carried out under the direction of Major G. H. Scott, Assistant Director in charge of Airship Flying." As he waited at the tower, Scott explained his interpretation of this phrase to his friend: he commanded the crew, who, he said, must "carry out his orders."

Scott was still impatiently waiting for Lord Thomson to arrive when two crew members passed by with tins of biscuits. He stopped them. "We don't need these tins. Put them in paper bags and get the tins off the ship. I want to save every pound of weight I can."

Indeed, R.101 needed to spare every pound; overnight the tower crew stuffed the airship to its limit with essentials. The hydrogen gas had flowed through a twelve-inch-diameter underground pipe to the tower, where, with great care, workers topped off the gas bags. One crew member joked: "What's the use of pumping gas into a bloody colander"—a reference to the holes discovered by Irwin. The hydrogen was produced by Woodis Rogers, a Cornwall man as likely to speak in verse as prose. In the hydrogen plant, Rogers blew steam across four tons of finely ground red-hot iron ore, which stripped the hydrogen from the steam, leaving the oxygen embedded in the iron and so giving a nearly pure stream of hydrogen gas.

The crew balanced the lifting force of the hydrogen with nine and a quarter tons of water ballast and a ton each of drinking water and lubricating oil. And, finally, they filled the fuel tanks with twenty-five tons of heavy oil, distributed equally around the ship in thirty tanks to keep it in trim. Once the tower crew finished their work, the flying crew arrived to take over.

Among that flying crew was Yorkshire-born Joe Binks, assigned to the rear engine car with the dour Arthur Bell. Binks wore the new uniform of crew members: a reefer jacket with buttons of black instead of the officers' gold, his hat badge constructed of ungilded cloth. He had slung over his shoulder a Sidcot suit, a one-piece wool-lined leather flying suit. When he wore this suit, his fellow crew members thought he looked like an enormous teddy bear. Other than his flying clothes—the lining of his Sidcot suit, a thick sweater, a leather cap and wool-lined boots—Binks, like all crew members, was allowed only fifteen pounds of luggage. He carried a small linen satchel of personal items into which he had tucked his vaccination record and passport; the Crown's Emigration Authorities would inspect the papers of everyone aboard before the ship slipped the tower.

Before he walked to the tower, Binks said goodbye to his youngest son, Derek. How sad to miss the boy's fourth birthday, three days away. Instead of sharing cake with him, Binks would mark the arrival in Egypt, the end of the first leg, with the cask of ale, shared with his thirty-five crew members—the seventy-pound cask carefully apportioned on the ship's manifest as two pounds per crew member.

Meanwhile, Harry Leech, the foreman engineer with round-rimmed glasses, stood nearby trying to console his crying seven-year-old daughter; she worried that her father would not return. As Binks and Leech walked toward the elevator, Leech's wife raced after him and handed him a "good luck" sprig of white heather.

Binks and Leech boarded the ship just as Vincent Richmond, R.101's designer, arrived at the tower, accompanied by his wife and elderly mother. Richmond thought of R.101 as the first ship of a fleet. He was convinced that if the British government and industry spent as much capital on airships as on shipping—the provisions of harbors, for example—the airship could achieve the same number of ton-miles as the seagoing ships but in less time. Yet, nine months earlier, in January of 1930, Richmond had realized, as he wrote a friend, that a ship the size of R.101 "is not inherently suitable to carry one hundred passengers over journeys to the East of 2,500 miles nonstop, at all times of the year." To overcome R.101's limitations, Richmond had worked with Michael Rope all year to design the next generation of airships. Richmond characterized the fleet in a speech at the British Association for the Advancement of Science as composed of airships that would "constitute the largest moving structures in the world." He added that "there is no reason why the airship should not become the safest form of transport yet devised."

Richmond had, nevertheless, stowed in his luggage—he was given a more generous allowance of forty-four pounds—a small medal of St. Christopher, the patron saint of travelers.

At 5:15 p.m., Lord Thomson's chauffeured blue Daimler pulled up to the tower. Scott had wanted Thomson to arrive at five for the six o'clock departure, but his aide thought an hour "a rather long time to keep" a Secretary of State waiting, so on the way they had stopped for tea in Shefford. Thomson emerged from the Daimler in a dark overcoat, accented by a white handkerchief in his breast pocket and a black homburg hat.

As he approached Scott, Thomson turned to his aide. "This is a voyage I've been waiting for all my life, and more than ever since we started along this airship trail in 1924. I've never looked forward to anything so much." Indeed, he'd hoped for R.101 to fly to India as early as 1927. For Lord Thomson, the success of R.101 and the airship fleet that followed promised to create his "all-red girdle of air transport" that linked the vast British Empire. This achievement, he felt, would propel him to the top ranks of the government, perhaps as the next Viceroy of India, or even Prime Minister.

Walking toward the elevator, Thomson asked a crew member for a summary of the weather. "It looks," the man said, "as though it may blow up a bit with a spot of rain for a short while." This delighted the Air Minister. "To ride the storm," he had written a friend, "has always been my ambition and who knows but we may realize it on the way to India, but not, I hope, with undue risk to human lives." Just then a slight breeze blew across the fields of the Royal Airship Works. R.101 wobbled at the tower.

Just three days earlier the Imperial Conference, a quadrennial gathering of the Commonwealth leaders, had convened in London. Already gathered in the Foreign Office's Locarno Suite were all the Commonwealth Prime Ministers (Australia, Canada, Newfoundland, New Zealand, South Africa, and the United Kingdom), the Maharaja of Bikaner representing India, and Mr. P. McGilligan for the Irish Free State. With his typical flair for the dramatic and to demonstrate the speed of airships, Thomson intended to travel from Britain to India and return before the end of the forty-five-day conference. There he would present his ambitious airship program for the Empire.

Thomson, a skillful orator, had, no doubt, rehearsed the scene many times: in his mind's eye, he stood in the barrel-vaulted Locarno reception room and opened by reminding the delegates that he had left for India on October 4th, three days after the start of the conference, and returned to meet with them on October 20th, the twentieth day of the gathering. His travel time from India was a mere four days; he was rested, he told them, because riding in an airship was like "sitting there as part of a bubble up in the blue with a feeling of detachment and serenity"—an arresting vision for the delegates, still exhausted from a grueling ten to fifteen days of travel.

With the delegates hooked by a vision of a tranquil cross-continent journey, Thomson would enthrall them with details of a fleet of next-generation supersized airships, ships a third larger than R.101 that would zip along at seventy-five miles per hour and travel 5,000 miles without refueling. To start this fleet, he suggested that the delegates appropriate £2,750,000 to build two of these airships, the first constructed in two years and the second in eight months, along with the necessary infrastructure. These new ships would be too large to fit into the sheds at the Works so they had to be enlarged, and mooring towers must be built across the Empire. Thomson proposed to start with a second tower at the Works and three towers along imperial routes: in New Brunswick, Canada for the Atlantic route, and in Malta and Basra for the Indian route. This, he predicted, would spark a network of towers and in twenty years every seaport in the world would have one.

For now, this expansive plan and his speech were only on paper, though. Thomson planned to refine his speech while en route to and from India in consultation with Richmond. So he told his aide, who toted a bulky bag of state papers, "I was going to work on them on the voyage, but I've got those speeches to draft, letters to write and that conference paper to put together for when we get back. So I'll leave this lot behind."

Thomson's aide returned the unnecessary briefcase to the Daimler, and his boss walked to the mooring tower, where he shook Scott's hand and greeted Richmond. They chatted, while the green Works van pulled up again, loaded with Thomson's baggage: two green cabin trunks, four suitcases, two twenty-six-pound cases of champagne, a three-pound dress sword, and a 129-pound carpet. "My precious carpet from Sulaymaniyah," said Thomson. "We'll have it down for the dinners at Ismailia and Karachi to do the thing in style." At each mooring point, he planned a celebration on board R.101 for local officials, where, as the ship's Flight Instructions firmly noted, "the Ship's steward will have to supply all crockery and cutlery etc., and have all tables ready."

Once the crew finished loading all 254 pounds of the Air Minister's luggage, Thomson, Scott and Richmond entered the elevator. Richmond turned to his wife. "Good-bye," he said, "and keep the flag flying." The elevator doors snapped shut, and the men, now shadows on the frosted glass joined the other passengers on board: the monocled Sir W. Sefton Brancker, Britain's Director of Civil Aviation; Major Percy Bishop, an AID inspector; Squadron Leader W. Palstra, who observed for the Australian government; Squadron Leader W. O'Neill, Britain's Deputy Director of Civil Aviation, India; and James Buck, Lord Thomson's valet.

Meanwhile, an exhausted Noel Atherstone remained at the tower's base and smoked his last cigarette before departure. He was drained from ninety-six straight hours of preparation for the

India flight. It had begun three days before, on October 1st, with an overnight test flight of the lengthened R.101. The ship had flown from the Works to London, passed over Southend, and spent the night over the East Coast. Atherstone and Irwin planned to fly for thirty-six, even forty-eight hours, in order to stress test the cloth cover by flying for at least six of the hours with all five engines at full power. However, after eleven and a half hours, they halted the flight: an oil cooler failure shut down the starboard forward engine and precluded any high-speed tests.

At four o'clock in the morning of October 2nd, Atherstone took command and guided R.101 from Yarmouth at the edge of the North Sea back to the Works. He was pleased that the ship handled better than before the refit; he had expected it to be "semiready and in a nearly totally unairworthy condition." At 6:45 a.m. Atherstone returned to the nose cone to prepare the cables for landing and Irwin took command.

Then Scott intervened. As the ship approached the tower, he ordered a guy wire lowered too soon. It entangled the tower and delayed the landing by three hours. Atherstone hoped Scott would not blunder on the flight to India, that he would only observe, as ordered by the Air Ministry. But Atherstone was aware that Scott had disregarded his non-executive status on R.100's flight to Canada in late July.

Floating into Quebec, Scott had ordered R.100 to pass through a thunderstorm, instead of going around it. In the turbulent air the ship shot up from an altitude of 1,200 feet to 4,500 feet, the last 1,000 feet in fifteen seconds. The violent winds ripped the fabric on the starboard elevators. The ship safely arrived in Montreal, but Scott's rash decision could have destroyed it.

Although Atherstone hoped Scott's status as non-executive Admiral would prevent his interference with R.101's operation, there was no remedy for Scott's capricious scheduling of the airship's flights. He had set R.101's departure for India early on the morning of October 4th, a mere forty-eight hours after the return from its overnight test flight—no time to move the ship to the shed and conduct a detailed inspection of its cover as Irwin had planned. And for a weary Atherstone this short timeline caused another "flap and panic" to "get everything on the top line." The urgency decreased a little when, a day before the flight, Scott moved the departure from morning to evening.

To prepare for the India flight, Atherstone supervised the last-minute replacement of a defective emergency trouser-shaped ballast bag and ordered a thorough examination for all the others. He managed the purging and refilling of the gas bags because the hydrogen purity in several of them was low—the oxen skin kept hydrogen from escaping, but let air seep into the bags.

Atherstone also enforced "Flight Instruction #32": "No photographs are to be taken under any circumstances whatever on the route between the English Coast and Egypt whilst passing over European Countries, Colonial Possessions in North Africa or the Territory of Syria. This instruction must be strictly observed." He confiscated all personal cameras from the crew and passengers and delivered them to Irwin. Only "Mr R. Blake," an engineer in the midship port engine car, was allowed to take pictures of "items of interest en route." These "items" included Lord Thomson, the Secretary of State, in conversation, Irwin and Scott in the control car, and passengers at lunch and in the lounge. Atherstone also reminded the passengers and crew that no letters or parcels could be carried; he would enforce a five-pound fine for each letter he found. The minutiae of the orders distracted him from the importance of this flight.

For Atherstone, his dream of becoming captain of R.101 was at stake. He hoped to take full command of R.101 once the fleet expanded and Irwin was promoted to the newest ship of that fleet.

For that to happen, Atherstone knew R.101 must dazzle the world. "The future of airships," he thought, "very largely depends on what sort of show we put up." That show was enhanced by the new uniforms, yet, in his opinion, their last-minute appearance also highlighted the disarray of the "powers that be," his collective term for the Works' senior staff and the Air Ministry.

When Atherstone had argued just a year earlier for new uniforms, the Air Ministry rejected his suggestion. It was only the *Graf Zeppelin*'s arrival at the Works with its smartly uniformed crew that panicked the Air Ministry into a rush to try "to get stuff in time" to manufacture uniforms. But they insisted that the men pay for them themselves. The Air Ministry advanced Atherstone and his crew members twenty pounds each to purchase a uniform and other kit for the trip to India, plus five pounds pocket money for "subsistence" once they reached their destination. "Typical," he thought, "of the Air Ministry methods."

Therefore, although he had confidence in the newly rebuilt ship, his doubts about the project management of R.101 led him to think "luck will figure rather conspicuously in our flight."

Beyond luck, the journey would also test Atherstone's skills as a pilot. He was assigned by Irwin to work the elevators for the flight across England. This most critical task of all—maintaining R.101 at a constant altitude—was usually performed by a coxswain, but a forecast of rough air caused Irwin to assign Atherstone. No crew member could "feel in his boots" the motions of R.101 in the air as well as Irwin's trusted wartime colleague, First Officer Noel Atherstone. This duty, Atherstone knew, would tax him because, he said, "the ship's captains are in a very difficult position of having to keep watch in flight, that is really quite wrong."

In contrast, the *Graf Zeppelin* carried three watchkeepers besides the captain. And on the U.S. airship *Akron* neither captain nor first officer kept watch: it carried three watchkeepers and three navigation watchkeepers. For the trip to India, Captain Irwin, First Officer Atherstone, and Second Officer Maurice Steff would rotate in three-hour shifts—a daunting schedule to the sleep-deprived Atherstone.

He took a long, last drag on his cigarette. He would have no time for the smoking room.

At 5:30 p.m., when Atherstone stationed himself in the nose cone, the noisy bustle of loading the ship abated, giving way to a tense silence as the crew prepared for the critical steps needed to slip the tower. Through the voice pipe Irwin commanded: "Flying stations." At this, Atherstone directed his crew to detach the supply pipes for fuel, water, and the cables for electrical power and telephone. Next, he ordered the bridge withdrawn and the ventral hatch closed. The crew and passengers were now *isolatoes*, as Herman Melville once described the crew members on the *Pequod*. To alert any air traffic that R.101 was about to depart, a red light flickered atop the tower. In the reflected glow the ship's shiny nose shone with a pink-tinged shimmer.

From the control car a spotlight shone on the rear engine car. The light spilled into the car and alerted engineers Binks and Bell to prepare for orders. Soon, the lights flashed on their telegraph and its pointer rotated from "stop" to "start low." Binks cranked the small gas-driven starter engine. A sound like a lawnmower echoed throughout the grounds of the Royal Airship Works. The small engine drove the pistons of the heavy-oil Beardmore engine in spasmodic jerks until the larger engine started with a low, throaty rumble. The rear engine was warmed up and ready so Bell slid the telegraph lever to "slow" to signal the engine status to the control car.

The spotlight moved to the midship port engine where another set of engineers readied their starter engine—each of the five cars was assigned a crew of two engineers. A single percussive burst from its starter engine rang out, followed by the low roar of its heavy-oil engine. The spotlight flicked to the starboard engine, then forward to the port engine where the same cycle occurred, each starter engine rattling like machine-gun fire in the tower's dome. With four engines started the spotlight was shone on the last engine, the forward starboard engine. The click of the gas valve from its starter engine, a burst of ominous black smoke, then silence. Then a second hiss, and a third, and a fourth; the result only black smoke. On the eighth try, twenty minutes later, a percussive hiss, a burst of white smoke, and the dull roar of the larger engine.

As the rumble of all five engines filled the air, Atherstone pressed his ear against the voice pipe anticipating orders from Irwin. "Prepare to slip," Irwin said. He wanted all crew in position for slipping. Atherstone, the strict taskmaster, already had his crew in place so he immediately repeated the command to the tower: "Prepare to slip."

"Take the strain off the wire," ordered the officer in charge of the tower. A tower hand turned a wheel and drew the wire tight, ensuring the bowl-shaped pendant rested firmly in the cup at the end of the tower's hefty arm, which still tightly held the airship.

"Out stops," commanded the tower officer. The tower hand withdrew the pins holding the ship's pendant in the mooring arm. The pins dangled from a chain; it rattled in the wind. Now only a short wire tethered the airship to the tower.

With the ship floating freely, Atherstone gazed at a small, liquid-filled gauge in the bow, marked in increments of quarter-tons "heavy" and "light." This gauge worked like a level to show whether or not R.101 was in trim from front to back. The bow also had indicators to measure the yaw and side strain, but these never worked well, so Atherstone ignored them. He ordered the tower crew to "ease up on the wire"—to slowly pay out the main cable. The indicator on the bow gauge reported the ship was sinking, so Atherstone issued a one-word status to Irwin: "heavy." In response Irwin released a half-ton of water ballast. It cascaded from the ship in fine droplets, glittering in the tower's floodlights. Atherstone's gauge now indicated "light." He reported to Irwin, "Ship lifting." The gas bags, he told Irwin, were 96 percent full, and so the ship could rise to 1,000 feet.

Irwin ordered, "Stand by to slip," quickly followed by, "Slip."

At 6:36 p.m. the mighty airship was free of the tower. As the cable dropped, a rising wind blew R.101 from the tower. Within seconds of departing, the giant airship tilted toward the ground. Irwin quickly ordered the release of four tons of ballast and the ship's nose slowly righted itself. On orders from Irwin, the engineers engaged the ship's five propellers. They slowly rotated, with a regular, muffled beat, not a droning like an airplane, but a clank like a piece of metal beaten rhythmically.

The airship rose, its control car glistening in the floodlights and an oblong luminous rectangle shining from the windows of the promenade decks, where silhouetted figures waved farewell. A few periodic bursts of light appeared from beneath the ship as crew members signaled with flashlights to family below. At the ship's tail, red and green lights illuminated the Union Jack on an RAF ensign hung from the rudder. The ensign rippled in the wind as the ship faded into the night sky.

The much-anticipated and planned-for first test flight to India of the great airship R.101—the dream of so many—was underway.

CHAPTER NINE

TO RIDE THE STORM

OCTOBER 4–5, 1930

N OT SATISFACTORY," thought Joe Binks as three tons of ballast water cascaded by the open door of his rear engine car. To Binks, this torrent looked larger than usual for departing from the mooring tower. The ballast water mixed with rain and was swept through the car by the frigid wind, yet Binks was warmed by the heat radiating from the car's engine a foot from him. No cover or enclosure protected him from this monster of an engine—nine feet long, a foot and a half wide, and weighing nearly two and a half tons—its exposed surface so hot that when the rain struck the engine it evaporated into small clouds of steam. This 650-horsepower locomotive engine filled the car with a deafening din as its eight cylinders spun the engine's crankshaft. The engine belched sulfurous fumes and filled the car with a diesel-like odor from burning oil. Burning heavy oil as fuel reduced the gasoline needed to twelve gallons, which was used to power the forty-horsepower starting engines. This gasoline was stored in small tanks that sat on trap doors so that, if fire broke out, an engineer could pull a lever and dump the tank and its flammable contents, the lever always in reach because the engineers operated from a workspace at the front of the car. At the moment, Binks shared this space—a three and a half feet by three-quarters of a foot—with fuel tanks, the telegraph, control levers, and two other men: Harry Leech, the foreman engineer, and the dour Arthur "Ginger" Bell, the other engineer assigned to the rear engine car.

As R.101 porpoised in the turbulent air, Bell thought, "Just a little trouble keeping her trimmed." The trim was best regarded, he'd learned from his many airship flights—his first in 1919 and the most recent the long trek of R.100 to and from Canada—as "the business of the officers."

The ship's instability didn't stop Mr. Leech from leaving the car. Throughout the flight Leech planned to shuttle among the five cars and use his engineering expertise to keep the engines running. He tucked his round glasses into the pocket of his Sidcot suit, leaned out the car's open door, and grabbed the ladder. Fifteen feet from him, the propeller spun, its suction tugging Leech from the car. Once on the ladder the prop wash was so powerful that it could lift him parallel to the ground, turning him into a human flag tethered to the ladder only by his firm grip. Leech inched his way up the ladder as the rain pelted him, until he passed through a hole into the safety of R.101's hull.

Once in the hull he traveled forward along the ship's walkway, the plywood flooring bending under him. He headed for the two engine cars slung near the ship's center. When he reached the new bay at midship, he paused for a respite from the racket of the ship's engines. Standing still, he was aware of the ship's motion. Leech thought the airship pitched and rolled more than usual; he had never felt it roll this much in flight, only at the tower. He compared it to movements he'd experienced when riding on the Royal Navy's submarine chaser blimps, where he had been an engineer. He hadn't felt this much motion even when two of those ships crashed.

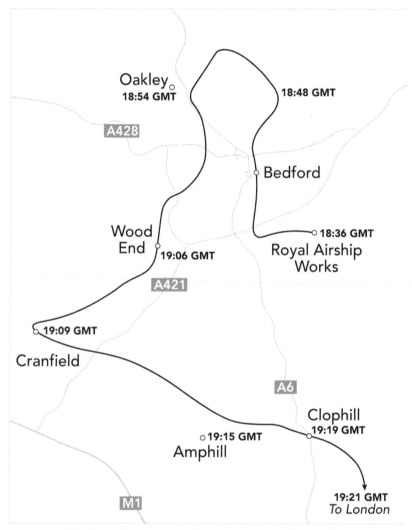

Oakley
18:54 GMT

18:48 GMT

A428

Bedford

Wood
End
19:06 GMT

18:36 GMT
Royal Airship
Works

A421

19:09 GMT

Cranfield

A6

Clophill
19:19 GMT

19:15 GMT
Amphill

M1

19:21 GMT
To London

The First Forty-Five Minutes of R.101's *Final Flight*

R.101 *departed from the Royal Airship Works mooring tower at 18:36 GMT on October 4, 1930. The airship stayed close to the tower until either Irwin or Scott decided it should continue on to India.*

Leech watched the surge of the giant gas bag above him: wind from the ventilators in the cover rushed over the bag and rattled it back and forth but his quiet contemplation lasted only a moment because the walkway was the main thoroughfare from bow to stern. Soon, Michael Rope, R.101's engineering genius, arrived. Rope, like Leech, continuously roamed the ship; while Leech shuttled between the engine cars below the airship, Rope climbed to the top of each gas bag. He worried that their wire netting—let out to enlarge the bags and increase their lift—might allow the surging bags to smack into the sharp bolts of the metal frame. Leech stopped Rope and pointed to the surging bag above them; Rope assured him that the bag's wire netting kept it from touching the framework. As Leech continued to the midship engine cars, Rope climbed one of the ladders built into the framework and disappeared between two gas bags.

Nearby, Arthur Disley, a radio operator, stood at the center of R.101 and examined the mass of colored wires in the ship's main junction box. He doubled as the ship's electrician, a natural use of the skills of a radio operator because the cantankerous radio equipment required constant repair and maintenance. While an operator must be agile with the telegraph key, literacy in Morse code was mere entry-level knowledge. Disley was trained using *The Admiralty Handbook of Wireless Telegraphy*, which devoted 899 pages to fundamental principles of electricity and magnetism, generators, motors, vacuum tubes, circuits and included—aptly for Disley's work—an appendix on "Resuscitation from Apparent Death by Electrical Shock." Disley grabbed the leads of the ammeter built into the junction box and verified the load on all the circuits. He started with the three huge aluminum core cables— aluminum to reduce weight—that connected electrical generators in three of the engine cars to the junction box. They pumped 220-volt, three-phase power to the box. Next, he tested the separate circuits that, over the four miles of wiring in R.101, fed electricity to the kitchen, passenger quarters, and the radio room, the latter's wires a contrasting color because of the importance of radio to the ship's operation. Once he'd tested all circuits, Disley walked the length of the ship inspecting every one of R.101's 130 lamps, each in a fitting specially designed to prevent the escape of sparks from a short circuit—a spark that could ignite the five million cubic feet of hydrogen on board. Disley discovered only one bulb burned out: at frame NO. 4, just above the two aft engine cars. He changed it and then returned to the radio cabin, where he could smell dinner being cooked next door in the galley.

As Disley worked in the radio cabin and Leech inspected the other engines, Binks left the rear engine car to rest in the crew quarters, while Bell tended the engine. Although the two men worked together during departure, they would now, a half-hour into the flight, alternate in three-hour shifts starting in ninety minutes, with one man sleeping in their shared bunk, and the other in the car monitoring the engine and awaiting telegraphed orders from the control car to change speed. Or, if fire broke out, pulling a handle to jettison the small gasoline tank of the starting engine. Before resting, Binks ate a snack of bread and cheese, pickles, and hot cocoa, but before he could finish word arrived that the rear engine had stopped.

Binks hurried along the ship's walkway to the opening above the rear engine. He scurried down the ladder, the wind whipping across him at fifty miles per hour, and dropped into the car. Bell explained that the oil pressure had fallen. Unlike a gasoline-powered engine where the oil pump spreads liquid oil to lubricate the engine, here the oil was the fuel: the pump vaporized the oil, converted it to a mist, then sprayed an exact quantity at a precise time into the engine. So important was this action that the engine's inventor called the oil pump the engine's "most characteristic feature." The sequence of actions was so complex—the pump contained seventeen moving parts—that the pumps often failed.

Only a few moments after Binks arrived, the oil pump failed and Bell shut down the engine. He sent Binks up the ladder to get Leech, the engine expert. But Binks' exit was blocked: First Engineer Bill Gent was descending the ladder. Gent, a longtime airship veteran—a proud member of Scott's heroic Atlantic crossing—supervised the engine car operators and helped Leech with keeping the engines in repair. The experienced Gent knew that on long flights he must let his engineers rest whenever possible. Besides, the car was too small for a crowd and in a few minutes the shuttling Mr. Leech would arrive. So he ordered Binks back to the crew quarters to sleep.

Routine set in across the airship despite the failure of one engine. It would surely be up and working again soon. In the dining room above Binks, Savidge and his assistants served the passengers a cold meal—no time now for Savidge to delight the crew with his cartoons and caricatures. While the passengers ate, four riggers patrolled the ship looking for any problems with the cloth cover or the gas bags. They climbed into the framework to inspect the gas release valves and to examine the ship's outer cloth cover. Often they came across Rope sitting atop a gas bag watching it rattle in its wire netting, approaching within inches of the metal framework. The riggers, also, often passed Leech on the walkway as he traveled between visits to the engine cars.

At 8 p.m., almost ninety minutes into the flight, a new watch of First Engineer Gent's crew shimmed down their ladders to their shiny, egg-shaped engine cars, the prop wash billowing their Sidcot suits, knives dangling from their belts, beating in the wind against their thighs. Joe Binks, part of this next watch, arrived in the rear engine car, pleased to see engine NO. 5 churning away. Leech and Gent diagnosed the problem as a faulty pressure gauge, much less serious than a broken pump. Soon after Binks arrived, the tired Bell ascended the ladder, happy to leave the heat, smell, and noise of the engine. He headed to the crew quarters for his supper, then to rest in their shared bunk, number thirteen, still warm from Joe Binks' body. Once there, Bell picked out the plasticine he'd stuffed into his ears as protection from the clamor of the engine.

The oil pressure in engine NO. 5 dropped as R.IOI neared a standard landmark: the white clock tower of the glass-covered Metropolitan Cattle Market in Islington, north of London. Binks grabbed the speed lever and pulled it toward himself to reduce the engine to half speed. He and Gent watched the oil gauge: they hoped the pressure would hold steady. It continued to fall so Gent signaled with his hands for Binks to shut down the engine. The only sound in the car now was the distant drone of the other four engines and the whistle of the wind through the open doors.

Above them Leech, on one of his many cycles between engine cars, noticed the engine stop. He scrambled down the ladder. He acted the moment he landed on the car's floor, conditioned by his time-critical work on Malcolm Campbell's finicky race cars. Leech ordered Binks to lock the propeller to prevent the engine's shaft from turning, then to remove the port oil covers to expose the engine's interior. Binks lay on the car's floor and slid forward next to the engine, the space barely larger than the width of his shoulders: he could squeeze along the full length of the engine on either side in a space a foot and a half wide at the front of the engine, narrowing to a tight ten inches at the back, where the engine butted against the rear wall. Through the rear wall the crankshaft connected to the propeller. Once Binks removed the last of the port-side inspection covers, he crawled backward to make room for Leech and Gent. The engine's insides now exposed, the two smaller men scooched along the floor, careful to avoid the eight hot exhaust pipes, and examined the engine's bearings, connecting rods and oil system. Leech's expert eye detected no defects, so Binks again slid across the car's floor, positioning himself to replace all eight inspection covers while the two senior men examined the relief valve on the opposite side of the engine.

As they studied the engine, R.101 passed over the cattle market and then London. The airship flew headlong into the wind, but with Binks' engine NO. 5 still out, the four remaining engines thrust R.101 forward at a ground speed of a mere twenty miles per hour. Once past London, the ship headed for the English Channel and France. But first, it had to rise to 1,200 feet to fly over the chalk hills of Surrey.

The passengers, unaware of engine trouble, listened in the lounge to a broadcast of Elgar's "Pomp and Circumstance" from Queen's Hall in London, the horn section of the BBC Symphony Orchestra almost masking the howling wind outside. A few intrepid passengers stood on the promenade decks, their backs turned to the brightly lit lounge so their eyes could adjust to the darkness. The city lights of Crockenhill, Otford, and Plaxtol passed under them, then darkness below until a final burst of luminosity from Fairlight Cove, east of Hastings. Three hours after leaving the mooring tower, R.101 swept past the cove's sandstone cliffs into the darkness of the Channel. With nothing more to see, they returned to the lounge, the somber strains of Elgar long gone, replaced by the upbeat Ambrose and his Orchestra playing the popular "My Baby Just Cares for Me."

Far below the passengers, unable to hear their music, Binks organized metal disks and springs to repack the engine's relief valve—the cause, Leech determined, of the drop in oil pressure. As Binks worked, Leech peered out the open door. The weather, he thought, was deteriorating. R.101 dove toward the Channel, coming so close that Leech saw the white spume of its waves.

As the airship neared the Channel, a calcium phosphide flare dropped from the control car. With it the crew measured R.101's drift caused by crosswinds. The water-activated flare hit the Channel's surface and burst into a brilliant white flame. The wind was so strong on this flight that the control car dropped a flare every ten minutes or so. The flaming white spot on the waters sped off to the right and behind the airship. The wind blew from the southwest at forty-four miles per hour, modulated often by fierce gusts. To compensate for this crosswind, R.101's nose pointed into the wind. The ship now flew slightly sideways in the air, but its center traveled nearly due south.

A few minutes before 11 p.m., nearly four and a half hours into the forty-hour flight to Egypt, Binks yanked on the starting cord of the small gasoline-powered starting motor; it revved to life with a high-pitched whine. Binks opened the larger engine's throttle: it fired without a sputter. He shut off the starting engine and pushed the speed lever away from him until the engine ran at top speed. All returned to normal in the engine car: deafening noise and a diesel-like stench of heavy oil.

R.101, now in mid-Channel, was 155 miles from the mooring tower and 130 miles from Paris. It flew at an air speed of sixty-three miles per hour now that Bink's engine NO. 5 was operating. The wind beat on the cloth cover with a greater, more sustained force than in any of R.101's test flights. The Middle Watch now took over. The bone-tired Joe Binks, his body aching from hours curled up on the floor, nestled against a hot, smelly engine, was relieved to see Arthur Bell sliding down the ladder. Once Bell replaced him, Binks ascended the ladder and headed along the walkway to bunk number thirteen, still warm from Bell and still reeking of diesel. Alf Cook, fresh from the midship engine car, joined Binks. Cook, a small man with a startling resemblance to Charlie Chaplin, told him that he had never seen the wind so strong while flying on an airship, the ship even coming several times so close to the Channel that he could see the waves.

R.101 chopped through the air over France after midnight, while most passengers and off-duty crew slept. The exhausted Atherstone slept, worn out from operating the elevators in the gusty wind over England. Savidge had laid the breakfast dishes, set for 7:30 a.m. sharp, and then retired. Apart from those assigned to the Middle Watch, only two others were awake: the stalwart Rope, who climbed through the framework to monitor the surging gas bags, and the indefatigable, roving Leech, who chatted with Bell in the rear engine car.

Satisfied that all was well with engine NO. 5, Leech climbed up the ladder toward the hull. The weather, he thought, was "very rough," caused by the "the wind and rain being terrific." He traveled along the walkway to the haven of the smoking room for a well-earned cigarette before turning in—his first since leaving the Works. He settled on a bench fastened to the starboard wall, the bench's soft cushion a relief, after lying on the hard floor of the engine car. The windowless room's metal walls were a pristine white in contrast to the gritty engine cars. It was quiet, the only sound a soft rustle of air drawn up by the ventilator in the ceiling. The gentle rocking of the ventilator was the only trace of the ship's motion through the gale force wind outside. Leech sat in solitude, satisfied that all five engines were running well.

It was a few minutes before two in the morning.

As Leech dozed, the ship was a few miles north of the small town of Beauvais, just over forty miles (sixty-five kilometers) north of Paris. It flew in trim and a little nose-up. With all five engines operating at full blast the airship maintained an air speed of sixty-three miles per hour, although the high winds slowed it to a crawl of twenty miles per hour ground speed. The ship flew at an altitude of 1,200 feet, but turbulence forced R.101 to oscillate around this height by 200 or 300 feet.

At 2 a.m., the Second Morning Watch took over, yet Joe Binks was asleep in bunk number thirteen—"out to the world," as he described his deep sleeps. The smell of a steaming mug of cocoa roused him, a gift from George Short, the engineer of the watch. Short shared good news with Binks: engine NO. 5 ran well. Binks slipped on his Sidcot suit and ran 150 feet along the walkway to the opening in the hull above engine NO. 5. He noticed in the distance Michael Rope hoisting himself into the framework and disappearing into the dark surging bags. Binks slid down the engine car ladder as quickly as possible.

Bell smiled and pointed to the engine car clock: it was three minutes past two, a gentle reminder that Binks was late. Binks leaned in to learn of the engine's performance during Bell's shift. Above the din of the engine, Bell detailed the engine's oil pressures and temperatures over the last three hours. Binks felt the ship shift under him—a motion different from the dips when mooring at the tower, or even the dives after the RAF Display in July. Binks thought it traveled "further." Even the more experienced Bell noticed the ship canted at "a terrific angle."

In the smoking room, the ship's plunge forced Leech to slide on his cushion along the smoking-room bench. A soda-water siphon and some glasses slid off a nearby table, but stayed intact. When the ship returned to horizontal, Leech picked them up and replaced them on the table.

The ship's dive woke Disley in his cot near the radio cabin. Groggy, he felt the ship right itself. At the same time, in the rear engine car, the engine telegraph rang and its lights flickered: the pointer rotated to "slow"—the control car ordered the engine slowed from 825 to 450 revolutions per minute. Bell pulled the speed control lever toward himself. R.101 dove again, a dive steeper than the first.

As the ship dove, Disley was completely awakened by the gongs clanging for the engines to go slow. A coxswain stormed by the radio cabin with a loud but calm cry of "We're down lads," and then hurried to the crew quarters to roust all hands.

The coxswain ordered a rigger just exiting the crew quarters to run to the front of the ship and release a half-ton of emergency ballast. Disley started to rise out of his bed in response to the coxswain's cry. Suddenly his bed tilted. His head was lower than his feet. He noted that the tilt was greater than when a thunderstorm had forced R.100 to dive near Trois-Rivières, Canada. Disley knew that the slowing engines would generate less electricity, and that some circuits must be shut off. He reached above his bed. He worried that the electrical current might ignite a fire, so better to turn off all circuits. He turned off one of the two circuits, but before he could reach the second, the ship dove steeply.

R.101 smashed into the ground nose first.

At midship, Leech knew that the ship had crashed, but was disoriented. He prepared for a "violent blow," but heard only a loud "crunch" as the metal framework at the nose collapsed—too mild a noise, it seemed to him, for a catastrophic event.

But then, an explosion blew open the door and threw him against the floor, the brilliant white flash momentarily blinding him. His training as a mechanic took over: the explosion's sound, he thought, was a "woof ... like lighting petrol on the floor" and not the ignition of hydrogen. His analytical mind recorded the color: "very white," not at all, he thought "like hydrogen flame."

His analysis ended when the upper deck fell into the smoking room and a girder trapped him in a space only three feet high—the deck above rested on the back of the inbuilt benches. From the collapsed decks, crew and passengers screamed and moaned as fire ravaged the ship. The blown-open smoking-room door exposed the control room, now engulfed in flames. The smoking room filled with thick fumes. Leech, now deprived of air, choked.

A white flash stunned Disley, still in his bed. He heard the clatter of radio equipment, books, and lamps—anything not firmly affixed to the ship. Within seconds a wall of fire surrounded him. It roared like a furnace—"awful, awful," repeated Disley to himself. He rammed his body into the fabric wall of his cabin and rebounded. Again and again he bounced off the wall until he sunk to the floor, leaned against the wall exhausted, and offered a prayer. "My fate is sealed," he thought.

The impact tossed Binks, his back to the direction of travel, on his rear. As the engine car skidded along the ground, its bottom caved in. The electrical lamp in the car flickered, then extinguished. In the darkness, the wreckage about them released a long, drawn out rumble like distant thunder. Seconds later the debris surrounding the two men burst into flames. The metal walls of the engine car reflected and intensified the light from the flames and bathed the two men with a fierce glow.

"We are caught," thought Bell as he looked at the fire raging around the car. Binks glanced at the fuel tank for the starter motor: it contained twelve gallons of explosive gasoline—no time to jettison it now. Flames entered the car and burned a trail across the floor toward the fuel tank. Binks and Bell grabbed oil-stained rags, wrapped them around their hands for protection, and beat the flames. "Hopeless," thought Binks. "Looks as though all is up, Bell!" he said.

Bell wanted to run through the flames, but Binks convinced him to crouch in the shelter of the car. The fire encroached on them. Binks said he hoped they would suffocate before they burned to death; "far better," Bell agreed, "than being roasted."

The heat softened the metal roof of the engine car: it sagged like a sheet of paper. Acrid smoke filled the car and Binks peered through its door. The ship was burning from bow to aft. He thought briefly about the pride and confidence he'd had in the ship. Even reflected on what a "blow" this was to the Royal Airship Works. He and Bell shook hands as death approached. Somber and silent, they resigned themselves to their fate.

In the smoking room, thick, acrid smoke smothered Leech. He struggled to lift a bent girder, and with great effort managed to free himself. He grabbed the leg of the built-in bench and ripped it from the inner wall of the ship. It tore an opening to the outside. He stuck his head through it, gulped in fresh air, then squeezed through the opening. He stood outside the ship, but the cellon windows from the promenade deck blocked his path to safety. The crash knocked the panes from their frames and they now were ablaze on the ground. Propelled by fear of the burning ship beside him, Leech ran through the maze of burning windows until he felt wet, cool grass.

In his bunk, a dispirited Disley lay on the floor; his attempts to beat a hole through the cloth wall had proved futile. The fire raged around him like a tornado. Then, without warning, he felt the floor break, exposing a torn section of the cloth cover below him. He enlarged the hole by beating on it with his fists, punching in a frenzy until he broke through, his hand striking cold ground—a sharp contrast to the blaze behind him. He squeezed his body through the opening and crawled along the seam of the cloth. And then he collapsed.

In the rear engine car, Binks and Bell huddled. Flames engulfed the car. Then, without warning, a half-ton of water thudded on the roof of the engine car. It rushed through the open door and smashed the men against the wall, but it doused the flames. "Splendid and merciful water—our savior," thought Binks. To avoid inhaling smoke the drenched men slapped over their mouths the charred rags they'd used to beat the flames. Binks hesitated to rush from the car; although there was a fire-free path to the edge of the shattered framework, he could see no farther. Was it safe? But Bell darted from the car and Binks followed, reacting instead of calculating. The two men ran over the charred ground through red-hot, glowing wreckage. They ran until they fell against French soil. Safe now, they looked back at the wreckage as the rain beat on them and the gale-force winds blew black smoke into their eyes.

"Hello, hello! Anybody out? Where are you?" cried Binks.

"Here's one—Mr. Leech," replied Leech, obscured by smoke. "Where are you and how many are you?" Binks and Bell identified themselves and fumbled their way to Leech.

The three dazed men surveyed the wreckage. The imposing R.101, the great machine to connect the vast geographic sweep of the British Empire, was now a tangle of debris on the ground. Only the rudder at the stern still stood tall. Rags and strips of fabric hung from it and fluttered in the wind, the center section rocking on its hinges, swinging aimlessly.

Sixty feet in the air, at the tip of the stern, almost untouched by any flames, the ship's RAF Ensign flapped in the wind—the Union Jack on the flag was partly burned, but the RAF roundel was intact.

Forward from the rudder, the girders of the ship's framework were twisted, its round rings distorted. Long gone from most of the framework were the delicate gas bags and plasticized cloth cover—both vaporized by the raging fire. Only Rope's ingenious wire netting remained, like a giant spider web spun over the ship's carcass. The polished aluminum exterior of a crushed engine car glistened in the flames. The collision with the ground rotated the car 180 degrees, its propeller now facing the wrong way. Beside the ship a row of gilded pillars towered over the wreckage: the remains of the lounge.

The ship's nose was buried in the spongy ground of a small

grove of hazel and oak; the steel mooring pendant that clattered on the cables and snapped into the mooring tower arm with a "most gratifying" click was now caked with mud. The ground was littered with quotidian articles: suitcases, fur-lined boots, charred shaving brushes, a tin of cigarettes, a ticking watch, and, untouched by the flames, the latest issue of *Wireless World.* And the stores, so carefully stowed by the chief steward, were strewn on the ground: a few loaves of bread, and a still-labeled tin of plums, its juice leaking from the can. From this debris, a charred crew member rose, but then fell back into the flames.

This snapped Binks, Bell and Leech from their shock. They lurched toward the burning wreckage and raced to an engine car. They smashed its windows to free any survivors. Leech cried: "Is there anybody …." Inside they saw an engineer, his body carbonized, still clutching a wrench in his hand. The inferno drove them back, so the three men circled the blazing ship to search for survivors.

Leech heard a voice from inside. He grabbed a piece of the burning wreckage and used it as a torch. He rushed back into the red-hot girders and freed Disley, the radio operator, who was unconscious at the edge of the ship. The men also found two more engineers, including the Chaplin-lookalike Alf Cook, and two riggers, both severely burned. Binks called for survivors. No replies. No sign of Thomson, Scott, Irwin, Atherstone, or any other officer or crew member.

The only sound was the hiss of rain evaporating as it struck the smoldering wreckage of R.101.

United Kingdom

R.101 left from the Royal Airship Works at 18:36 GMT on October 4, 1930. As it departed, the winds increased in strength.

Cardington

London

As the airship crossed the Channel, it encountered winds so fierce that it often traveled at a ground speed of only thirty miles per hour.

English Channel

Beauvais

At a few minutes past 02:00 GMT on October 5th, R.101 crashed in a field to the west of the small town of Beauvais. Of the fifty-four people aboard, eight survived the crash. Two of those survivors were badly burned and died a few days later.

Paris

France

Route of R.101's Final Flight

PART IV: THE POSTMORTEM

THE CAUSES OF R.101'S CRASH

A FEW MOMENTS BEFORE DAWN a week later, on the morning of October 11, 1930, in a cemetery a half-mile from the Royal Airship Works' mooring tower, the fragrant smell of freshly turned earth filled the air. Flares illuminated the edges of a forty-by-forty-five-foot hole in the ground—the communal grave for R.101's dead—as workers removed the last shovelfuls of dirt. As the sun rose, the gravediggers departed, replaced by other laborers who decorated the grave with thousands of flowers and wreaths—a floral aroma now displaced the odor of loam.

At four o'clock in the afternoon, Royal Air Force trucks moved the coffins of R.101's crew and passengers from the nearby Bedford train station to the grave near the Works. They drove through the town in silence: the BBC halted all transmission from 10 a.m. to 5:15 p.m. to honor the fallen; Bedford banned all traffic and ordered all stores and shops closed. Five hundred police officers lined the three-mile route from station to grave, behind them thousands of mourners, most dressed in black and holding flowers.

As a band played "Abide with Me," pallbearers lay the forty-eight coffins in four rows of twelve and covered each one with a Union Jack. Each coffin was adorned with a small label fabri-

cated from the metal of R.101's framework. Fourteen of the plates
bore names, including those of Captain H. Carmichael Irwin,
First Officer Noel Atherstone, Michael Rope, the Works' engineering genius, and Vincent Richmond, the ship's designer. The
other thirty-four plates read "To the memory of the unknown
airman who died on October 5th"—the blazing inferno had charred
the bodies beyond recognition. Among the unidentified remains
were the ship's steward, Albert Savidge, Lord Thomson, and
Major George H. Scott, Britain's pioneering airship pilot. For-
ty-six of the dead were killed within minutes of R.101's impact,
the other two, both riggers, were severely burned and died a few
days after the crash.

The crash happened a few minutes after 2 a.m. near the town
of Beauvais, France. By then, R.101 had traveled 250 miles from
the Works' mooring tower. On every inch of that journey, winds
slowed the ship's progress and rain pummeled its cover, a more
sustained assault than on any airship in the history of aviation.
The weather worsened as R.101 neared Beauvais. The ship passed
near the town because of a navigation error by the tired crew.
With no watchkeepers, the ship's officers were exhausted and
prone to error from sleep deprivation. The ship's flight plan charted
a course ten miles west of Beauvais because the town was well
known for its high winds and local turbulence—winds so strong
that they once collapsed the choir vaults of the town's thir-
teenth-century cathedral.

In the turbulent air at 1,500 feet above Beauvais, R.101 rose and
fell by 200 feet as its nose hunted for stable air. In the fierce winds,
the ship's cloth cover, battered by seven hours of flight, ripped
open along the top of the ship. Rain pierced the now exposed
paper-thin gas bags. As hydrogen escaped, R.101 sank to the
ground. The distressed ship skidded, at perhaps twenty or thirty
miles per hour, across a field and into a grove of trees. As the ship

slid, its nose bounced.

The impact was not violent—Leech reported a loud "crunch," which he characterized as too mild a noise for a catastrophe—and many on board might have survived except for a string of chance events.

The impact crushed the control car and sheared the aluminum pipes of the centralized ballast system, releasing tons of water into the car. The ballast ignited the water-activated navigation flares stored in the corner of the control car—the "very white" flame observed by Leech—which in turn ignited the hydrogen in the gas bags. The fire shot through the crew and passenger quarters, trapping everyone except those in the rearward engine cars, the fireproof smoking room, and the radio room. The hydrogen-fueled fire dehydrated the bodies of those trapped inside until their heads shrank to the size of a fist.

Although R.101's cover was subjected to bruising winds and pelting rain for far longer than any airship, the cover was also weaker than that of other airships. Its fragility was a consequence of Vincent Richmond's unwavering belief that R.101's debut would spark demand for a fleet of airships. To prepare for this, he pioneered techniques to speed up production, starting with R.101. Richmond believed that the bottlenecks in mass-producing airships occurred when construction steps required laborers to work suspended from the shed's ceiling. He minimized this time-consuming overhead work with R.101's novel nut-and-bolt framework and by waterproofing the ship's five-and-a-half-acre cloth cover with a plastic-like coating before lacing it to the framework. Although the precoating saved time, the cover, now stiff, cracked when stretched onto the airship's frame and, as Michael Rope noted in his June 1930 report, this decreased the cloth's strength so there was "no margin of safety for flight in rough atmosphere."

Rope's conclusion prompted Richmond to replace the cover and waterproof it on the ship. Although Richmond told a newspaper that replacing the cover "was an easy and comparatively inexpensive job," he and his staff at the Works battled against time to replace the cover before R.101 was scheduled to depart for India in the fall. Unable to carry it out in time, Richmond ordered any remaining sections of the original cover strengthened with fabric bands—three-inch-wide strips spaced three feet apart and fastened with a rubber-based glue.

These patches were inspected in late September by Frederick McWade, the inspector assigned to the Royal Airship Works. On his last inspection before the newly lengthened R.101 left the shed for its test flight, McWade examined the cloth cover aft of the nose and near the fins. He saw areas where the rubber glue was smeared over the original cover, but no patches were applied. He knelt and touched the cloth: his finger passed through the cover. On these sections where the cover had rotted, Richmond ordered reinforcing strips glued on. McWade reinspected the craft and concluded that "the work of placing these reinforcing strips in position on all suspected weak positions was completed to the satisfaction of the RAW [Royal Airship Works] Inspection Section and also the AID [Aeronautical Inspection Directorate]."

When the ship left the shed for its only test flight before departure for India, these patched sections of the remaining cover were still weak.

Key members on R.101's partner ship R.100 noticed problems with R.101's cover. A day or so before R.101's test flight, Nevil Norway, an engineer helping design R.100, visited the Works. Although R.100 was built at Howden, 140 miles north of the Royal Airship Works, its point of departure for its trip to Canada was the Works' mooring tower, and upon its return, the ship had been housed in shed NO. 2.

R.100's captain, Ralph Booth, Irwin's counterpart, wanted to show the ship's engineer something strange. Booth handed Norway a few square yards of R.101's cover and asked him, "What do you think of this?" Norway flipped the silvery fabric over and ran his fingers along the two-inch-wide patches covered by the rubber-based glue. As he flexed the cloth, it crumbled.

"Good God, where is this from?" said Norway.

Booth explained that it was from R.101. Norway hoped all "this stuff" had been removed from the ship. "They say they have," said Booth. Yet as the ship left the shed for its test flight before India, the Works had replaced almost 90 percent of the original cover with cloth waterproofed in place, but 33,000 square feet of the original cover—an area the size of half a football field—remained.

The deficiencies of these sections might have shown up in a long test flight before R.101 departed for India, but the ship's only test flight before India was the one cut short by engine failure. Irwin told Booth a day or so before the refitted airship left the shed that he "hoped" to "fly thirty-six or forty-eight hours at a reasonable cruising speed in bad weather in order to thoroughly test out the ship." After sixteen hours, an engine failed and R.101—its cloth untested at high speed—returned to the mooring tower. The proper action would have been to schedule a second test flight and to delay the departure for India, but, instead, fifty-eight hours after its return, the ship departed for India.

A delay might also have resolved the mystery of why the ship flew "heavy" on its test flights to the RAF Display in July, causing it to suddenly dive. Irwin thought the behavior was caused by the automatic valves releasing gas from the bags. When he investigated he discovered holes in the gas bags. These holes, of course, evoke an image of the catastrophic collapse of a bag and the crash of an airship. Indeed, a gas bag could rapidly deflate from a giant rip. If one of the fifteen gas bags in R.101 collapsed, the crew would feel the ship's tail drop, and then the ship itself fall by 500 feet. The elevator coxswain would force the helm down hard to check the angle of inclination, and the captain would rev the engines and discharge ballast aft to bring the ship to an even keel. Although holes conjure such a vision, the reality of holes in airship gas bags was much more mundane. Only the hydrogen below a hole in a gas bag escapes because hydrogen is lighter than air, any above will remain in the bag. So, to cause a sudden deflation, the hole must be at the top of the bag, and it must be large. More often small holes in the gas bags caused a slow leakage of gas and required the tower crew to refill the ship's bags more often. To the ship's crew the holes were most often a nuisance: to find a hole in the vast surface of a gas bag could take a week. We can never be sure that the behavior seen in the July flights played a role in the ship's demise, but that the source of this behavior was never resolved surely highlights the degree to which the ship was untested before its flight to India.

Not only, then, was this untested flagship airship, the hope of the Empire, flying patched up, but the chain of command for the entire enterprise was at best unclear, at worst frayed and, ultimately, deadly.

The Air Ministry was fuzzy about whether Irwin or Scott was in charge of the test flights and final flight. Even a day before the doomed flight, Irwin was unclear on his and Scott's roles. He asked Sir John Higgins, a senior Air Ministry official, to clarify their responsibilities. "I thought," said Higgins to Irwin, that the roles were "quite clear." He then elaborated with a detailed yet hazy and imprecise description.

Scott, as Assistant Director (Flying), Higgins told Irwin,

would discuss with the captain or the navigator and the meteorological officer the general weather conditions and as a result

166

would decide on the course to be taken, flying height and the speed of the airship. He would also advise on the amount of fuel and water ballast to be carried. The captain of the airship was entirely responsible for the preparation of [the] ship for the flight and that it was airworthy and well founded in all respects before the flight commenced. He was responsible for maintaining the ship in correct flying trim throughout the flight and carrying out the general orders in regard to course, engine speeds, etc. as laid down by the Assistant Director (Flying). He was entirely responsible for the flying organization of the ship and the discipline of the crew.

To help Irwin understand better, Higgins continued with an analogy: Scott's role was like that of

a senior officer in charge of the flight of aeroplanes proceeding from, say, Cairo to Cape Town. This senior officer would issue orders to all pilots of the machines as to the height at which to fly, the course to be taken and the arrangements made for communicating with him during flight.

This scenario left Scott in charge of scheduling flights, and so the responsibility for departing to India without a proper test flight lies with him. Yet, ultimately, the greatest share of blame for the R.101 disaster rests on the shoulders of Lord Thomson.

At every step in R.101's development, Thomson, the Secretary of State for Air, used the airship for PR stunts: a tea, or a tour, or a ride for a VIP. These requests, which often arrived via Thomson's aide, Major Louis Reynolds, burdened the overworked Irwin and Atherstone. "I wonder," Atherstone thought, "if Reynolds realizes what Irwin is up against, because if he does then he ought to be publicly shot for putting such almost impossible tasks to us."

Although this meddling diverted Irwin and Atherstone from testing the airship and training its crew, of graver consequence was Thomson's belief that R.101 was an all-weather craft.

Throughout R.101's year of flying, Thomson never grasped the airship's limitations. In early October, when he invited the MPs for a ride he wished for a "fresh breeze" of forty to fifty miles per hour to show them that "the ship does not roll much." A few days later, after his ride on R.101's second flight, Thomson told reporters he "rather regretted that the weather conditions were so fair," and that he had hoped for "a stronger wind ... as he wished to see the behavior of the airship in rough weather."

Later that month, after the Works' meteorological office forecast bad weather with gale-force winds, R.101 was moved from tower to shed. As predicted, a tremendous storm roared through the British Isles, sweeping from the southwest across Ireland, where the rain and hail ripped tiles and bricks from roofs. Then it hit Wales, where it flooded hundreds of houses, driving families to their rooftops. It smashed into England's south coast and created waves that beat against Admiralty Pier and that rose as high as the gallery of the lighthouse.

Yet Thomson objected to sheltering R.101. He expressed his displeasure to Sir John Higgins, who relayed to the Works' senior management that the Secretary of State "was rather annoyed at the airship being put back" into the shed because of the storm, and that he thought it "unnecessarily cautious." Higgins defended the Works: he explained "rather fully" to Thomson that it was "culpably foolish" to leave an untested R.101—it had only flown twice—at the tower.

And eight months after the MPs' flight, canceled because of bad weather, Thomson told delegates at the Fourth Imperial Press Conference that airships could fly to Perth by passing through the "Roaring Forties," the powerful westerly winds in the southern hemisphere that swept sixteenth-century ships from Europe to the East Indies. These winds, he claimed, would be no problem for British airships because "we now have some magnificent skippers training in this country who can handle their ships in the most appalling conditions." And on R.101's flight to India he hoped to "ride the storm," as he wrote to a friend. His belief in the all-weather performance of airships, prompted him often to quote a zeppelin expert that an airship "is the safest conveyance on land, sea or in the air that human ingenuity has yet devised."

This belief led Thomson to deviate from the original plan for developing giant airships. Higgins counseled a "slow and sure policy." He told Thomson that "the right policy to pursue is to go steadily on with the progressive experiments and thus to enable the full results of our extensive program to be achieved." But under Thomson, the Works' mission crept from the development of experimental crafts to the construction of commercial airships, ready to heft large payloads to India. Once R.101 was viewed as a commercial ship, Thomson's influence pressured the Works' management, chiefly Colmore and Scott, into grave errors.

The first error was to insert the additional bay before the flight to India. When the Works first proposed a refit to increase the airship's lift, they suggested a two-part plan: shave weight, fly to India, then, after that demonstration flight, split the ship in two and add an extra bay. "In relation to the future operation of the ship," wrote the Works in bureaucratic prose, "as distinct from the first demonstration flight [to India], an important improvement can be obtained by inserting an additional bay in the structure."

The Works proposed this additional bay so R.101 could have enough lift to operate between Britain and India a few months out of the year. Colmore, at least, realized that R.101 could not fly in any weather, but could, with the extra lift from a new bay, travel on longer flights in the summer, or over the sea where the air was smooth. The Works noted that the additional bay "could not, of course, be carried out in time for the first flight as now proposed." Yet Thomson, pushed for the bay to be added before the India trip. "The best course," he responded when asked to approve this plan, "would I think be: (a) To make the various alterations you suggest ...; (b) To insert the extra bay; (c) To make every effort for a flight with fifty-five tons disposable load to India and back at end of Sept. 1930."

The time spent installing this new bay would have been better used on a full test of the ship and the replacement of the entire cover. The ship should have traveled to India with the most minimal of crew, or, better, the demonstration flight should have been canceled once the Works decided the ship was too heavy for regular service to India.

The second error was to tie R.101's departure date for India to Thomson's political needs. In December 1929, Thomson let the Works know, through Higgins, that he would like R.101 "ready to go to India by the last week of September." He wanted the flight to precede or overlap with the Imperial Conference at which he planned to pitch an ambitious extension of the airship program to delegates from across the Empire. In response, Higgins cautioned Thomson that R.101 might not be ready. "I told the Secretary of State [Thomson]," Higgins reported, "and kept on telling him, verbally, all along, from quite early in the year, that he must not count absolutely on the airship being ready to go out to India, and that unless when we tried it, it was satisfactory, he would not be able to go at that time."

And the Director of the Works, Reginald Colmore, cautioned that

the break up of the S W [southwest] monsoon occurs about this time, generally about the middle of September, and squally conditions must be expected from then on to about the middle of November. It would be preferable to carry out the flight either before the break of the monsoon, or say, late in November, as the conditions on the route are likely to be considerably more favorable.

Colmore knew the weather well. He always carried in his pocket a report based on studies by the Works' meteorologist that showed the estimated fuel requirements for the England–India route for every month of the year and would frequently pull it out and discuss its implications with others at the Works. Colmore also questioned "the importance attached to the flight taking place" in late September. But he learned that "if the ship did not succeed in getting the Secretary of State [for Air] to India in time for him to arrive home for the Imperial Conference, no further money would be available for airship development and none would be asked for."

And he succumbed to that fear of losing the entire program.

Colmore and Scott felt pressured to set R.101's departure date no later than October 4th; any date after that and Thomson would miss the conference. That departure date "was biased," said Booth, the experienced captain of R.100,

> by the fact of the Imperial Conference coming off, and the psychological moment in airships when they could carry the Secretary of State to India, and bring him back to time. It biased their judgment agreeing to fly. If that Imperial Conference had not been coming off, I feel confident that they would have insisted upon more trials, as was done in the case of R.100 before she left for Canada.

Colmore yielded to the pressure to schedule the departure timed to the Imperial Conference, and even quietly arranged for an Imperial Airways plane to be on standby to return Thomson to England should the conditions not be ideal for R.101 to return from India in time to deliver the Secretary of State to the Imperial Conference.

The pressure on Colmore and others at the Works was noted

by Alfred Pugsley, a young engineer at the Royal Airship Works, later knighted for his contributions to engineering. "All were agreed," Pugsley recalled, "that governmental, and indeed, popular pressure, led by Lord Thomson in his enthusiasm for the journey to India, had at the last stages unduly harried and hurried designers, constructors, and crew alike." And so, driven to depart by Thomson's political strategy, an untested R.101 flew into tremendous storms.

And although the management failed the airship, the airship also failed its management.

In 1926, Britain's Director of Civil Aviation hailed R.101 as the "greatest adventure in construction engineering of our time" and, yet, in charge was Vincent Richmond, R.101's chief designer—a man with no training in engineering and no experience designing any airborne craft. Richmond studied chemistry at the Royal College of Science, and his sole practical experience with airships was in creating the waterproof finish applied to the outer cloth covers of airships and small military balloons. His engineering experience was limited to a short stint, before the First World War, designing docks for S. Pearson and Sons, a large construction firm.

Sometimes Richmond's decisions shocked his engineering staff. When he ordered the gas bag netting let out to gain more lift, a Works' engineer noted that this "violated the essential feature of Michael Rope's careful design." To make up for Richmond's sketchy technical training, his staff at the Works had to "balance the gaps in his engineering knowledge," as a colleague discreetly phrased it; or, as another delicately said, they "supplemented" his technical knowledge.

For example, Harold Roxbee, an engineer at the Works, pointed out to Richmond an error in his design for R.101's framework: the cross-section of the ship near the tail would not be symmetrical and this would disrupt airflow over the airship. The cigar-shaped framework of all airships arose from a set of rings spaced along a central axis and linked from back to front by long girders. At least twenty of these girders, Roxbee explained to Richmond, were used in all airship designs, but because Richmond designed R.101 with only fifteen girders the cross-section of R.101 as it tapered to its tail lost its symmetrical, nearly circular shape.

Roxbee pleaded with Richmond to increase the number of girders, but Richmond dismissed this suggestion. When R.101's framework was assembled, the section near the tail was indeed a distorted circle. Roxbee solved the problem by retrofitting—an action never desired by an engineer. He had the girders twisted as they neared the tail to keep the cross-section circular.

After R.101's crash, the young Roxbee thrived as an aeronautical engineer and his development of the gas-powered turbine for jets earned him a knighthood.

Criticism of Richmond's R.101 design wasn't limited to the Works' staff. Two of the greatest airship engineers of Richmond's era thought R.101's framework deficient. Ludwig Dürr, the chief architect for the Zeppelin Company, praised R.101 in public—"I regard R.101 as one of the best airships ever designed and constructed," he told Richmond a month before the ship's crash—but in private he expressed reservations about the design. Dürr worried that the ship's unbraced rings, in contrast to the wire spokes of the zeppelin frame, could never be made light enough. Their weight, he thought, reduced payload and fuel, which hampered R.101's potential as a commercial vehicle because its range would be far too short. And even more severe was the opinion of Britain's most experienced airship designer.

Barnes Wallis designed four of R.101's predecessors: NO. 9 in

1916, NO. 23 in 1917, NO. 26 in 1918, and R.80 in 1920. From 1924 to 1928, he designed R.100, contemporaneous with Richmond's design of R.101. Although the designs of both R.100 and R.101 were state secrets, Richmond sent, uninvited, drawings of R.101 to Wallis.

"It is the crudest piece of design which I have ever seen," Wallis thought when he reviewed the work. He dismissed Richmond as a mere "Works' Manager" and not "a technologist in any sense of the word." As he bundled the drawings to return to Richmond, Wallis concluded that R.101 was a mass of mistakes and unfit to fly. He tacked an icy note to the returned papers: "Until it has been shown unsatisfactory I prefer the arrangement we have worked out for R.100."

Two factors propelled Richmond to the top ranks of British airship designers. First, although he had no practical experience designing airships, he had, for a British citizen, a singular store of theoretical knowledge of zeppelin designs because of the Treaty of Versailles. The treaty mandated that "Dirigibles able to take the air, being manufactured, repaired or assembled ... must be delivered to the Governments of the Principal Allied and Associated Powers." To accomplish this, the victors formed an Inter-Allied Commission. As Britain's representative, Richmond toured Germany free to inspect every zeppelin ship, visit every airship factory, and view blueprints of the most advanced designs of the zeppelin engineers. Richmond showed such interest on his tours that the German officer in charge of the Schutte-Lanz Works, a now forgotten rival of the Zeppelin Company, reported to his superiors, "I got the impression that Mr. Richmond will probably take up airship matters in the future." He continued: "Mr. Richmond seems to be interested in an airship undertaking in England or India."

Yet theoretical knowledge, however detailed, was not enough

alone to catapult him to the top ranks because Britain had experienced airship engineers: Barnes Wallis, of course, but also C. I. R. Campbell.

Campbell was Chief Designer of Airships and Superintendent of the Royal Airship Works. "He was undoubtedly," claimed *Flight*, a British aviation magazine, "our foremost airship designer." Campbell designed, in 1921, the British airship R.38, at the time the largest airship in the world, although small enough to fly through the central ring of R.101 with twenty feet to spare on each size. To create this airship Campbell drew, in contrast to Richmond, on years of engineering training and experience. After graduating with the highest honors in engineering from the Royal Naval College, Campbell designed and built seagoing ships for the Navy, until in 1915 they put him in charge of all airship design in the Admiralty, where he honed his skills. The outcome of that training was R.38, "the first ship of purely British design," reported *Flight*, "and not a copy of previous German ships."

In the early morning of August 24, 1921, R.38 took to the sky for a day of flight. Campbell rode on the ship as an observer, as did his design team—"the cream of the airship services," said *Flight*. In the late afternoon, R.38 sped through the air, piercing a bank of white clouds to emerge into the sunlight, as the crew, in high spirits, tested the ship's controls at high speed. Over an estuary of the North Sea near Hull, the ship's captain ordered the fin controls to be moved rapidly to show the airworthiness of R.38 to cross the Atlantic; the crew heard a violent crack, then a few sharp explosions, followed by two loud explosions that shattered windows in hundreds of shops and rattled houses two miles away.

The ship's backbone, its metal framework, snapped in two, and, engulfed in flames, R.38 plunged into the Humber River. Forty-five of the fifty-one on board died; among the dead were Campbell and his team. The disaster robbed Britain of its most capable airship experts, leaving few in the government's employ with knowledge of airship design.

When Britain decided in 1924 to revive its airship program, they turned to one of the few who had worked on British airships: Vincent Richmond. This accidental engineer was charged with designing R.101, a task described by R. V. Southwell—knighted years later for his technical achievements—"as hard as can be set before an engineering designer." Although Richmond intended to design a "novel" and "radical" airship to a "British standard" that surpassed the time-tested zeppelin designs, he instead created an overweight airship. To avoid a structural failure like R.38's, Richmond decided upon a framework with thick, heavy rings— he lacked the engineering finesse to design a strong, yet lightweight structure. This heavy framework required a last-minute "refit" to gain fourteen tons of lift. The time spent on this refit would have been better used for more test flights, which perhaps might have detected problems with this ship's cover long before its flight to India.

In sum, then, this overweight airship also carried a burden created by the political structures surrounding it. Lord Thomson and Major Scott created an environment where they and their underlings overrode the safety recommendations of inspectors, violated safety regulations by approving flights to serve public relations needs, and overworked R.101's officers by requiring them to double as watchkeepers. The result was a confluence of four interlinked factors that destroyed R.101: navigational errors by an overworked and sleep-deprived crew, abnormally stormy weather, the weakness of the ship's outer cloth cover, and the storage of water-activated flares in the control car. These events resulted in R.101's dive into a grove of trees and its subsequent explosion as it skidded across the ground.

STORIES OF THE SURVIVORS AND
THE FATE OF BRITISH AIRSHIPS

AFTER R.101'S CRASH, Harry Leech, the engine expert, received from King George V the Albert Medal for "at grave risk" rushing into the burning wreckage and "disentangling a companion from the network of red-hot girders." For the rest of his life he worked on engines and as an engineer. Throughout the 1930s, he fine-tuned the engines used by Sir Malcolm Campbell to set land and water speed records. Leech beamed with delight when Campbell's car roared across the Bonneville Salt Flats at 300 miles per hour and cheered when Campbell's boat thundered across Lake Maggiore in the Alps at 127 miles per hour. In the 1940s, Leech maintained the engines for Campbell's son, Donald, when he tried to set water speed records. In the 1950s, Leech worked at the engineering department of the University of Southampton and at South Hants Hospital, where he used his engineering skills to build a cesium unit to treat cancer. He died at age seventy-seven in November 1967.

Outliving Leech by a few years was the rear-engine car operator Arthur "Ginger" Bell, who died in December 1973, aged seventy-five. For years, Bell lived at NO. 18 East Square in Shortstown, less than three miles from the giant sheds, although a reminder of his airship adventures was closer to home. From his house he could walk 300 feet or so and reach a street named, in his honor: Bell's Close. A few streets over was Bink's Court, named in honor of his colleague Joe Binks.

After R.101, Binks dabbled in airships again: he joined a small team that developed *The Bournemouth*, a tiny airship, a mere twenty-seven-feet long, built in 1951 with private funds. Its builders hoped to revive airships. Binks was the last of R.101's survivors to die, in June 1974, aged eighty-two.

After Noel Atherstone's death in the crash, his wife, Susanna, was paid £10 3s. for his wages for October 1st to 5th, less income tax of £5 15s. and 10 shillings and 6 pence of charges for personal telephone calls from Canada. He called home several times from Montreal while serving on R.100. The Air Ministry considered deducting the five pounds advance issued for pocket money in India—"presumably lost in R.101," they wrote—and the twenty-pound advance to purchase a uniform and kit for the trip to India—"uniform lost in R.101," they also noted—but in the end they waived these deductions. It would look unseemly to have one of R.101's widows pay money *to* the Air Ministry. They awarded her a yearly pension of, as they spelled out precisely in a letter, "£191.12.6 (one hundred and ninety-one pounds twelve shillings and six pence)," specifying that it will be paid "while you remain unmarried and of good character." Her children, Richard, aged nine and a half, and Anne, seven and a half, received a yearly allowance of £31 18s. until they reached age eighteen. Susanna Atherstone remarried four years after the crash, was widowed again in 1948, and lived until 1976, when she died at age eighty-one. She preserved Atherstone's diaries, which are currently stored by his granddaughter in a bank vault in Southwold in Suffolk.

After the R.101 disaster, Britain's commitment to airships weakened. In May of 1931, Prime Minister Ramsay MacDonald told the House of Commons that Britain should not "continue to build new ships," but neither should the country conclude "that the experiments and our experience have been so discouraging that we will let the matter rest" and "scrap everything." He proposed a "middle course": maintain the Works as a "nucleus" for "scientific experimental interest in airship development," although he reminded the House that "there will be no new construction, no placing of large ships on order at all." He noted that Britain's only existing airship, R.100, rested on trestles, its gas bags deflated, in one of the two giant sheds at the Works. The ship was, he said, "very much out of condition by lack of use." Indeed, after its successful Atlantic crossing in July 1930, R.100 had not flown again, not even for a short flight. R.100 would become "a sort of experimental ship," said the Prime Minister, and undertake no "long-distance spectacular flights." He estimated the costs of this diminished airship program as £120,000 in the first year, £130,000 in the second, and £140,000 each year thereafter. This new, stripped-down program lasted only six months: in mid-November 1931, the government sold R.100 for scrap.

By early December, a salvage team had removed the ship's tables, beds, decoration, staircase, and flooring, which were sold to yacht owners and to those, said the head of the salvage firm, with a "sentimental interest." The ship's cloth cover and gas bags were removed and scrapped; the engines detached and sold. And now, with R.100 a mere metal carcass, workers attacked it with hammers, hacksaws, hatchets, and axes. They lopped off the tail and fins, which fell into an untidy heap on the shed floor. The ship's nose smashed to the ground with a grinding sound that echoed throughout the giant shed. With the nose off, they hacked the ship apart from front to back, cut the frame into small pieces by blowtorch, then piled the scrap in a heap, and steamrolled it flat.

An undignified end for a ship that flew 20,000 miles without incident. Britain never again built or flew an airship.

For Britain as a world power, the impact of R.101's failure had significant consequences. The human capital and the outlays expended on airships—over £2 million in 1930 currency—diverted energy and funds from Britain's nascent aviation industry, the foremost in the world when they started R.101. By 1930, Britain lost the lead to the United States, where the Douglas Aircraft Company produced, in 1934, the DC-3, which revolutionized commercial aviation.

And for the politicians who desired to sustain the Empire, the failure of a dominant British aviation presence spelled disaster. With the loss of aviation superiority, Britain lost in the next round of imperialism. Germany, Britain's aviation rival, built a strong commercial air presence throughout Europe, Asia, South America, and Africa. The German government, eager to dominate air routes, funneled money to Lufthansa, which became hugely profitable: it flew more miles and carried more passengers than all other European companies combined. Yet the British had in their grasp the innovation that could have ensured Britain remained a dominant world power.

While teams of government-funded workers built airships, Royal Air Force member Frank Whittle toiled in near obscurity to create a jet engine. Whittle repeatedly sought government funding of his revolutionary engine, but failed each time. In 1935 he let his patent on the engine lapse, rather than pay the five pound renewal fee. Although the British government eventually funded his efforts, their support came too late. The United States took the lead when Boeing developed, in the mid-1950s, the first commercially successful jetliner, the 707.

Remnants of Britain's airship program still exist. Approach Bedford from the south on the A600 and the giant sheds can be seen in the Great Ouse River Valley. The sheds were used for a time by the Department of the Environment to test firefighting methods—they were so large that firefighters could build a house, set fire to it, and extinguish it with their test equipment. Over the years the sheds have housed lighter-than-air crafts, mostly meteorology balloons, or hot-air balloons used to train paratroops. More often they are used for theatrical spectacles or to shoot movies—*Batman Begins*, *The Dark Knight*, and *Inception* were filmed in shed NO. 2.

If you search the grounds surrounding the sheds, you can discover the twelve-foot-square concrete bases of the mooring tower's legs, although the tower was torn down during the Second World War, its scrap reclaimed for the war effort. The only trace of R.101, though, is its charred ensign displayed on the wall of St. Mary's Church in Cardington. The ensign is framed in oak and below it is a bronze tablet that lists the forty-eight victims of R.101.

Perhaps the most elaborate memorial was to the quiet, unsung engineering genius Michael Rope. His wife, Doreen, funded the building of a small Catholic church near the family's farm at Kesgrave, Ipswich. The church was finished in June 1931, less than a year after Rope's death. At its dedication a foundation stone was laid on behalf of Rope's eight-month-old son, Crispin, born shortly after the crash. A scale model of R.101, constructed from metal salvaged from the wreck, hangs from the chancel arch. The quiet Rope's memorial grew beyond the church: his wife used insurance funds to create a foundation to support the disabled, to relieve poverty, and to promote the public understanding of science. Among the projects supported by Doreen Rope, who died in 2003, was a hospital for treating leprosy in Bolivia, and one in Uganda to help families destroyed by AIDS.

Hours after R.101's crash, sections of the ship's still smoldering metal framework were hacked to pieces by firefighters and gendarmes. They ripped into the wreckage with blow torches, chisels and metal saws, chasing away swarms of rats attracted by the plastic coating on the few scraps of cover that survived the fire. They found five bodies in the control car, and in the crew and passenger quarters they uncovered twenty more bodies. Within a day, the rescue effort stopped.

To cart away the remains of R.101, the British government hired Thomas W. Ward and Company, Shipbreakers of Sheffield—a firm famous for using an elephant to cart scrap. They promised to remove the wreckage "expeditiously and quietly" and to "prevent souvenir hunters getting any part of it." The firm's workers finished the demolition begun by the rescuers and soon the airship's "novel" and "radical" framework was no more than tidy piles of metal. The compacted eighty-ton framework returned to Britain in two consignments; the first aboard the steamer *Fraternity* on December 19, 1930; the second aboard the *New Pioneer* on Christmas Day. R.101's remains shared space in both ships with a cargo of processed food and meat. When the vessels arrived in Liverpool, the wreckage was transported to Sheffield, where the firm melted the scrap, and sold it to the Zeppelin Company.

They used it to create the zeppelin LZ 129, an airship better known as the *Hindenburg*.

ACKNOWLEDGMENTS

Many people lent a hand to improve this book. Alexander Poole, of Poole's Family Research, scoured the British Archives to locate hundreds of documents about R.101 and delivered over 1,000 pages on the airship. Librarians of the Lighter-than-Air Collection of the Akron Public Library were helpful when I spent the better part of a week there studying the transcripts of the Simon Inquiry into R.101's crash.

Viewers of my YouTube channel, *engineerguyvideo*, read an early manuscript of the book. From that mass of typographical errors, infelicities, and fuzzy writing they extracted enough to provide insightful comments. Their feedback sharpened the arguments in the book, alerted me to obscure sentences, and highlighted what was missing. I appreciated greatly the careful read and detailed comments from (in alphabetical order): Marc Dumouchel, Robert Fox, Bill Pike, Gary Schultz, Eric Seale, Robert Sido, Mordecai Veldt, and Robert Zeh.

Carl Lennertz's line editing on this improved manuscript helped create a book more accessible to readers. Bela Cunha did a superb job of copy editing the final manuscript.

Appendix A is a list of Britain's attempts to build passenger airships prior to R.100 and R.101.

Appendix B is a list of all the passengers on the R.101's ill-fated flight to India.

The appendices that follow contain four documents from the British Archives. These documents reveal the thoughts of those creating and managing R.101.

Appendix C is the press notes released on October 1, 1930, three days before R.101's departure to India. This sixteen-page document describes R.101's route to India, details the food and supplies aboard, notes the location of signal towers, lists passengers, and shares short biographies of the officers and personal details of the crew on board.

Appendix D is a report by Vincent Richmond and Michael Rope on their trip on the *Graf Zeppelin* from the Royal Airship Works to Friedrichshafen, the home of the Zeppelin Company. The report reveals the deficiencies, in their eyes, of the *Graf Zeppelin* as a passenger ship and also highlights the impoverished state of the Zeppelin Company.

Appendix E is a fascinating report by the Works' fabric manager and resident chemist on how to construct a gas bag from animal intestines. The attention to detail highlights the difficulties in producing an airship in an era before plastics and other synthetic materials.

And, lastly, Appendix F is a heart-wrenching document: it is a report signed by Colmore, but likely written by Richmond and

Rope, that details R.101's subpar lift and the Works' drastic measures to reduce the weight of R.101.

The documents in appendices E and F are from an investigation led by Sir John Simon into the causes of R.101's crash. These two appendices are from the supplemental material generated by that inquiry. See the Bibliography for details.

BRITISH PASSENGER AIRSHIPS PRIOR
TO R.100 AND R.101

After the First World War, Britain attempted to build and operate five passenger airships: R.33, R.34, R.36, R.38, and R.80. All failed. In total these ships cost the British government £1,825,000 ($8,690,476) and flew about 1,400 hours—an hourly rate, then, of £1,300 ($6,200). All of these ships were much smaller than R.101, the largest being about half the volume. The volumes listed below for each ship are in millions of cubic feet. For comparison, the volume of R.101 was 5.510 million cubic feet.

R.33
First flight: March 6, 1919
Decommissioned: April 1928
Hours flown: 735
Volume: 1.950

This airship was built by the Royal Naval Air Service for use in the First World War, but was not completed before hostilities ended. In 1920 the airship was turned over to civilian authorities. When the British government halted all airship development in May 1921, R.33 was mothballed. The airship flew again in 1925 when British airship development was resumed. It was used for promotional flights and for testing. By November 1926 the airship's framework showed fatigue and so the ship was dismantled in 1928.

R.34
First flight: March 14, 1919
Decommissioned: January 1921
Hours flown: 495
Volume: 1.950

R.34, the ship flown by Major Scott across the Atlantic in 1919, flew in bad weather and struck a hill in a North Yorkshire moor in late January 1921. The impact damaged two propellers. The ship limped to the Howden Airfield on half power in search of the safety of its shed, but strong winds kept it from entering it. The crew moored the airship on the ground—Howden had no tower. Strong gusts of wind during the night battered the airship against the ground. By morning its framework was damaged beyond repair and so it was hacked to pieces and sold for scrap.

R.36
First flight: April 1, 1921
Decommissioned: June 1926
Hours flown: 97
Volume: 2.100

On June 21, 1921 Major Scott erred in landing this airship at the tower. The ship's nose collapsed. The ground crew toiled for five hours to untangle the damaged airship, but as they released it and lowered it to the ground, the wind rose. It took another five hours to reach the shed. As the ground crew moved R.36 into its shed, a gust of wind rammed the airship into the shed doors and destroyed the middle of the ship. Eventually it was determined to be beyond repair and was scrapped.

R.38
First flight: June 23, 1921
Destroyed: August 24, 1921
Hours flown: 70
Volume: 2.724

The British intended to sell this ship to the United States. Before delivery the ship's crew wanted one more test flight. So, on August 24, 1921, R.38 sped through the air, piercing a bank of white clouds to emerge into the sunlight as the crew, in high spirits, tested the ship's controls at high speed. As it flew over an estuary of the North Sea near Hull, the ship's captain ordered the fin controls to be moved rapidly. The ship's backbone, its metal framework, snapped in two and R.38 crashed into the Humber River.

R.80
First flight: July 19, 1921
Decommissioned: July 1925
Hours flown: 73
Volume: 1.200

This was the last rigid ordered during the First World War. Construction was begun in 1917, but by 1919 the British authorities decided it no longer had military value, though they continued production for commercial use. Its last flight was in September 1921. The ship was too small to be commercially viable. After that it was housed in a shed and its framework was used for stress analysis and destructive testing. It was eventually dismantled.

PASSENGER AND CREW ON BOARD
R.101'S FLIGHT TO INDIA

When R.101 slipped the mooring tower on October 4, 1930, the following people were aboard.

Passengers

1. Brigadier-General, The Right Honorable Lord Thomson of Cardington (Secretary of State for Air)—killed, body never identified.
2. Air Vice-Marshal Sir W. Sefton Brancker (Director of Civil Aviation)—killed, body identified on return to London.
3. Major Percy Bishop (Chief Inspector AID)—killed, body never identified.
4. Squadron Leader W. Palstra RAAF (representing the Australian Government)—killed, body never identified.
5. Squadron Leader W. O'Neill (Deputy Director of Civil Aviation, India)—killed, body identified on return to London.
6. James Buck, Lord Thomson's valet—killed, body identified on return to London.

Officials of the Royal Airship Works

7. Wing Commander R. B. B. Colmore (Director for Airship Development)—killed, body identified on return to London.
8. Major G. H. Scott (Assistant Director of Airship Development–Flying and Training)—killed, body never identified.
9. Lieutenant-Colonel V. C. Richmond (Assistant Director of Airship Development–Technical)—killed, body identified on

return to London.

10. Squadron Leader F. M. Rope (Assistant to Richmond)—killed, body identified on return to London.

11. Alexander Bushfield, AID—killed, body identified on return to London.

12. H. J. Leech, Foreman Engineer Royal Airship Works—survived.

Officers of R.101

13. Flight Lieutenant H. Carmichael Irwin (Captain)—killed, body identified on return to London.

14. Squadron Leader E. L. Johnston (Navigator)—killed, body never identified.

15. Lieutenant-Commander N. G. Atherstone (First Officer)—killed, body identified on return to London.

16. Flying Officer M. H. Steff (Second Officer)—killed, body never identified.

17. M. A. Giblett (Chief Meteorological Officer)—killed, body identified on return to London.

Petty Officers and Charge Hands

18. G. W. Hunt (Chief Coxswain)—killed, body never identified.

19. W. R. Gent (Chief Engineer)—killed, body identified on return to London.

20. G. W. Short (Charge-Hand Engineer)—killed, body never identified.

21. S. E. Scott (Charge-Hand Engineer)—killed, body identified at Allonne, France.

22. T. Key (Charge-Hand Engineer)—killed, body never identified.

23. S. T. Keeley (Chief Wireless Operator)—killed, body never identified.

24. A. H. Savidge (Chief Steward)—killed, body never identified.

Crew members

25. Flight-Sergeant W. A. Potter (Assistant Coxswain)—killed, body identified at Allonne, France.

26. L. E. Oughton (Assistant Coxswain)—killed, body identified on return to London.

27. C. H. Mason (Assistant Coxswain)—killed, body never identified.

28. M. G. Rampton (Assistant Coxswain)—killed, body identified on return to London.

29. H. E. Ford (Assistant Coxswain)—killed, body never identified.

30. P. A. Foster (Assistant Coxswain)—killed, body never identified.

31. E. G. Rudd (Rigger)—killed, body identified at Allonne, France.

32. C. E. Taylor (Rigger)—killed, body identified on return to London.

33. A. W. J. Norcott (Rigger)—killed, body never identified.

34. A. J. Richardson (Rigger)—killed, body identified on return to London.

35. W. G. Radcliffe (Rigger)—survived, but died at Beauvais, France on October 6, 1930.

36. S. Church (Rigger)—survived, but died at Beauvais, France on October 8, 1930.

37. R. Blake (Engineer) NO. 4 car—killed, body identified at Allonne, France.

38. C. A. Burton (Engineer)—killed, body identified on return to London.

39. C. J. Fergusson (Engineer) NO. 1 car—killed, body never identified.

40. A. C. Hastings (Engineer) NO. 3 car—killed, body never

identified.

41. W. H. King (Engineer) NO. 2 car—killed, body identified on return to London.

42. M. F. Littlekitt (Engineer) NO. 1 car—killed, body never identified.

43. W. Moule (Engineer) NO. 2 car—killed, body identified on return to London.

44. A. H. Watkins (Engineer)—killed, body never identified.

45. A. V. Bell (Engineer) NO. 5 car—survived.

46. T. H. Binks (Engineer) NO. 5 car—survived.

47. A. J. Cook (Engineer) NO. 4 car—survived.

48. V. Savory (Engineer) NO. 3 car—survived.

49. G. H. Atkins (Wireless Operator)—killed, body identified on return to London.

50. E. Elliott (Wireless Operator)—killed, body identified on return to London.

51. A. Disley (Wireless Operator/Electrician)—survived.

52. F. Hodnett (Assistant Steward)—killed, body never identified.

53. E. A. Graham (Cook)—killed, body never identified.

54. T. W. Megginson (Galley Boy)—killed, body never identified.

FLIGHT OF HM AIRSHIP R.101 TO
INDIA: NOTES FOR PRESS USE

On October 1, 1930, three days before R.101 left for India, the Air Ministry press office released this sixteen-page document to newspapers and other press outlets. It was written by C. P. Robertson, the Air Ministry press officer.

The document covers every aspect of R.101. It opens with the mission's purpose: "testing out the behavior of an airship on a long distance flight, more especially under semitropical conditions." It describes the infrastructure in place for the flight: the signal towers along the route, the meteorological information that will be communicated to the ship as it flies, and the towers in Egypt and India. The document lists all the passengers, officers and crew *scheduled* to fly to India. It contains detailed biographies of all key personnel, and lists for the crew their age, birthplace, and previous airship experience. Most revealing, though, is the mention of Scott only as an official of the Royal Airship Works who was riding on R.101. He is not listed as an officer. Scott objected to this characterization of his role when he saw these notes on the morning of departure for India, October 4th. In response to Scott's objections, Robertson issued a press release, written in consultation with Colmore, when the ship departed the tower. It included this line: "The flight has been carried out under the direction of Major G. H. Scott, Assistant Director in charge of Airship Flying."

The passenger and crew list in this document was outdated by the time R.101 slipped from the mooring tower three days after the press notes were issued. A. H. Watkins had replaced G. Watson as an engineer, E. Elliott had replaced C. W. Larkins as a radio operator, and Alexander Bushfield, an inspector with AID, had joined the flight.

This document has been reproduced with its table of contents and with the original pagination indicated. The spelling of place names as in the original document has been retained.

This document is extracted from the file "Responsibilities of Captain for R.101: Position of Major Scott and F/Lt. Irwin" located in the National Archives, Kew, Reference AIR 5/13.

Cover page

196

Page 1

Flight of HM Airship R.101 to India: Notes for press use

The flight of HM Airship R.101 to India via Egypt—the first flight of an Airship to either country is being undertaken as part of the Air Ministry's development policy for Airships with the object of testing out the behavior of an Airship on a long distance flight, more especially under semi-tropical conditions.

The flight is an experimental one, and in this respect it should not be forgotten that when the Airship was designed she was approximately twice the size of the largest Airship then built, and incorporates many novel features.

HM Airship R.101

The R.101 was designed by Lieut-Col. V. C. Richmond, Assistant Director of Airship Development (Technical) and was built at the Royal Airship Works, Cardington, Bedford. She is the largest Airship in the world having a gas capacity of approximately five and a half million cubic feet.

Since the Airship carried out home trials an extra section has been embodied in the ship, which has increased her length by forty-five feet and her gas capacity by about 500,000 cubic ft. The principal dimensions now are: Length 777 feet, maximum diameter nearly 132 feet and maximum height about 140 feet. As the result of the insertion of the extra bay, and by alterations to the parachute netting which enabled each gasbag to hold a greater volume of gas, her gross lift is now approximately 165 tons.

She is engined by five Beardmore "Tornado" 585 HP compression ignition heavy fuel oil engines. They are carried in five separate power cars. Two of the engines are of reversible type.

R.101 has the most spacious passenger accommodation of any airship yet built. It consists of a large Saloon lounge (Length thirty-three feet, width sixty-two feet) which stretches across the hull, with a raised promenade at either end from which excellent views can be of obtained; a separate dining room with seating capacity for fifty persons, a fire-proof smoke room (a feature which has not been installed in any other airship and has been made possible by the use of heavy fuel oil engines) and roomy passengers' cabins. There is also an electrically equipped kitchen and good lavatory accommodation.

The color scheme is white and gold, while the curtains are of cambridge blue.

Page 2

The experiment of collecting rainwater on the top of R.100 during the flight to and from Canada having proved highly successful a somewhat similar catchment system has been provided on R.101. Arrangements have been made for collecting water at two positions on the top of the hull and the water will be led from these points in order to supplement the water ballast.

The airship has carried out extensive home trials her total flying time, before carrying out tests after the insertion of the new section, being 103 hours.

A detailed description of the airship is given in separate notes entitled "HMA R.101."

Alternative routes

The flight will be made from The Royal Airship Works, Cardington, Bedford, to India via Egypt, where a stop will be made for refueling purposes at the Airship Base situated at Ismailia in the Canal Zone. This Base is equipped with a Mooring Tower similar in all respects to the one at Cardington, and also with a Silicol Hydrogen Plant which has an output of about 60,000 cubic feet per hour.

At Karachi, in addition to a Mooring Tower and hydrogen plant there is also a large housing shed, which is the largest building in the British Empire, being slightly larger than either of the Sheds at Cardington.

The route HMA R.101 will follow will be dictated by the Meteorological conditions prevailing at the time of departure, and the Captain will naturally shape his course during flight so as to take advantage of the most favorable winds.

The route can be divided up into two sections: (1) Cardington to Ismailia, (2) Ismailia to Karachi.

The following table shows possible alternative routes and the distances that would be covered:

Cardington to Ismailia

No.	Mercator Route	Nautical Miles	Statute Miles
1	Via Brest, Tafalla, Barcelona, Malta, thence to Ismailia	2,440	2,810
2	Via Toulouse, Narbonne, Malta, thence to Ismailia	2,235	2,570
3	Via Lyons, Marseilles, thence to Ismailia	2,075	2,390
4	Via Lyons, Marseilles, Malta, thence to Ismailia	2,170	2,500

Page 3

Ismailia to Karachi

No.	Mercator Route	Nautical Miles	Statute Miles
1	Via Alleppo, Euphrates, Baghdad and Persian Gulf and along the Persian Coast to Karachi	2,200	2,580
2	Via Desert Route, Baghdad and Persian Gulf and along Persian coast to Karachi	2,125	2,440
3	Via Red Sea and Gulf of Aden thence across the Indian Ocean	2,790	3,210

At far as the route from Ismailia to Karachi is concerned it is probable that the most Northerly route will be flown, by way of Alleppo, Baghdad and Basrah. The return flight will be carried out on more or less similar routes which will be decided at the time of departure.

Passengers, officers and crew

Lord Thomson, Secretary of State for Air, Air Vice-Marshal Sir Sefton Brancker, Director of Civil Aviation and Squadron Leader W. Palstra MC of the Royal Australian Air Force will fly on the airship to and from India. Squadron Leader W. H. L. O'Neill, MC will travel to Karachi as a representative of the Secretary of State for India.

The following officials from the Royal Airship Works, Cardington will be on board:

Wing Commander R. B. B. Colmore, OBE, RAF, *Director of Airship Development*

Lieut-Col. V. C. Richmond, *Assistant Director of Airship Development (Technical)*

Major G. H. Scott, CBE, AFC *Assistant Director of Airship Development (Flying)*

Squadron Leader F. M. Rope RAF, *Technical Assistant to Lieut-Col Richmond*

Mr. H. J. Leach, AFM, *Engineer*

Major P. Bishop, OBE, *Chief Inspector Aircraft of the* AID. Will travel as far as Egypt

Mr. J. Buck will be in attendance on Lord Thomson throughout the flight

The officers of R.101 are:

Flight Lieutenant H. C. Irwin, AFC, RAF *Captain*

S/Ldr. E. L. Johnston, OBE, AFC, *Navigator*

Lt.-Commander N.G. Atherstone, AFC. (RN RET.) *1st Officer*

Flying Officer M. H. Steff, RAF, *2nd Officer*

Mr. M. A. Giblett, MSC, (Superintendent of the Airship Division, Meteorological Office), will act as *Meteorological Officer*

The members of the crew are:

Chief Coxswain: G. W. Hunt, AFM

Asst. Chief Coxswain: W. A. Potter.

Asst. Coxswains: C. H. Mason, L. F. Oughton.

Riggers: S. Church, H. E. Ford, P. A. Foster, A. W. J. Norcott, W. G. Radcliffe, M. G. Rampton, A. J. Richardson, E. G. Rudd, C. E. Taylor

First Engineer: W. R. Gent, AFM

Chargehand Engineers: T. A. A. Key, S. E. Scott, G. W. Short

Engineers: A. V. Bell, J. H. Binks, R. Blake, C. A. Burton, A. J. Cook, C. J. Fergusson, A. D. Hasting, W. H. King, M. F. Littlekit, W. Moule, V. Savory. G. Watson.

Page 4

w/T Chargehand: S. T. Keeley

w/T Operators: G. K. Atkins, A. Disley, C. W. Larkins

Chief Steward: A. H. Savidge

Steward: F. Hodnett

Cook: E. A. Graham

Galley Boy: J. F. Megginson

The flying crew therefore consists of five officers and thirty-seven men, and the total number on board (unless there are alterations later) will be fifty-three. (Notes regarding the officials and crew are given in pages seven to fifteen.)

An airship normally flies with a two-watch crew but on the outward journey a three-watch crew is being carried so that the services of the third watch may be available on arrival at Karachi. When an airship is moored one watch is always on duty, a stand-by watch is in close attendance and undertakes maintenance duties during the day, and the third watch—the relief watch—is off-duty for twenty-four hours at a time.

As the conditions on the return journey from India are generally more unfavorable than on the outward passage it may be decided—particularly on the first flight—to curtail the numbers carried on the return passage in order that ample reserve of fuel can be carried to meet any adverse conditions.

Uniform

Dark blue uniform recently approved for the Air Ministry Airship Crews will be worn on the flight probably as far as Egypt, but at this stage it may be necessary to change into tropical kit, for which arrangements have been made. The blue uniform consists of a reefer pattern jacket with gold buttons in the case of the Officers and black for the men, peaked cap, and badge consisting of a circle surmounted by a crown in the center of which are the words "R.101" and on the circle "RAW Cardington." Similar badges will be worn on the khaki tropical kit.

It should be noted that the Crew of R.101 is entirely composed of civilian personnel, with the exception or two officers and one NCO of the Royal Air Force, who are seconded for duty on Airships.

page 5

Food supplies, etc.

On each section of the flight, i.e. Cardington to Ismailia and Ismailia to Karachi, four days' rations will be carried consisting of two days' ordinary ration, one day's reserve ration, and one day's emergency ration. The total amount of food will amount to 837 lbs., which will be taken on board at Cardington and Ismailia on the outward flight and at Karachi and Ismailia on the homeward flight.

About 500 gallons of drinking and washing water will be carried during the flight.

Meals will be served in the Dining Room and will be cooked in the electrically equipped kitchen close by.

The Airship will be cleared by Customs, Emigration and Medical Authorities before leaving Cardington and the necessary papers will be available for clearance in Egypt and India.

The amount of luggage allowed to each Officer or Passenger is thirty lbs., and to each member of the Crew fifteen lbs.

Signals organization

HMA R.101 is equipped for long-wave transmission and for long and short-wave reception. Her call sign and registration mark is GFAAW. (The wave lengths are not being disclosed and it is hoped that private persons will not attempt to transmit messages, as the Airship will be fully occupied in receiving meteorological information and in transmitting essential messages.)

The signal organization in divided into five zones, the operating wireless ground stations being:

Cardington: Cardington to Marseilles 70° E. Long.

Malta: Marseilles 70° E. Long. to Crete 25° E. Long.

Ismailia: Crete 25° E. Long. To Ismailia

Ismailia: Ismailia to Head of Persian Gulf 48° E. Long.

Karachi: Head of Persian Gulf 48° E. Long. to Karachi

The Airship will be in communication with these Stations in the order shown, and similar arrangements will be in force on the return flight.

The main chain of communication will be entirely by Royal Air Force Wireless Stations, with the exception that the Station in India is the Indian Government Civil Station at Karachi.

During each stage there will be certain routine times both for the transmission and reception of messages. Progress reports will be dispatched by the airship each day at midnight (GMT), 6 a.m. (GMT), noon (GMT), and 6 p.m. (GMT).

The Karachi W/T Station is also fitted up with radiotelephony so that the Captain of the Airship will be able to speak to the mooring Tower officer during landing.

page 6

Special attention has been devoted to the provision of adequate meteorological information throughout the flight. The principal reports which will be supplied and picked up are:

a. A selection of the regular synoptic reports issued from the Meteorological Office, Air Ministry via the Air Ministry W/T Station.

b. Special reports from the Meteorological centers at Cardington, Malta, Ismailia, Baghdad, and the Indian Government Station at Karachi.

c. Weather messages from steamships at sea.

d. Regular synoptic reports from Continental countries on the route and adjoining territories.

The Meteorological Officer will prepare on board the Airship special weather charts every six hours, similar to those drawn daily at the Air Ministry, and the route followed will be mainly based on the deductions made from these charts.

Staff at overseas air bases

The airship bases at Ismailia and Karachi are under the control of airship officers who were sent recently from the Royal Airship Works. Flying Officer H. R. Luck, RAF is in charge at the former station and Lt. Commander H. W. Watt, RNR, of the latter. The nucleus of the mooring tower crew for each station were also sent from England. Additional men are being provided on the spot by the Royal Air Force and a certain number of Egyptians and Indians are also being employed.

page 7

Notes on officials and officers

Wing Commander R. B. B. Colmore, OBE, RAF, *Director of Airship Development*, is the Air Ministry director under the Air Member of Council for Supply and Research, responsible for all airship activities. His directorate is organized in five main divisions; research and design; flying; organisation; construction and maintenance; and finance and administration. Both of the first three divisions is in charge of an assistant director; a works manager is responsible for the fourth and a secretary and accountant for the last. The director has his headquarters at the Royal Airship Works, Cardington, Bedford, where the airship R.101 was designed and constructed and which is also the base for Britain airship operations. The trials of R.100 and R.101 have been carried out at Cardington.

Wing Commander Colmore was born at Portsmouth in 1887, was educated at Stubbington House, Fareham and in HMS *Britannia*. He became a Sub-Lieutenant in the Royal Navy in 1907 and was promoted Lieutenant in 1909. He retired in 1911 and on being mobilized at the outbreak of War become a Lieutenant-Commander. He served with the Armored Car Division at Antwerp in 1914 and commanded the armored car section which was employed at Gallipoli in 1915 and later in the same year was Commanding Officer in the first campaign against the Senussi tribes on the Egyptian borders. He was transferred to the Airship Section of the Royal Navy Air Service in 1916 and after serving at the airship station at Barrow became Commanding Officer of the airship base at Mullion, Cornwall. While holding the command he evolved a novel scheme of dealing with the submarine menace by a system of combined patrols of airships, seaplanes and aeroplanes in conjunction with surface craft. This method proved so successful that Lt. Col. Colmore (as he become on formation of the Royal Air Force) was appointed a 1st class Staff Officer, Aircraft Operations, Plymouth, with a view to the same principles being applied against submarines along the whole British Coasts, and in this connection he was later posted as Chief Staff Officer, Aircraft Operations, with Commander-in-Chief, Grand Fleet, based at Dundee. The war ended, however, before the system came into general operation.

After the War he was granted a permanent commission as Squadron Leader, Royal Air Force, and was attached as Staff Officer for Airships to the Department of the Controller General of Civil Aviation, Air Ministry.

When it was decided in 1924 to proceed with the development of airships he was appointed Deputy Director of Airship Development in the department of Air Member of Council for Supply and Research and became Director at the beginning of the present year. He is seconded from the Royal Air Force for airship duty. He was on board R.100 during her Canadian Flight in July and August this year and represented the Air Ministry during her stay in Canada.

Major G. H. Scott, CBE, AFC, *Assistant Director of Airship Development (Flying)* was born in 1889 at Catford, Kent, and was educated at Richmond School, Yorks, and the RN Engineering College, Keyham. From 1908 he was engaged in general engineering until the outbreak of War when he joined the Royal Naval Air Service as a Flight Sub-Lieutenant. After service at Farnborough, in HMA *Eta* and at Kingsnorth [*page 8*] he proceeded in 1915 to the airship station at Barrow and became captain of the *Parseval* P.4. The following year he was appointed to the command of the airship station at Anglesey and in 1917 became captain of R.9, the first British rigid airship to fly, and was also appointed Experimental Officer, Airships, at Pulham airship base. On the formation of the Royal Air Force he was given the rank of Major.

Towards the end of 1918 he was chosen to command R.34 and was awarded the AFC for his work on airships. In 1919 he commanded R.34 on its flight from East Fortune, Scotland to the United States and back to Pulham. For this he was awarded the CBE. This was the first flight of any aircraft to America and also the first outward and homeward flight.

He was demobilized from the Royal Air Force later in 1919. In 1920 he was appointed to the technical staff of the Royal Airship Works, Cardington. He is the inventor of the Air Ministry system of airship mooring to a tower, which is also employed in the United States.

In 1924 he was appointed officer in charge of Flying and Training in the Airship Directorate and in January of this year became Assistant Director (Flying). He visited Canada in 1927 to advise the Canadian Government on the selection of an airship base, which resulted in St. Hubert, Montreal being chosen and equipped.

Since the autumn of last year he has carried out extended trials of the two new British Airships R.101 and R.100, which are the largest airships in the world and contain many novel features compared with previous airship types.

He took part in the Canadian Flight of R.100 during July and August this year and was Officer in Charge of the Flight.

Lieutenant-Colonel V. C. Richmond, OBE, BSC, ARCS, FRAES, *Assistant Director Airship Development (Technical)* was born in 1895 at Dalston, London, and was educated at the Royal College of Sciences, London. He became Engineer to Messrs. S. Pearson & Sons, for Physical and Structural problems in connection with dock construction. In 1915 he joined the Royal Naval Air Service and was engaged until the end of the War principally on the construction of nonrigid airships. In 1920 he went to Germany with the Inter-Allied Commission of Control and during part of the time was in charge of the Naval Sub-Commission for the surrender of airships and seaplanes. In 1921 he joined the Airship Research Department of the Air Ministry and until 1923 was engaged on research into problems connected with rigid airship construction. From 1923 to 1924, during the cessation of airship activity in this country, he was in charge of the Material and Research Branch under the Director of Research, Air Ministry and since 1923 also, has been Lecturer in Airship Design and Construction at the Imperial College of Science. He joined the Royal Airship Works in 1924 as Officer in Charge of Design and Research, during which time the R.101 has been designed and construction in 1930 was appointed Assistant Director (Technical).

page 9

Flight Lieutenant H. C. Irwin, AFC, RAF, *Captain of* R.101 was born in 1894 at Dundrum, Co. Cork, Ireland, and was educated at St. Andrew's College, Dublin. He joined the RNAS Airship Section in 1915 and from 1916 to 1917 was Captain of Non-Rigid airships SS *Zero, Coastal* and NS Type in Home Waters and the East Mediterranean. He commanded R.33 and R.36 in 1920 and from the following year to 1924 was performing RAF duty at Service Stations and Staff duties at the Air Ministry. In 1925 he was transferred to the Royal Airship works, Cardington, and in 1926 again commanded R.33 when she carried out various experimental flights to gather technical data required in connection with the design of R.100 and R.101. From 1926 to 1928 he commanded the RAF School of Balloon Training on Salisbury Plain and in 1929 was again transferred to the RAW to take over command of R.101. He was a member of the British Olympic Athletic Team at Antwerp in 1920 and has repeatedly represented Ireland and the Royal Air Force in International and Inter-Service Athletic Contests. He is seconded for airship duty from the Royal Air Force.

Squadron Leader H. L. Johnston, AFC, OBE, Reserve of Air Force Officers,

Navigator of R.101, was born in Sunderland in 1891 and was educated at Tynemouth High school and the Marine School, South Shields. He is a qualified Master Mariner and originally served in the Royal Naval Reserve. He transferred to the RNAS (Airship Section) in 1916 and after commanding coastal type airships he later became Commanding Officer of Luce Bay airship station, in the South West of Scotland. On the formation of the Royal Air Force he was appointed Captain and later was promoted to the rank of Major. After the War he served in the navigation branch in the Air Ministry but later retired from the Royal Air Force. He was appointed to the Royal Airship Works, Cardington, in 1924 for navigational duties and was loaned for some time to Imperial Airways, Ltd., in order to open up European aeroplanes routes. In 1927 he was navigator to the Secretary of State for Air on the first Imperial Airways flight to India and back. He is navigator for R.100 as well as R.101 and in that capacity flew with the former on her voyage to Canada and return in July and August of this year. He is also an Air Ministry Examiner for Navigators' licenses. He recently organized the Guild of Air Pilots and Air Navigators of the British Empire and holds the position of Deputy Master in that organization.

Lieutenant-Commander N. G. Atherstone, AFC, RN (Retd.) *First Officer* R.101 was born in 1894 at St. Petersburg, Russia, and was educated at Larchfield, Helensburgh; Winton House, Winchester, and Charterhouse. He joined the Royal Navy as a Cadet in 1915 and was appointed to HMS *Highflyer* for training. On the outbreak of War he was appointed to HMS *Gibraltar* and served with the 10th Cruiser Squadron, Grand Fleet and Destroyers until 1917 when he transferred to Airships, becoming Pilot of Non-Rigid SS *Zero* and HS types. In 1918 he was appointed 1st officer of R.29 and was awarded the AFC. He returned to the Royal Navy in 1919 and retired in 1920 becoming resident in Australia. He was promoted Lieutenant-Commander RN (Retd.) in 1926 and returned to England in 1927 on being appointed to the Royal Airship Works, Cardington, for Airship duties. He was appointed First officer R.101 in 1929.

page 10

Flying Officer M. H. Steff, RAF, *Second Officer* R.101 was born in 1896 at Luton, Beds. [Bedfordshire]. He joined the Navy in September, 1914 and served in HMS *Inflexible* from 1915 onwards and was present at the battle of Jutland in 1916. He became a flight officer in the Kite Balloon section of the

RNAS in the beginning of 1918 and served in the Barrage Kite Balloons in Italy. He took part in minesweeping operations in 1919 in the Aegean Son, the Dardanelles and the Black Sea and in 1920 he was posted to the instructional staff of the School of Balloon Training in England where he served for four years. He proceeded in 1925 to the Royal Airship Works for Kite balloon experiments and was appointed 2nd Officer of R.101 last year. He has been loaned to R.100 for her Trial Flights, as 2nd Officer, and in that capacity flew with her to Canada and back in July and August of this year. He is seconded from the Royal Air Force for airship duty.

Mr. M. A. Giblett, MSc, *Meteorological Officer,* R.101, was born in 1894 at Englefield Green, Surrey, and was educated at the Universities of Reading and London. During the War he served as Meteorological Officer, Royal Engineers, in the North Russian Expeditionary Force, Archangel, and in 1929 joined the Meteorological Office, Air Ministry, being in the Forecast Division until the beginning of 1925 except during 1921 when he was detached for duty during the trial flights of airships R.80, R.36 and R.38.

When an Airship Services Division was created in the Meteorological Office, Air Ministry, in 1925 he was appointed Superintendent. He was a member of the Official Airship Mission which visited South Africa, Australia, New Zealand and India in 1927 to advise the Governments on the steps to be taken to provide the necessary ground organization for airship operations. He has also organized the necessary meteorological services for airship flights to Canada and on the route to Egypt and India. He is on the Council of the Royal Meteorological Society and is Meteorological Secretary of Section A of the British Association. He flew in R.100 as Meteorological Officer on her trip to Canada and return in July and August of this year.

Squadron Leader F. M. Rope, RAF, *Assistant to Assistant Director (Technical),* was born in 1888 at Shrewsbury and was educated at Shrewsbury School and Birmingham University where he took an engineering degree. He left the University in R.38 and until 1912 was an engineer to the British Electric Plant Co., Alloa. He then joined the Rio Tinto Co., London, Mining and Mechanical Engineers. From 1913 to 1914 he was employed on locomotive engineering by the Brighton Railway and from then to 1915 served in the same capacity with the Nigerian Government Railway, West Africa. He joined the RNAS in 1915 serving at Capel and Kingsnorth Airship Stations where he subsequently became Staff Officer in the Director of Research Department. From 1921 to 1924 he was Technical Staff Officer, RAF, Iraq and was then appointed to the Royal Airship Works, Cardington. He is seconded to the Royal Airship Works from the Royal Air Force.

page II

Mr. H. J. Leech, AFM, *Foreman Engineer, Royal Airship Works,* was born at Dudley, Worcestershire in 1890 and educated at Appleby. He served as an apprentice with the BSA Co. on motor car manufacturing from 1906 to 1911 and was engaged in this branch of engineering until 1916 when he joined the RNAS (Airship Section). He became an engineer on Non-Rigid Airships SS *Zero,* CP and C-Star types and the *Parseval,* and was an engineer on the SRI, an Italian Semi-Rigid, when she flew from Rome to England in 1918. He was demobilized in 1919 but rejoined airships in 1920 and was placed in charge of the Engine Shops at Pulham Airship Station. He remained there until 1924 when he was transferred to the Royal Airship Works, Cardington, and took charge of the Engine Shop where he has been engaged on test and research work and the development of the Diesel Oil Fuel Airship Engine.

Lieutenant-Commander H. W. Watt, RNR, *Officer in Charge of Karachi Airport,* joined the Royal Naval Reserve in R.38 and from 1914 to 1915 was engaged in Naval Patrol Work. He then transferred to the RNAS (Airship Section) becoming Captain of Non-rigid types and in 1918 was appointed Captain of HMA R.26. In the following year he want to Pulham Airship Station and took part in Airship Mooring Experiments but retired in 1920 and became resident in New Zealand. In 1929 he was appointed to the Royal Airship Works, Cardington, for training to take charge of Karachi Airport, Aeroplanes and Airships. He proceeded in August of this year to take up that appointment and also to make all local arrangements for the forthcoming Indian Flight of R.101, administered by the Government of India.

Flying Officer H.F. Luck, RAF, *Officer in Charge Airship Base, Ismailia,* joined the Naval Wing, RFC (Airship Section) in 1913 and commenced flying in airships on HMA NO. 4. He remained flying with this ship until 1915 when he became engaged on the construction and flying of Coastal Airships. In 1917 he was engaged on the construction and the flying of R.25 and in 1918 was flying non-rigid SS type airships and was Senior Flying Officer at a Mooring Out Station. In November 1918 he was appointed to the R.34 and flew in that ship on every flight which included the voyage to America and back in 1919. Between 1920 and 1921 he flew in R.33 and R.80 and from the latter year until 1929 he was engaged mainly on armament duties at various stations in the

Royal Air Force. He was then appointed to Royal Airship Works, Cardington to be trained in Mooring Tower duties and in August of this year proceeded to Egypt to take charge of Ismailia Airship Base and to make all arrangements for landing, refuelling and re-victualing R.101 at this intermediate Base on the Cardington to India Air Route.

page 12

Crew of R.101

Name	Age	Designation	Decorations	Birthplace	Remarks
Atkins, G. K.	30	W/T Operator	Nil.	London	Joined Airship Service 1917. SS.Z.16, SS.Z.37, SS.Z53 & 67. Coastal 3 & 5a.R.101 & R.100. *R.100 Canadian Flight.*
Bell, A. V.	31	Engineer	Nil.	Fambridge Ferry, Essex	Joined Airship Service Nov. 1919, R.33. Joined crew R.101 July, 1929. *R.33 breakaway crew.*
Binks, J. H.	37	Engineer	Nil.	Sheffield, Yorks.	Joined Airship Service 1925, R.33, Joined crew R.101 6.8.29.
Blake, R.	33	Engineer	Nil.	Westminster, London	No previous flying experience. Joined crew R.101 Oct. 1929.
Burton, C. A.	29	Engineer	Nil.	Hull, Yorks.	No previous flying experience. Joined crew of R.101 Oct. 1929.
Church, S.	25	Rigger	Nil.	Cardington, Beds.	No previous flying experience. Joined crew of R.101 Oct. 1929.
Cook, A. J.	27	Engineer	Nil.	Lambeth, London.	No previous flying experience. Joined crew of R.101 Oct. 1929.
Disley, A.	28	W/T Operator	Nil.	Lancaster, Lancs.	Joined Airship Service 4.3.29. R.101 & R.100. R.100 *Canadian Flight.*
Fergusson, C. J.	36	Engineer	Nil.	Gillingham, Kent	No previous flying experience. Joined crew of R.101 Aug. 1929.
Ford, H. E.	27	Rigger	Nil.	Kingsbridge, Devon	Balloons RAF from 27.4.20 to 25.5.29. Attached Cardington for construction R.37 & R.33. Joined crew R.101 1929.
Foster, E. A.	28	Rigger	Nil.	Bedford, Beds.	No previous flying experience. Joined crew of R.101 Oct. 1929.
Gent, W. R.	53	1st Engineer R.101	AFM	Northampton	Joined Airship Service 1915. Ships SS type, C.12, C.STAR, I.C.14.A, R.29, R.32, R.34, R.36, R.33, Joined R.101 1929. *Crew of R.34 to USA and return. R.33 breakaway crew.*
Graham, E. A.	28	Cook	Nil.	Ranelagh, Co. Dublin	Previously employed on Ocean going vessels & Messrs. Dudeney & Johnson Ltd., Bedford. Joined R.101 Sept. 1930.
Hasting, A. C.	30	Engineer	Nil.	East Ham, London	Joined Airship Service 1918. Ships R.33. R.80, R.38. Joined R.101, 1929.
Hodnett, F.	29	Assistant Steward	Nil.	Youghal, Co. Cork, Ireland	Joined Airship 23.4.30. Assistant Steward, *R.100 Canadian Flight.*

Hunt, G. W.	41	Chief Cox- swain.	AFM & Bar.	Twyford, Berks.	Joined Airship Service 1913. Ships "Beta" & Kite Balloons, Coxn. on SS types, C.P.14, 2nd Coxn. No.9, Chief Coxn. R.29, R.33. Joined R.101 as Chief Coxn. Aug. 1929. *R.33 breakaway crew.*
Keeley, S. T.	35	Chief W/T Operator	Nil.	Stufton, Diss, Norfolk	Joined Airship Service 1924. R.33. (*On board during breakaway*). R.101 & R.100. *R.100 Canadian Flight.*
Key, T. A. A.	35	Charge- hand Engineer	Nil.	Hastings, Sussex	Joined airship Service 1915. Ships-Exptl. SS, SS.8, SS.19 & others, R.36, R.33. Joined R.101 1929.
King, W. H.	32	Engineer	Nil.	Tonbridge, Kent	Served on Airships SS.Z18, R.29, R.36, R.33, joining R.101 1929. *R.33 breakaway crew.*
Larkins, C. W.	25	W/T Operator	Nil.	Blackheath, Kent	Joined Airships Sept. 1929. R.101 & R.100. *Crew on return from Canada.*
Littlekit, M. F.	29	Engineer	Nil.	Sherfield English, Nr. Romsey	No previous flying experience. Joined crew R.101 July, 1929.
Mason, C . H.	33	Assistant Coxswain	Nil.	Harringay, Middlesex	Joined Airship Service 1916. Ships SS & CP types No. 9, 2nd Coxn. of "Perseval" No. 6, R.33. Joined crew R.101 1929.
Megginson, J. W.	18	Galley Boy	Nil.	York	No previous flying experience. Joined crew R.101 & R.100 July, 1930.
Moule, W.	30	Engineer	Nil.	Wolver- hampton.	No previous flying experience. Joined crew R.101 Oct. 1929.
Norcott, A. W. J.	29	Rigger	Nil.	Royston, Herts.	No previous flying experience. Joined crew of R.101 Oct. 1929.
Oughton, L. F.	29	Assistant Coxswain	Nil.	St. Pancras, London	Joined Airship Service 1919. Ships R.24, R.33, R.36. Joined R.101 1929.
Potter, W. A.	32	Asst. Chief Coxswain	Mentioned in Dispatches	Yoxford, Suffolk	Joined Airship Service 1915. Ships C.1, R.9, R.23, R.31, Asst. Coxn. R.33. *Crew R.38, Survivor.* Joined R.101 Asst. Chief Coxswain 1929.
Radcliffe, W. G.	31	Rigger	Nil.	Bedford, Beds.	No previous flying experience. Joined crew R.101 Oct. 1929.
Rampton, M. G.	31	Rigger	Nil.	Binstead, Hants.	Joined Airship Service 1915. Ships SS.22, Coxn. SS 34, & others. R.31, R.33, R.34, R.9, R.23, R.36. Joined crew R.101 1929.
Richardson, A. J.	29	Rigger	Nil.	Wilstead, Beds.	No previous flying experience. Joined crew R.101 Oct. 1929.
Rudd, E. G.	25	Rigger	Nil.	Norwich, Norfolk.	No previous flying experience. Joined crew R.101 Oct. 1929.

Savidge, A. H.	32	Chief Steward	Nil.	Reading, Berks.	Steward White Star Cunard, Union Castle & Orient lines. Joined Airships 1921. R.36, R.101 & R. 100. *R.100 Canadian Flight.*
Savory, V.	33	Engineer	Nil.	London	No previous flying experience. Joined crew R.101 Sept. 1929.
Scott, S. E.	40	Charge-hand Engineer	Nil.	Leicester	Joined Airship Service 1921. Ships R.33 & R.101 (July, 1929) *R.33 breakaway crew.*
Short, G. W.	34	Charge-hand Engineer	Nil.	Maidenhead, Berks.	Joined Airship Service July 1918. Ships C.9, C.2, SS.Z, R.33. Joined crew R.101 July 1929.
Taylor, C. E.	33	Rigger	Nil.	Wilstead, Beds.	No previous flying experience, Joined crew R.101 Oct. 1929.
Watson, G.	25	Engineer	Nil.	Gillingham, Kent	No previous flying experience. Joined crew R.101 May, 1929.

British personnel at overseas airship bases

The following personnel from Royal Airship Works, Cardington, have proceeded overseas to Karachi and Ismailia respectively to take up airship duties:

Karachi		Ismailia	
Mr. P. Norton	Foreman m/Tower	Mr. C. Elliott	Foreman m/Tower
Mr. J. Westgates	m/Tower	Mr. E. Jones	m/Tower
Mr. J. Penney	m/Tower	Mr. H. McLellan	m/Tower
Mr. J. Holland	m/Tower	Mr. C. Pilsbury	m/Tower
Mr. T. Dutton	Foreman Shed	Mr. T. Wallace	Foreman Gas Plant
Mr. G. Alley	Foreman Gas Plant	Mr. J. Sharman	Gas Plant
Mr. J .Skinner	Gas Plant	Mr. H. Pretty	Gas Plant
Mr. A. Stansbury	Gas Plant		

page 16

Comparative table of airships

Nationality	Airship	Approx. Capacity. (cubic feet)	Gross Lift (tons)	Length (feet)	Diameter. (feet)	Height. (feet)	No. of Engines	Brake Horse Power	Max. Horse Power
British	R.9 (pre-war design)	889,300	25.6	526	53	76.6	3	2 at 180 Vickers 1 at 200 Maybach	610
British	R.33 & R.34	1,960,000	59.5	640	78.75	91.5	5	250 Maori Sunbeam	1,250
British	R.38	2,724,000	82.7	694.5	85.5	92	6	350 Cossack Sunbeam	2,100
British	R.100	5,000,000 plus	156.5	709	131	133	6	650 Rolls-Royce Condor	3,900
British	R.101	5,500,000	165	777	131' 8"	140	5	585 Beardmore "Tornado"	2,925
USA	*Los Angeles*	2,599,110	71.43 helium	658.4	90' 8"	104' 5"	5	400 Maybach	2,000
USA	New ships under construction 2	6,500,000	180 helium	785	132' 9"	146' 5"	8	Not known	4,480
German	*Graf Zappelin*	3,708,000	129	776	100	113	5	530 Maybach	2,650
German	New ship under construction	5,500,000	167	Details not available			8	Maybach ~595	~4,760

REPORT ON FLIGHT IN THE GRAF ZEPPELIN AND VISIT TO FRIEDRICHSHAFEN BY LIEUTENANT-COLONEL V. C. RICHMOND AND SQUADRON LEADER F. M. ROPE

This document was written by Richmond and Rope after their trip in late April 1930 on the *Graf Zeppelin*. The airship landed at the Royal Airship Works, where it picked up Hugo Eckener, the visionary who resurrected zeppelin-brand airships after the First World War. Eckener was touring the Works after meetings in London, at which he had discussed standardizing airship mooring before the Zeppelin Company started service to the United States in 1933. Vincent Richmond and Michael Rope returned with Eckener to the Zeppelin Company's headquarters in Friedrichshafen, Germany. They reported on their ride in the *Graf Zeppelin*, their observations of zeppelin's wind tunnel and airship designs, and their visit to the zeppelin factories in Germany.

Although the highlight of the report is their impressions of flying in the zeppelin, their observations of the Friedrichshafen factories reveal how the Zeppelin Company, called the "Firm" throughout, struggled financially. Richmond and Rope observed the manufacture of parts for Opel cars and the production of "large containers for petrol, milk and beer" from aluminum, but "nowhere was there any sign of airship work in progress." They also noted that the cash-strapped Zeppelin Company allowed the public, if they paid a fee, to mill around the *Graf Zeppelin*.

In the report Richmond and Rope mention LZ 128, an airship

in the early stages of planning. After R.101 crashed, the Zeppelin Company abandoned LZ 128 because of the public's fear of hydrogen-filled ships. Zeppelin then designed and built two airships—their last two airships—that used helium: LZ 129, known as the *Hindenburg* and LZ 130, the *Graf Zeppelin II*. These ships, though, eventually used hydrogen because the United States refused to sell helium to Germany for them, as it feared helium would transform zeppelins into invulnerable military weapons. Helium, explained a U.S. military officer, "reduces materially the danger of fire from incendiary bullets fired into them; it enables lighter-than-air craft to operate against heavier-than-air craft without the danger of fire from the balloon gas."

Additionally, the report contains three fascinating tidbits. First, Frau Eckener, Hugo Eckener's wife, confided to Richmond and Rope that Ludwig Dürr was "slow." Dürr was the chief architect of zeppelin airships: he helped build the first one, and was involved in the design of every one thereafter. He served as technical director until 1945.

Second, Richmond and Rope's pride comes through in this bureaucratic report when they mention "it was noticeable that they [the zeppelin designers] had in their possession several of the English technical papers on the subject of airships copiously annotated." Likely these were their own papers! This pride also appears when they analyze the wind tunnel results conducted by the Zeppelin Company. And of particular interest is their discussion of the echo sound equipment used to determine a zeppelin's altitude. Engineers at the Royal Airworks had also developed an instrument to measure altitude but it was removed before the flight to India.

Third, Richmond and Rope refer to the "Wembley incident." On the *Graf Zeppelin*'s route to the Royal Airship Works, the ship passed over Wembley Stadium where Arsenal and Huddersfield Town battled for the FA Cup. To honor King George V, who was attending, the zeppelin "bowed" by dipping toward the ground. It swooped so low that players complained that the airship blocked the sun and darkened the field. The *Daily Mail* reported "lively comment during the weekend" about the zeppelin's flight over Wembley. Although only hinted at by the *Mail*, the flyby reminded many spectators of the zeppelin raids of the First World War, especially when they learned that Captain Lehmann, who flew the *Graf Zeppelin* over Wembley, had bombed London in the war. As this report reveals, this anti-zeppelin sentiment was not shared by the British delegation, visiting the zeppelin works. "The British technical public," said a member of the delegation have "nothing but admiration regarding the skill and courage displayed" during the wartime zeppelin bombing raids.

This document mentions seven figures, but they are long lost. The spelling of place names as in the original document has been retained. I have inserted notes in brackets to help clarify ambiguities.

The original of this document is stored at the National Archives, Kew, Reference AIR 5/12. Its title in the archives is "Report by Lt. Col. Richmond and S/Ldr. Rope on their visit to Friedrichshafen, and *Graf Zeppelin* flight, 1930."

Contents

Itinerary

Saturday, 26th April. Left Cardington in the *Graf Zeppelin* 5:49 p.m.

Sunday, 27th April. Landed at Friedrichshafen 6:40 a.m. 1 p.m. visit to Dornier Works at Altenrhein. 4 p.m. returned to Friedrichshafen. Conversation with Dr. Dornier. 8 p.m. Dr. Eckener gave a complimentary dinner to the principal passengers of the *Graf Zeppelin* flight.

Monday, 28th April. a.m.: visited Zeppelin Works accompanied by Capt. Lehmann who conducted us to Dr. Dürr and Dr. Erlich. The morning was spent in a detailed examination of the Zeppelin Works, the new airship shed and the *Graf Zeppelin* in company with Dürr and Erlich. *p.m.:* Further technical discussion with the above.

Tuesday, 29th April. Escorted by Dürr and Erlich visited the wind tunnel, the foundries and the fuel gas plant. At lunch we were entertained by Dr. Dürr and Dr. Erlich. *p.m.* Interviewed Dr. Maybach and were escorted round the Maybach Motor Works by Herr Lutz. 5 p.m. interview with Dr. Eckener. 6 p.m. Dr. Eckener gave us a complimentary dinner, other guests being Doctors Maybach, Dürr, Ehrlich, and Capt. Lehmann

Wednesday, 30th April. a.m. Final interview with Dr. Eckener and further technical conversation with Dr. Dürr. At lunch we were entertained by Capts. Von Schiller and Fleming. *p.m.* Visited the Motor Gear Cutting Works at Lowenthal escorted by Dr. Ehrlich and Herr Dolt, Works Manager. 5:30 p.m. left Friedrichshafen.

Thursday, 1st May. 9:30 p.m. arrived Bedford.

Flight of the *Graf Zeppelin*

The ship left the ground at 5:49 p.m. and was soon put up to cruising speed on all engines which was observed from the speed indicator to be between 31 and 32 meters per second (70.5 MPH approx). The smell of the fuel gas in the passenger cabin, which was very noticeable when the ship was at rest, was found to be not entirely dispersed when the ship was underway. The vertical windows were found to be a great benefit to the passengers and the open windows caused no unpleasant draught. It should be appreciated that the living saloon was comparatively small and well shut off from the rest of the ship. When the door to the control car was opened, an appreciable draught was felt from the windows.

It was observed that the saloon which was heated by radiators fed with hot water from the auxiliary engines, was kept at a very pleasant temperature.

The sound of the engines was quite appreciable, the most noticeable feature being the beats when two wing engines were nearly in step. The various instruments were examined in operation and are reported on more fully below.

The Officers very courteously allowed most of the passengers to visit the control car and to remain there if they so desired. Indeed one very noticeable feature of the trip was the extreme pains taken for the comfort of the passengers. The itinerary was carefully planned so that the ship passed over all the most interesting vicinities. The food and drink were very good, a special menu having been printed for the trip. The facilities for washing are well thought out, though somewhat inadequate.

The ship reached London soon after six o'clock, and at 6:30 p.m. was over the Houses of Parliament, the height having been reduced to only 300 meters, and the engines throttled down (21 meters per second). After circling London, the ship passed along the Thames and at 6:50 p.m. over Greenwich, the speed and height were again increased. The ship practically followed the coast of Kent round to Dover which was reached about 8:15 p.m. Here a message which had been prepared by Col. The Master of Sempill and signed by Dr. Eckener was transmitted to S. of S. [Secretary of State, Lord Thomson]. The ship then proceeded by way of Ostend and Zeebrugge to Brussels in order to allow the passengers to view the illuminations.

The passengers all went to bed between eleven and twelve o'clock, and most of them reported having slept soundly the next morning. We were roused at daylight and the ship was found to be over Friedrichshafen at 4:45 a.m. As there was a considerable amount of mist about and the landing party had not been ordered for this early hour, the ship was taken across Lake Constance to view the sunrise in the mountains in the region of Bregenz. The ship returned over Friedrichshafen about 6 a.m. with a considerable amount of mist still about. It was noticeable that the pilots made regular use of the echo sounding gear to determine the height of the ship. It was also noticeable that numbered boards were placed on the landing ground close to the tee to indicate the ground temperature (see below). Owing to the limited dimensions of the aerodrome, the pilots followed their usual practice of making a high landing with long trail ropes (100 meters). The ship was brought to the ground without incident at 6:40 a.m. and walked over to the vicinity of the shed where side guys were attached to the trolleys on the handling rails. There was very little wind and only three men were employed on each side guy in coupling up to the trolleys and moving them. It was noticeable that as the process of moving the side guys definitely located the ship, no other precautions had to be taken so that it moved strictly on the centerline of the shed.

Some of the passengers left immediately by motor-car and others proceeded to the Kurgarten Hotel. It was noticeable that there were many visitors to the aerodrome, and it was subsequently discovered that it is now a regular practice of the Zeppelin Company to allow such visitors to view the ship at any time on a payment of a small charge. These visitors are not allowed to go on board. No special escort is provided for them.

In subsequent conversation, the Flying Staff appeared to be considerably worried over the Wembley incident. Capt. Lehmann said that he had only passed over the football ground, which was previously quite unknown to him at the special request, first by telegram and later by letter, of Colonel The Master of Sempill. Two extracts from the German newspapers on the subject are attached to this report. On the whole they seemed to have taken the incident in a very good spirit. It was noticeable, however, that the *Daily Mail* which can normally be obtained the following day in Friedrichshafen, was on Tuesday confiscated by the police, presumably on the ground of unfavorable comment on the *Graf Zeppelin*. This was confirmed by the effort which Capt.

Lehmann strenuously made to endeavour to obtain a copy of the paper for us.

At the dinner given by Dr. Eckener in the evening, most of the Flying Staff were present with their ladies, but none of the technical staff other than Count Soden who is head of the Motor Gear Cutting Works (an allied firm). Group Capt. Gossage, Air Attache, [Ernest Leslie Gossage] was also present. Dr. Eckener made a cordial speech of welcome in which he referred in rather vague terms to co-operation with Great Britain. He especially thanks Col. The Master of Sempill for the arrangements made for his welcome in London. Col. Sempill in reply said that as he was leaving early next morning but Group Capt. Gossage and Colonel Richmond were remaining, he did not feel it out of place to reply to Dr. Eckener. He referred to the wartime flights of the German airships for which he said the British technical public at any rate had now nothing but admiration regarding the skill and courage displayed. He referred to the pioneer work done by Count Zeppelin and his associates, which was all fully appreciated in airship circles in England. He also stressed the value of co-operation but again in somewhat vague terms.

Technical information

Dr. Eckener kindly invited us to spend at least three days in Friedrichshafen, and had evidently instructed his staff to give us the fullest possible information and it was indeed noticeable that to none of our questions did they make evasive or hesitating replies. We reciprocated as far as possible and repeatedly requested them to put to us any points on which they required further information regarding English practice. It was noticeable that they had in their possession several of the English technical papers on the subject of airships copiously annotated.

The principal members of the technical staff appeared to be as follows:

Dr Dürr in charge. Dr. Dürr is apparently one of the oldest members of the Zeppelin Company having been associated in the early days with Count Zeppelin and acts in the capacity of Chief Engineer, since he is in charge not only of work directly connected with the construction of the airship, but also with the other enterprises of the Company, such as their foundry work and manufacture of aluminum tanks and containers of various kinds for the trade. He was also apparently responsible for liaison with the subcontractors for the new shed which is to be erected at Lowenthal. Dr. Dürr whose knowledge of English is extremely limited showed us the utmost courtesy. It was somewhat surprising, however, that at the dinner given by Dr. Eckener, Frau Eckener confidentially volunteered the information that he was now regarded as rather "slow."

Dr. Erlich is in charge of general airship design. He was prisoner at war in England, and speaks extremely good English. He acted as principal interpreter during our visit and displayed the utmost endeavours to be helpful.

Herr Schirmer—the young Engineer in charge of the Wind Tunnel work.

Herr Forster, who was one of the men left in England when the ship returned to Friedrichshafen, is in charge of the Stressing Work.

Dr. Sturn is in charge of all Machinery questions.

Herr Besch in charge of Ground Handling Equipment is an Ex-Naval Constructor and is at present in Pernambuco [Brazil] erecting a stub-mast for the forthcoming visit of the *Graf Zeppelin*.

Herr Hilligarde [most likely this was Erich Hilligardt]—in charge of Electrical Installation and Instruments.

Airship sheds

The new shed at Friedrichshafen is 250 meters long by 46 meters high by 50 meters wide inside (820' x 151' x 164'). The whole of the steelwork is inside, the outer vertical walls being made of brick. The floor is concrete covered with wood and apparently considerable importance is attached to this latter feature. It is considered to ease many of the erection problems, and it has been suggested that it has an effect in minimizing corrosion of the structure. It was noticeable that the steelwork employed appeared to be considerably lighter than that employed in England.

In commenting on this, Dr. Dürr said that the Government Regulations under which it was built were quite as strenuous as those laid down in America, and he was surprised to hear that apparently our own regulations had led us to employing a heavier structure.

A small lift was installed at the center of one side of the shed. Double travelling gantries were fixed to the overhead runways on each side of the shed (four in all) provided with winches. From these were suspended horizontal wooden platforms. The doors at each end of the shed were of the curved type running on circular tracks above and below. It was stated that these were not unduly expensive and in any case doors of this shape gave greater clear length inside the shed for less vertical well area.

Dr. Dürr considered that the shed was large enough to accommodate a ship up to 250,000 cubic meters air volume (8.83 million cubic feet).

The operating shed to be erected at Lowenthal has not yet commenced, but Dr. Dürr stated that it is hoped to have it completed by next spring. Its dimensions are up to 270 meters long by 49 meters high by 50 meters wide (886′ x 161′ x 164′).

Workshops

A tour of the workshops showed how excellently the Firm contrived to keep their staff together by the manufacture of various items for the trade. The foundries are extensive and have a good deal of casting work in hand, principally for engine details not only for the Maybach Works, but also for Motor Car Works such as the Opel. Casting is being carried out in aluminum, silumin and elektron. Silumin, however, is only being produced for special high-class work owing to its extra expense over aluminum. The die castings work appeared to be of a particularly high order, some of the items being quite elaborate such as part of the crankcase for the Opel engine.

Amongst other things, we noticed a large casting in silumin for the Maybach twelve-cylinder diesel engine. This was stated to be a heavy engine of about 400 HP for railcar work from which they hoped later to develop an airship engine.

It was noticeable that for the production of elektron castings, 5 percent of sulphur was used in the sand to prevent burning.

In either shops, very large containers for petrol, milk and beer were being constructed from welded aluminum, but nowhere was there any sign of airship work in progress which agreed with Dr. Dürr's statement that they were not yet ready to commence the construction of LZ 128, except that in the big airship shed, the girder structure used for erectional purposes was under way.

Some elaborate metal jigs for the construction of triangular girders were observed in one of the shops.

The Graf Zeppelin

Aerodynamics The following dimensions were given for the ship:

Max. diam.—30.5 meters (100.1 ft)

Length—236 meters (775 ft)

Air volume—121 cubic meters (4.275 million cubic feet)

Max. gas volume—114,000 cubic meters (4.05 million cubic feet)

A convention appears to be adopted for what is called the "declared" volume to represent the condition in which the ship normally leaves the ground. This is taken as 95 percent of the full gas capacity. In this case, however, it was stated that the "declared" volume is 105,000 cubic meters (3.71 million cubic feet) which is considerably less than 95 percent (namely 92.1 percent).

In the wind tunnel which is of the Eiffel-jet type, the models of various ships including the *Graf Zeppelin* and the new ship now under design were viewed. The fan in the tunnel which is driven by two 240 HP Maybach engines gives a wind speed of 46 meters per second (151 foot per second) on a jet of 2.9 meters dia. (9.5 ft). It was noticeable that the mesh of the honeycomb was rather small (about 1½″). All models are made to exactly the same volume and are about 2 meters long. Considerable importance is attached to placing all models in exactly the same position for test, as 30 percent variation in the drag has been experienced by varying the position. The models are hollow and constructed of sheet steel mounted with spiders on a central tube and finally covered with plaster of paris. They present a remarkably neat and elegant appearance. This technique is preferred to the use of wood owing to the tendency of the latter to warp.

The measurements made do not appear to be as complete as these made in the British tunnel. For instance, no measurements of the damping coefficient are carried out and indeed it was stated that no calculations on stability whatsoever are made. This is left to past experience and trial in the air, not always with successful results, as is evident from the alternations which have had to be made to the fins of the *Graf Zeppelin* (see below). Fairly elaborate pressure plotting experiments are carried out with bunches of internal tubes which are connected, eight at a time, to a multiple photo manometer. Certain results were exhibited in the form of curves, but it is not quite clear whether these are exactly on the same basis as employed in this country. Dr. Dürr promised, however, to write us fully on this matter and since the results of our own experiments have now been published in R. & M. 1168 and R. & M. 1169 we promised to send these in exchange. ["R. and M." refers to "Reports and Memoranda," specifically here these reports: Jones, R., and Bell, A. H., "Experiments on a Model of the Airship R.101," ARC RM-1168, London, His Majesty's Stationery Office, 1926; and Jones R., Bell, A. H. "The distribution of pressure over the hull and fins of a model of the rigid airship R.101, and a determination of the hinge moments on the control surfaces." ARC RM-1169, London, His Majesty's Stationery Office, 1926. Here "ARC" is an abbreviation for the Aerospace Research Council.]

From such observations as we were able to make, it appeared that the resistance coefficient from the bare hull of the *Graf Zeppelin* on the basis normally employed in England is 0.0147 (R.101—0.000725). It is noticeable that the *Graf Zeppelin*, owing to the limitations of the shed in which it had to be built, has an exceptionally high block coefficient = 0.7 (R.101—0.59). The calculations as to the speed of the ship (see below) do not agree with the above value for the resistance coefficient, but this is the common experience of the Firm. The fact that their experience is different from ours in this respect is probably due to the nature of their tunnel. Both on the full-scale and in the tunnel, however, the resistance is surprisingly low compared with that of the *Bodensee* and *Los Angeles* in view of the high block coefficient of the *Graf Zeppelin*, and this result was more or less unexpected by the Firm.

We feel that the Company's wind tunnel results may be influenced by a certain amount of turbulence in their wind tunnel, which would explain the variation of drag with position of the model, and on modern theory prevalent in this country would serve to reconcile matters more nearly with the full scale results.

Apparently no experiments are made with engine cars in position, but the passenger car has been included. From a chart exhibited to us it was clear that the Firm are in the habit of making the usual correction of static pressure drop along the tunnel. They stated that experiments were made on the hinge moments of the rudders and the pressure distribution.

It appears that the Firm are still somewhat concerned regarding the loading on the rudder since we noticed in the ship itself equipment in place for measuring the pressure distribution on the bottom rudder.

We endeavoured to discover the exact maximum speed of the ship. Dr Ehrlich gave this as 36 meters per second, but stated that he thought on one occasion they had obtained as much as 37 meters per second, although he did not care to place much reliance on this figure. Capt. Lehmann said that possibly when the ship was new and thoroughly tuned up 36 meters per second might be obtained, but he now preferred to put the maximum speed at about 35 meters per second. Other Officers (Schiller and Fleming) quotes the speed as 33 to 34 meters per second. These figures correspond to 73.8 MPH at the worst and 80.5 MPH at the best.

The propellers were stated to have a diameter of 3.4 meters (11.15 ft) and an efficiency of 85 percent (excluding car interference effects). Our own calculations on such data as is available regarding these propellers would put the efficiency more nearly at 70 percent on the basis, at any rate, which is commonly employed in this country for such calculations. Probably the most reliable method of estimating the full scale drag of the ship is on the basis of the horsepower absorbed at cruising speed.

There was general agreement that the cruising speed of the ship was 32 meters per second (71.6 MPH) at which the propellers run at 1400 RPM and the horsepower absorbed was stated to be 380 per engine. We discovered, however, that this horsepower was estimated from gas fuel consumption probably at a height of about 2,000 ft. which corresponds to a ground horsepower of about 410.

We noticed in the gas supply mains to the engine cars that Venturi meters were fixed for measuring the consumption.

For the horsepower and propeller efficiency stated, the *overall* resistance coefficient of the ship works out at 0.01015 or taking the efficiency of the propellers at 70 percent—at 0.0109 (R.101—0.0115). These results are exhibited and compared with R.101 in Figure 1 attached to this report, the curves of which are taken from R. & M. 1119. [Jones, B.M. "Skin friction and the drag of streamline bodies" ARC RM-1199, His Majesty's Stationery Office, 1929.] On the basis of these curves which represent modern theory regarding the effects of turbulence, the results do not appear as inconsistent as might be expected at first sight, if it be accepted that the conditions in the Friedrichshafen tunnel are turbulent. The fact remains, however, that it is quite evident from the full scale results on the *Graf Zeppelin*, its shape which in the past would not have been regard as very good in this country, has a remarkably low drag coefficient, indeed lower than that of R.101.

With the object of gaining further light on this question, Dr. Dürr very kindly undertook to make and test a model of R.101 in his tunnel, if we would reciprocate with similar tests on a model of the *Graf Zeppelin* in our own tunnel. It is hoped that this procedure can be agreed to, as we feel it will throw valuable light on what is a most vital question in airship design.

These facts serve to illustrate the necessity which has been recently strongly urged by us of comparing the merits of various shapes under turbulent conditions in the wind tunnel instead of merely under the conditions of smooth laminar flow which has been employed hitherto.

Structure The general arrangement of the structure of the *Graf Zeppelin* does not exhibit any noticeable departures from previous zeppelin practice except for the inclusion of the axial corridor which is located rather below the center of the ship, in addition to forming a partial support for the fuel gas bags, it also forms a support for the automatic gas valves which would otherwise be somewhat difficult to deal with in view of the presence of the fuel gas bags below.

It will be evident from Figure 4 that the total head of hydrogen is not so great as in previous ships, which did not carry fuel gas bags. This means reduced pressure on the bulkhead wiring. In addition, the axial corridor helps to support the pressure on the bulkheads (in a similar manner to the axial girder in R.100), and these two facts combined serve to reduce what would otherwise be the very high loads to be carried in the transverse frames. It should be remembered also that the diameter of the transverse frames of the *Graf Zeppelin* is considerably less than that of the British airships (100 ft. as compared with 130 ft. approximately), and even in the new ships which the Firm are designing of approximately the same capacity as the British ships the diameters will be smaller since the fineness ratio is to be 6 as compared with 5.5 in the British ships.

We discovered from a conversation with Dr. Dürr that it was the combination of these facts which led him to the opinion that in the new ship he could successfully employ the same type of transverse frame as they used in the *Graf Zeppelin*. Nevertheless he expressed the opinion that it might be necessary to change to the R.101 type of frame when building ships of still greater capacity in the future.

The question of weights was discussed, and the Firm stated that it was not their habit to publish such data in Germany, and we informed them that similarly so far in this country, we had not published any comprehensive details regarding the weights of the British ships. They offered to exchange a schedule of weights on a quid pro quo basis, provided their information was not published in this country. We said we thought this would be acceptable to our authorities. It is hoped that this procedure can be agreed to, as the information likely to be obtained from the Zeppelin Company in this respect should prove very valuable.

In conversation with Dr. Eckener, we suggested that one of the directions in which technical cooperation between different nations would prove beneficial was on the subject of factors of safety, since this was bound up with such international matters as certificates of airworthiness and rates of insurance. Dr. Eckener thoroughly agreed, and we suggested that in the first instance we should send particulars of our Airworthiness Regulations (R. & M. 970) for comment by his technical staff. [This refers to *Report of the Airworthiness of Airships Panel*, London, His Majesty's Stationery Office, 1925.] Incidentally Dr. Eckener expressed the opinion that the factors of safety commonly employed by his Company were rather less than our own.

Very little novelty was observed in the structural detail. It was noticed, however, that the bracing of some of the girders was of the improved type shown in Figure 2 attached to this report, and it is understood that this is to be employed still more extensively in the new ship. Particulars of the principal channel sections employed for the construction of the girders were also obtained, and are shown in Figure 3. It was stated that the strongest girder in the *Graf Zeppelin* was capable of withstanding an end load of 15 tons, such girders being employed in the transverse frames. An examination of the particulars given in Table 3, however, shows that none of the sections referred to there are likely to be capable of giving a girder to sustain such a high load as this.

Dr. Ehrlich referred to the curves of girder efficiency given in Colonel Richmond's paper to the Institute of Naval Architects. [Richmond, V. C. "Some Modern Developments in Rigid Airship Construction," *Transactions of the Naval Architects* Vol. LXX 1928 p. 173–209; this paper is summarized in "HM Airship R.101," *Flight* April 12, 1928.] On this curve he had marked points to correspond to the efficiency of two of the Zeppelin Company's girders. These showed that at an I/K of 27.2, the efficiency factor was very nearly 10. This corresponded with the efficiency of the best of all duralumin girders in R.101, but was not so high as the efficiency of the composite steel and duralumin girders.

We discussed with Dürr the nature of the material to be employed in bracing members such as shear wires. He stated that all the bracing wires in the *Graf Zeppelin* were of the solid drawn construction, the thickest being 3.4 mm. We estimate that these should be capable of sustaining a tensile load of 1½ tons. The endings employed on such wires are of the bent, bound and soldered type, but it is evident that the limit has been reached with regard to the thickness of wire with which such endings can be made.

The load of 1½ tons as a maximum in the bracing wires of the *Graf Zeppelin* appears to us to be remarkably low, and we think it probable that the wires must be doubled or trebled in some places to give the necessary shear strength, though we had no opportunity of actually observing this.

The Firm's objection to flexible bracing wires was stated to be the low coefficient of elasticity. We pointed out to them, however, that if flexible cables of the straining cord type are employed, the coefficient of elasticity is quite reasonable. For the larger wires which would be necessary in their new ship, the Firm stated that they proposed to experiment with swaging on end connections, but we think that such long thick rods are likely to prove troublesome during erection being very liable to receive permanent kinks.

We carefully examined the bow of the *Graf Zeppelin*, and were also shown a detailed drawing afterwards. The general arrangement for the support of the bow spindle is somewhat similar to that of R.101, except that the aft end of the spindle is radially supported by girders instead of tie rods as in the case of R.101. It was stated that the bow was strong enough to sustain a lateral breaking load of 28 tons, though certainly in our opinion without a detailed examination of the strength of the members, the construction looked somewhat too light to carry such a heavy load. The bow spindle has only a short overhang (415 mm between the forward bearing and the suspension point), and the ship would undoubtedly foul the Cardington mast head unless the mast was fitted with a special adaptor cone.

It was noticed that the bearings worked direct on the surface of the spindle, and the Firm stated that this was made possible by the employment of a special steel for the construction of the spindle. The diameter of the spindle at the forward bearing was about 250 mm, which is considerably larger than that of R.101's spindle. The spindle tapers considerably towards the aft and where the inner diameter is only about 65 mm which would not be capable of passing the stopper normally employed on the mooring ropes of the British ships. The casting at the forward end of the bow was noticed to be of elektron metal.

We discussed the use of this material for airship work with Dr. Dürr and discovered that this was practically the only place in the ship where it was employed. He did not seem to have any very definite views about its further employment in future airships.

We did not notice any instrument in place for measuring the lateral force on the bow, and the arrangement of the spindle did not appear to lend itself particularly well to the inclusion of such an instrument.

The fins were noticed to be remarkably wide for their depth, so much so that we suspect from our own experiments in this country that they are not particularly efficient. Owing to the fulness of the shape of the tail, the fins are relatively long in comparison with their depth, which is again not a particularly efficient arrangement. It is evident that the fins have given a certain amount of trouble, and Dr. Eckener stated to us that the ship was originally too unstable. Since first they were constructed, however, the horizontal fins have been increased in size, and the bottom fin has had a projecting piece added, and a deeper rudder fitted to correspond.

From our observations of the steering of the ship in flight, it appeared that it was not particularly stable in direction, though Capt. Lehmann blamed this on the lack of experience of the rudder coxswain.

It was noticed that the surface of the fabric in the fins was very well supported by a system of light intermediate ribs and it is evident that the support of the fabric has given the Firm considerable anxiety since their experience on the Atlantic flight when the fabric was badly torn.

We were informed that one complete turn of the wheel in the control car corresponded to a movement of the rudder 3 degs. The travel of the main control was stated to be 2 meters.

Valves The automatic valves which were of the conventional type were stated to be capable of allowing a rate of rise of 10 meters per second (approx. 2,000 ft. per minute) with a super-pressure of 10 mm at the valve. This was stated to be equivalent to a super-pressure at the bottom of the gas bag of about 1 mm, as the valves were located above the axial corridor are considerably above the bottom of the bags.

Blau gas installation The *Graf Zeppelin* is fitted with seventeen hydrogen gasbags. Fuel gasbags are fitted underneath twelve of these extending from the fourth bag from the nose to the third bag from the tail inclusive. The suspension of the fuel gasbags is illustrated diagrammatically in Figure 4. These bags are made of exactly the same material as the hydrogen gasbags, which we were informed had a strength of 800 kilograms per meter width (45 lbs. per inch approx.).

A noticeable feature of the arrangement was the fact that when the fuel gasbags are empty, the hydrogen bags are not of sufficient volume to completely fill the hull space. On the other hand, no special support is provided for the bottom of the hydrogen bags when they are up to pressure, the strength of the fabric being considered sufficient to sustain the super-pressure which is only of the order of 1 mm at the bottom. The support of the fuel gasbags is of a very rough and ready character, and is sufficiently indicated in Figure 4.

An alarm communicating with the control is fitted under each fuel gasbag in the roof of the keel indicating when the ship has reached a pressure height or when the Blau gasbags have been completely filled in the shed. As far as could be ascertained, this alarm consists of a simple dome which when pressed down by the gasbag against the action of a spring makes an electrical contact. Two of these alarms are made to give quantitative measurements of pressure by the action of a contact moving over a resistance coil.

The principle gas main is of 100 mm dia. and is located at the top of the keel, and passes from end to end below the twelve fuel gasbags. It has three filling points, one in the form of a flexible fabric pipe at the forward end for filling from the mast, and two tee connections one forward and one aft, for filling in the shed. There are flexible joints in the main at intervals, made of ordinary rubber hose fixed with metal clips which are bonded together. The main is provided with isolating valves of the type shown in Figure 5, so that the fuel gasbags are divided into three groups, corresponding to the three engine positions. Gas is, however, only drawn from one bag in each group at a time. The bags are connected to the main by a simple branch piece, provided with an isolating valve and the connection to the bag is made in that portion of its lower surface which forms the roof of the keel.

The branch mains supplying the power cars are of 60 mm diameter. Immediately above each engine, the branch main is connected to the automatic suction valve illustrated in Figure 6, and from this four separate branch pipes, pass to the four carburettors (two at each end of the engines). Immediately before entering the carburetor, each of these branches is provided with a suitable flame trap. This trap is extremely simple in construction, and consists mainly of eight layers of fine gauze supported between by two layers of heavier gauge. The disc area of the gauze is about 120 mm in diameter. This flame trap appeared to be so simple and light in construction as compared with similar devices contemplated in this country that we asked the Firm if they would be prepared to supply one on repayment for experiment in this country. This they readily agreed to do. They stated that it was quite effective either for Blau gas or hydrogen.

The object of the automatic suction valve illustrated in Figure 6 is to prevent gas passing through the engine and into the exhaust pipe, except when there is suction on the induction pipe.

For the same reason the engine is started on liquid fuel only since otherwise the Firm were emphatic that there was serious danger of a big flame of gas or even an explosion in the exhaust pipe.

In the supply pipe to the particular engine car which we visited, it was noticed that a Venturi meter was fixed for measuring the fuel gas consumption.

The density of Blau gas at present preferred appears to be between 1.1 and

1.05.

Dr. Eckener stated that the gas being slightly denser than air, it always percolated down to the keel where there was ample ventilation to clear it away. Although this was advanced as an argument in favor of safety, it might be equally said that since the most likely sources of ignition will lie along the keel of the ship, it would be better to have a gas which is less dense than air.

The consumption of gas per horsepower hour was given as 0.135 cubic meters (4.77 cu. ft.) at 0 °C, 760 mm pressure and 1.05 density. This corresponds to a weight of gas burnt of 0.404 lbs per HP hour.

If allowance be made for the weight of hydrogen saved in the space occupied by the Blau gas, then the figure of 0.404 lbs per HP should be reduced to 0.366 for the purpose of comparison with all liquid fuel burned in a normal installation. Against this, however, must be offset any excess of the weight of the Blau gas installation itself over the corresponding installation for liquid fuel. In any case it must be borne in mind that the installation actually employed is one combining both liquid fuel and fuel gas.

It was stated that the composition of the liquid fuel normally employed is 80 percent Benzole, and 20 percent Petrol.

It was stated that the calorific value of the gas normally used is 15,800 kilogram calories per cu. meter at RTP (1,775 BTUs per cu. ft). This figure appears to us to be somewhat higher than has been stated in previous publications.

Auxiliary machinery & electrical installation The *Graf Zeppelin* has now been fitted with a special cabin to carry the auxiliary machinery only. We regard this as a most useful and progressive feature. The cabin which is located immediately aft of the passenger car is egg-shaped with about one-third projecting outside the outer cover. It is gas tight as far as the interior of the hull is concerned, having double doors for entry which constitute a gas lock. It is well-ventilated to the outer air by openings in the bottom. In it are located the two auxiliary engines, two dynamos for cooking, two for lighting, the Gyro compass and the electric switchboards. Only one of the auxiliary engines with its train of dynamos is used at a time, the other being held in reserve.

These engines are of the type normally employed in the Wanderer Motor Car, and have an output of about 12 HP. They are run on Blau gas. They are started by means of the ordinary motor car starting gear run off the ship's accumulators. The generators used exclusively for cooking are rated at 110 volts, 72½ amps (8 kilowatts). They are enclosed DC machines running at 2,000 RPM and manufactured by Siemens Halske.

The other electrical services of the ship are maintained by batteries in conjunction with smaller generators running at 24 volts, and cannot be run for over thirty minutes off the batteries. For this reason, it is necessary to keep the auxiliary engines running if any protracted stop is made in the course of a flight. The Gyro compass was stated to take about three hours to set itself after first being started up.

The auxiliary engine can in an emergency be started by means of a strap on a pulley.

Fans are provided for cooling the radiators of these engines, but a certain amount of cooling is also provided by the fact that the hot water is passed into heating radiators in the passenger saloon.

Visits to Maybach Motor Works & Lowenthal Gear Gutting Works

It is not proposed to comment at length on these Works since a very full report was recently rendered by AD/RDE. It was quite evident in the course of our conversations with Doctors Eckener and Maybach that they were very anxious to persuade us to use the Maybach engine in the British ships, and they were therefore extremely pressing in their invitations to visit the Maybach Works.

We pointed out that the horsepower of this engine was rather too low for our purpose especially as it was ungeared, and in order to draw as much information from them as possible, expressed surprise that the engines were normally only run at 400 HP and that the efficiency of the propellers employed was as low as 65 percent. This produced some discussion between Dr. Eckener and his Constructors regarding new propellers, and also elicited the information that a gear for the Maybach engine was well advanced, or which the Firm promised to give us details (see below).

Dr. Ehrlich informed Dr. Eckener in our hearing that new propellers were being constructed, and should be ready with a month or two. As far as he can ascertain these propellers will probably give better efficiency and absorb more power at a cruising speed, but are liable to reduce the top speed of the ship. Dr. Maybach was emphatic that the engine was capable of a considerably greater continuous power output which he suggested might be made as much as 500 HP.

It was evident that the resonance characteristics of the shaft were so adjusted with the aid of the coupling as to make 1,400 RPM the most comfortable speed for cursing. It was not clear, however, why this particular speed with its corresponding power of 400 HP with existing propellers was fixed upon.

At the Gear Works, we were shown a drawing of the reduction gear to be employed on the Maybach engine for airship purposes. This gear is of the Farman type, and it is to be bolted directly on the engine without the interposition of a coupling. It is designed, however, to drive a tail shaft, and it is possible that it might be found necessary to insert some form of flexible coupling in this shaft. The gear is to be carried in a simple dome-shaped casing made of silumin, and provided with cooling veins on one side. We saw some of these castings in the process of manufacture.

We noticed that one of the bevels has forty-two teeth, and the other twenty-four teeth, but no arrangement is made for inclining the bevels to give other reduction ratios than 2:1. The large bevel was roughly 8″ in diameter, and the small one 5″ in diameter. The length of the teeth was estimated to be about 2½″. No arrangement is made for taking the airscrew thrust in the gearbox, but only the thrust of the vertical bevel. The low speed shaft is spigotted into the crankshaft with a plain bearing.

The whole gear is oiled from the engine via the crankshaft.

We were told that 95 percent of the steel employed for gears in this Factory was of the oil hardening type, we noticed that the gears were held in a special press during quenching to prevent distortion.

In the Maybach Works we were shown copies of the results of the endurance test carried out on the airship engine. This appears to have been run at 1,600 revolutions for 225 hours. The horsepower was given as 550 at 1,300 feet above sea level. During part of the run, the power appears to have been raised to the equivalent of 605 at sea level.

We noticed that the Firm were manufacturing a considerable number of 150 HP Diesel engines for railcar work. These were of the six-cylinder in-line type with air injection. The Firm stated that they had adopted this method of injection because the compressed air was useful for other purposes in the railcar and also because it gave greater economy at low speeds.

We observed that the bottom half of the crankcase of these engines were manufactured of silumin, and that long vertical steel bolts were employed between the cylinder head and the main bearing caps.

Blau gas plant

A new plant for the production of Blau gas has been erected at Friedrichshafen, but was not in operation at the time of our visit, as it has been found necessary to make certain alterations in order to adjust the temperature in the oil cracking retorts. At present supplies of gas are being obtained in high pressure wagons from Bitterfeld. This gas referred to by the Firm as Lehner gas is transported in liquid form at a pressure of about forty to fifty atmospheres. One truck is stated to be capable of transporting seven tons of liquid. The density of this gas at atmospheric pressure is 1.4 and has to be diluted with hydrogen. As far as we could gather, it was being manufactured from waste fat products.

The new plant at Friedrichshafen is manufactured by the German Blau Gas Company, Augsburg and consists of four units. Each unit is built up of an oil vaporizer, a superheater, or retort, and a condenser. The total cost of the plan was stated to be 150,000 marks (£7,500). The output of each of the four retorts was stated to be 120 cubic meters per hour (4,240 cubic feet per hour). The cost of the gas thus produced is stated to be 60 pfennigs per cubic meter (17/– per 1,000 cubic feet).

Incidentally Dr. Dürr stated that hydrogen was produced in the Friedrichshafen plant at about one-third of this cost.

The main retorts are heated by water gas. They consist of about 300 vertical tubes of small diameter through which the oil vapor passes. The cracking temperature is between 400°C and 500°C.

It was stated that the oil employed is ordinary "gas oil."

The gas is cooled in the condenser by further supplies of oil. The gas as produced in this manner is of somewhat low density, and has to undergo two further processes. In the first it is mixed with hydrogen, and the mixture is passed over steam heated nickel where apparently the catalytic action causes the hydrogen to combine with certain constituents of the gas. The next process is to submit the gas to high pressure in order to remove certain constituents. The exact pressure employed for this purpose is not known. We noticed, however, that the compressor was marked for a maximum pressure of eighty atmospheres, and the Lehner gas at twenty-five atmospheres.

The density of the gas produced up to this stage is apparently about 0.95 at atmospheric pressure, and it was stated that it is finally treated with a small proportion of Lehner gas to bring its density up to the desired figure of 1.1 to 1.05.

The gas in the compressed form is passed for storage into a special building equipped with a large number of ordinary size gas storage bottles.

Operational details including instruments

We endeavoured to obtains some general views from the Flying Personnel regarding water ballast. Captain Fleming stated that for long flights they rarely carried more than about 3½ tons, and he seemed to regard 5 percent of the gross lift of the ship as about the maximum likely to be required at any time.

He expressed the opinion that possibly landing to a mooring tower might introduce special requirements in addition to this. The only protection employed against the freezing of water ballast is the old method of dissolving a certain amount of calcium chloride in the water. We referred to the now well-known objection to this practice, namely that it might cause serious corrosion in contact with duralumin. The Firm considered, however, that this was merely a question of taking proper precautions and the alternatives of using glycerin or ethylene glycol were too expensive.

We noticed that the *Graf Zeppelin* carried reserve water in a very neat form of rectangular ballast bag provided with a long neck which could be tied up. We were unable to ascertain, however, the precise purpose for which this was reserved.

The ship carries about 600 kilograms (1,332 lbs) of spare machinery parts including a propeller on long flights, and also a small sling for lifting engines.

The question of experience in vertical currents during the *Graf Zeppelin*'s world flight was discussed at length. No accurate estimate appears to have been made of the maximum rate of rise or fall experienced by the ship, but Captain Lehmann stated that an allowance of ten meters per second (approximately 2,000 feet per minute) made on the gas valves was ample to cover any movements which they had experienced. The greatest extent of the vertical movement which the ship had undergone was stated to be 300 meters (approximately 1,000 feet) on more than one occasion. It was stated that the only occasion on which the ship had been forced down to a within a few hundred feet of the sea was when the fabric tore on the horizontal fin. Members of the crew were sent out on the fin to examine the girder work for which purpose it was necessary to reduce the speed. The ship was then struck by a heavy squall of rain and began to descend. It was impossible to open out the engine in order to regain the height before getting the men back again into the ship, and this accounted for the low altitude to which the ship descended.

It was noted that extensive use was made of the echo sounding gear to determine the exact height of the ship especially just prior to landing. On long flights we were informed that it was the regular routine practice to determine the ship's height accurately at 8 a.m. each day and set the barometer accordingly. The method employed was stated to give an error of loss than one percent at a height of 200 meters (656 feet) even in the hands of an inexpert operator. With an expert operator reasonably good readings could be obtained up to a height twice this.

The sound is produced by an ordinary 11 mm rifle firing a blank cartridge through a vertical tube and we were informed that for first-class accuracy it was important to have the ship on an even keel at the moment of firing. We were also informed that experiments with the type of instrument which employs a siren to make the sound had not been successful.

Details of the Behm sounding instrument which it is understood was employed in Germany, are well-known in this country. We had no opportunity of witnessing the use of the instrument fixed in the *Graf Zeppelin*, but the description given us by Captain von Schiller does not appear to agree very well with the details previously published in this country.

As described to us, the effect of firing the shot was to release a pendulum, the oscillations of which were carefully counted. The effect of the echo was stated to be to deflect the pendulum sideways from the scale over which it was swinging and the reading on the scale when this occurred was carefully observed.

Prior to landing, the meteorological data usually called for in this country is supplied by wireless. In addition large boards marked with figures are laid round the landing tee to indicate the ground temperature, barometer, and wind.

We observed that the ship carried a recording electric thread thermometer similar to the type used in the Cardington Meteorological Office. This instrument appeared to be giving three records, presumably one for the atmosphere and two for the gasbags. It was noted that the ship also carried an Assman psychrometer. In addition to the ordinary aneroid the ship carried a continuously recording instrument.

Considerable importance was obviously attached to accurate statoscopes and inclinometers. In addition to the ordinary aneroid a low-range instrument usually referred to in this country as a landing altimeter, was carried. In addition to this a very sensitive aneroid manufactured by Askania was observed. This instrument has a range of twenty meters rise or fall from zero, which could be set at the will of the coxswain by pushing the pointer to the mid position to which it could be set at any moment. Two instruments of the Thermos Flask and Leak type were carried to indicate the rate of rise and fall.

The pilots expressed the opinion that the Askania instrument referred to above used in conjunction with a stopwatch was the most accurate means available for determining the rate of rise or fall. Two bubble inclinometers were carried of different sensitivity.

For determining the air speed of the ship, an air log appears to be preferred to a Pitot tube, which is in agreement with our own experience in this country. The method of recording the airspeed is interesting. The same instrument is used for indicating the speed of revolution of the engines through the medium of a multiple switch which can be connected to each of the engines in turn or to the air log. The indicating instrument is a frequency meter of the tuned reed type manufactured by Hartman and Braun. The transmission between the engines or the air log and the indicating instrument consists of a simple type of alternating current generator which transmits impulses through electric leads to some form of vibrating mechanism in the frequency meter.

The pilots referred to what they considered to be a very useful form of ground speed indicator which has been evolved in Germany, but was not yet fitted to the *Graf Zeppelin*. This consisted of a coarse wire spiral rotated by an electric motor, the speed of rotation being capable of adjustment at will. The spiral rotates over a slot through which the ground is observed. The speed of rotation is adjusted until the lines of the spiral appear to remain stationary with respect to the ground. The rate of rotation of the spiral then gives an indication of the ground speed.

Very great importance was obviously attached by the pilots to the use of the Gyro compass, which is now installed in the *Graf Zeppelin*. The compass is carried in the auxiliary machinery cabin with a repeater in the control car, and also a second repeater giving a continuous autographic record. This compass was stated to weigh 150 kilograms (331 lbs) including one repeater. This weight was considered to be amply justified in view of the greatly improved steering which resulted therefrom. It was stated that the improved steering increased the actual air speed of the ship by 1 to 2 meters per second (say 3 miles per hour). It should be borne in mind, however, that the more stable the airship in direction, the less will be the value of such a device, and we have already commented elsewhere on the fact that the *Graf Zeppelin* is apparently somewhat lacking in directional stability.

Experiments are contemplated in this country with a gyroscopic turn indicator which as far as can be seen should be just as effective as the Gyro compass for ensuring good steering for less weight.

It was observed that a single engine room telegraph dial was used for each pair of wing engines. Each dial, however, carried two independent handles. There were no marks on the dials corresponding to full speed on the engines, and we were informed that on the comparatively few occasions when full speed was used, it was customary to send for the chief engineer and instruct him verbally or alternatively to give three rings on the engine telegraph gongs.

The question of mooring and handling airships was discussed at some length especially with Dr. Eckener. He stated that he had studied American methods at some length, and also that he was impressed with what had been done in England but would like to have more experience regarding operations to and from a high mast. Dr. Eckener said that he regarded this as an important international matter on which he hoped we should all finally come to as close an agreement as possible. It was evident that he had not yet made up his mind on the subject, as he stated that it was proposed to carry out certain experiments in Germany, but that he hoped to be ready to discuss the matter about next August, when he suggested a conference on the subject should be arranged between representatives from America, Germany and Great Britain. We could gain little information regarding the exact nature of the experiments proposed except that we observed that a small stub-mast was lying on the Lowenthal Aerodrome, and Dr. Eckener referred to attempting to land at this mast with the aid of blocks and side guys somewhat similar to those employed in England for landing to a high mast. Dr. Eckener stated that he was satisfied that an airship could ride at a stub-mast provided it was made heavy on the aft car, but he was by no means satisfied that successful landings could be made to such a mast, except under exceptional weather conditions. Until he had made his experiments, he preferred to preserve an open mind on this question.

We discussed with Capt. Lehmann the necessity for keeping an airship trimmed up by the nose during the process of hauling into a mast, and pointed out that this might involve difficulties with the stern of the ship as it approached the ground. He reported that close to the ground, the air flow should be practically horizontal, but it was obvious that he had not thought very deeply on the matter especially with regard to the downward kiting effect caused by the main hauling in wire.

Capt. Fleming objected to the considerable weight of the ropes which had to be carried for landing to a high mast.

A short discussion also took place on the subject of mechanical handling on the ground. Capt. von Schiller referred to the difficulty which might be caused by the noise of the tractors employed in such an operation and referred to the Citroen tractor manufactured in France, which was provided with rubber tracks, and was much quieter than the ordinary type. He was against the use of sunken rails owing to the difficulty of their becoming clogged with stones and ice, but Capt. Lehmann considered that the sunken type of rail was essential and that if properly designed and maintained should not lead to any difficulty.

Capt. Fleming volunteered an interesting explanation of the circumstances which have been previously reported under which the *Los Angeles* assumed an almost vertical position whilst riding at the high mast at Lakehurst. He stated that the stability wheels or rollers had been loaded with lengths of heavy chain. Owing to the fact that they were not being carefully watched, he thought that some of this chain was resting on the ground and hence provided a drag which prevented the ship from rotating in an azimuth under the action of change in wind direction. A fresh cold breeze was probably thus enabled to strike the ship on the tail, and this accounted for the subsequent events.

Projected design of new ship LZ 128

The following general points regarding the new zeppelin airship which is now being designed were obtained in general conversation. The ship is to have a capacity approximately equal to that of the British ships. It is to have a fineness ratio of barely six. The block coefficient is to be 0.65. It will have thirty-six longitudinals all of equal strength, and transverse frames of a similar design to that employed in the *Graf Zeppelin*. It is admitted that the strongest girder required in the ship will have to withstand an end load of approximately twenty tons.

The ship is to carry eight Maybach engines mounted in tandem, but we were unable to ascertain the exact arrangement proposed for the engine cars. The Firm stated that they did not like the tandem arrangement, but this was only a temporary measure until they could obtain engines of greater horsepower. They hoped to realize a cruising speed of 36 meters per second (80.6 MPH). Observing that this speed is higher than the cruising speed of the *Graf Zeppelin*, we asked for their views on this question. The designers stated that they were naturally averse to being asked for a very high speed, but this requirement had been laid down by the operating staff. We questioned them as to whether this was result of experience gained under bad weather conditions or whether it was merely with the object of shortening the time of passage. They stated that it was the latter reason.

The passenger car is to be located entirely within the hull of the ship, but bulges are to be fitted on the sides of the ships in order to provide vertical windows. It is interesting to note that the Firm have arrived at the same conclusion as ourselves regarding this point.

The accommodation is to be sufficient to carry not more than thirty passengers, but the Firm consider it essential that it should be on a fairly luxurious scale. They also consider that they will be fortunate if the structure weight of their passenger accommodation does not exceed eight-and-a-half tons.

Visit to the Dornier DOX machine at Altenrhein and subsequent conversation with Dr. Eckener

The following brief observations may be of interest if the facts stated are not already known to the Air Ministry Officers who have previously inspected this machine. This visit was arranged by Col. The Master of Sempill, and the Firm very courteously sent a launch to take the party across Lake Constance on Sunday afternoon. We were escorted round the Works by Herr Bernard whom it was understood acted in the capacity of Works Manager.

Subsequently on our return to the Kurgarten Hotel at Friedrichshafen, we encountered Dr. Dornier himself. A number of searching questions were put to him by Col. The Master of Sempill, all of which appeared to be answered very frankly. Amongst other things, Dr. Dornier stated that the Jupiter engines in the DOX are only good for a continuous HP of 300 and that at a greater output than this, they give continuous trouble. He hopes that the Curtis Conqueror engines which are being substituted, will give a continuous output of 420 to 430 HP without trouble. The extra weight involved in the radiators will be compensated for by the lower fuel consumption after ten hours flight.

This mean propeller efficiency of the tandem combination was stated to be 60 percent. Dr. Dornier stated that apart from the engines, the modifications required in the machine were trifling, and would cost less than 1,000 dollars.

The controls which consisted originally entirely of metal tubes were found to have insufficient elasticity, and consequently a length of flexible steel cable had been inserted. The back step is being sharpened by a few degrees to give a smoother braking on landing, thought it was admitted that this might affect the take off.

Dr. Dornier contemplates a still larger machine in which the wing area will be increased by about 100 sq. meters, but we gather that this represented a maximum which would satisfy him for a considerable time to come.

We referred to the very heavy duralumin sections which it had been necessary to develop for this machine, and Dr. Dornier stated that he would prefer to employ steel except for plating, but could not obtain the necessary sections in Germany.

We noticed that some of the channels and plates employed were as much as [fraction illegible in original]″ thick. We also noticed some large 4″ steel tubes in the struts and enquired if these were made of high tensile steel. We were informed that these were made of comparatively low grade material (thirty-two tons per sq. inch) and were manufactured by the Mannesman Tube Company.

Col. Sempill asked Dr. Dornier if he was still a believer in the use of stub wings in place of wing tip floats, and was informed that Dr. Dornier whilst not regarding them as ideal, still thought they were the best solution available at present.

Arrangements are now being made whereby fuel or mail can be carried in these stub wings.

Dr. Dornier stated he was now working on a now four-engine machine which differed in many respects from the Super Wal. [For details see "A New Dornier Super-Wal," *Flight* March 22, 1928.] Apparently he hoped great things from this machine. Both the factories at Pisa and Mansell were working on this machine.

The allied company which he was forming in America and which was financed by General Motor Ltd. had only reached the stage of surveying a suitable site near Philadelphia. His company in Holland had just completed an order for forty machines and were now working on twelve more for the Dutch East Indies. Dr. Dornier also stated that day bombing machines were being built in Japan to his design. [This was likely the *Do Komet III* built under license by Kawasaki.]

We observed that there was a good aerodrome for land machines in the possession of the Dornier Works at Altenrhein with a clear length of about two kilometers.

We were informed that when the new engines are installed in the DOX it is proposed to carry out an endurance flight in the Mediterranean of 4,000 to 5,000 kilometers. If this is successful, an attempt will be made to cross the Atlantic. Dr. Dornier emphasized the ease with which the machine can be handled in the air and stated that it had ridden out six-foot waves on Lake

Constance without any sign of distress.

[Signed] V. C. Richmond, F. M. Rope

RAW

Cardington,

7th May, 1930

MANUFACTURE OF THE GAS BAGS OF R.101

This document was written by the Works' fabric manager and resident chemist, J. W. Ward Dyer. He prepared it, in November 1930, for the Simon Inquiry. At the Works, Dyer created and maintained the airship's cloth cover and the gas bags. In this document he detailed the creation of a gas bag from 50,000 oxen entrails. Dyer's training as a chemist shines through as he discusses the solutions, varnishes and glues applied to the skins. He became fascinated by airship fabrics while studying at the University of London. His MS thesis, there, in 1920, was on "The chemical and mechanical changes accompanying the decay of certain types of non-rigid airship fabric, together with considerations on some aspects of the weathering and protection of fabrics." He continued this line of research at the Works, where he tirelessly searched for the perfect airship fabrics. For example, to find the right cloth for R.101's cover he once shone a mercury vapor lamp on a piece of cotton for a week until it turned biscuit yellow and "showed a complete loss of strength."

This document focuses on the preparation of the animal entrails to create a gas bag. Dyer calls them "skins," but the gas bags were constructed from oxen cecum—the intraperitoneal pouch at the beginning of the large intestine. Although today we would use a synthetic material, none were acceptable at the time. No plastic or rubber had the three qualities of cecum that were ideal for a gas bag: the cecum was thin, and so lightweight, it was flexible, and nearly impermeable to hydrogen. In the first half of this document Dyer describes the production of a gas bag from arrival of the animal entrails packed in salt to the assembly of the processed entrails into a gas bag with a volume of 250,000 to 500,000 cubic feet. One marvels at how he ever arrived at the precise steps—soaking in glycerin, the exact temperature of the gluing room, the humidity of the assembly shop, and the fine sandpaper used to abrade the edges before final assembly. In the second half of the document he describes the types of cotton appropriate for gas bag construction, the composition of the glues used, how the strength of the seams was tested, how to repair a gas bag in situ, and the time to deflate a gas bag with a volume of 500,000 cubic feet.

This document is item NO. 67 in the supplemental materials assembled for the Simon Inquiry. It is at the National Archives, Kew, Reference AIR 5/905.

MR. JOSEPH WILLIAM WARD DYER, MSc (Lond.) AIC, Fabric Manager and Chemist, Royal Airship Works, Cardington, will say:

The gasbags are made of a cotton fabric lined with goldbeater skin, these two components of the bag being united by a special form of glue. The separate processes in making the gasbags are as follow:

- Scraping the skins.
- Laying the skins.
- Gluing the sheet of skin to the cotton fabric.
- Cutting the complete skin and fabric sheet to its correct shape.
- Joining these sheets together to form the bag, and after various fittings such as filling and emptying valve sleeves and handling patches have been attached finally varnishing the material on both faces. Those operations are described in detail below.

Scraping the skins

The skins are taken from the salt in which they are packed and washed in warm water, scraped free from excessive fat and other foreign matter, again

246

washed and soaked overnight in a 5 percent solution of glycerin in water.

Laying the skins

The next process is to assemble the individual skins so as to form a large sheet of skin ready for gluing. Such a sheet will form a large component of the finished part, for example, the whole end of a small bag, one-half or one-third of the end of a large bag or a quarter or one-fifth of the body of a bag. This will be readily understood by a reference to the model. The skin sheet at this stage is made rather larger than and roughly the same shape as the component part of the bag which it is intended to cut from it when the fabric has been glued to it. The assembly of the skins into this sheet is carried out by laying them one at a time in a wet condition with the margins of adjacent skins overlapping about half an inch on a smoothly stretched canvas cloth which rests on a board to give it firm support, so that the skins laid on it can be firmly pressed down and smoothed out. The board slopes away from the worker at an angle of about 50° and below the board in front, the canvas on which the skins are to be laid is wound on a roller. The canvas continues upwards away from the worker and on to a second roller at the back of the bench. It will be clear that the board, the canvas and the rollers must be slightly wider than the width of skin sheet it is desired to make. As the work progresses, the canvas is wound from the front roller to the back roller bringing fresh stretches of it over the working board in turn to be covered with the overlapping skins in the way referred to. Beyond the upper edge of the sloping board, the cloth carrying its assemblage of skins on the way to the second roller at the back of the bench passes over supporting slats of wood. It is thus well ventilated: the skin sheet therefore, dries and is readily peeled from the canvas before the latter is rolled on to the second roller. The canvas is thus merely a background on which the skin sheet is assembled and the sheet as it leaves this stage is merely a sheet of skin with no fabric attached to it. It may be termed two-ply skin sheet, for on the working board referred to each width of canvas as it comes up from the roller is covered with a double layer of the wet overlapping skins. From the glycerin water in which the skins have been worked, the dry skin sheet retains a little glycerin. This slightly increases its flexibility as glycerin is hygroscopic and goldbeater skins are rendered flexible by the presence of moisture. Small holes in the goldbeater skins as received or made in the act of scraping them are of quite common occurrence. These are patched with small cuttings of wet skins in the act of laying the skins on the board. It should he stated that no adhesive of any kind is used to make the individual skins unite into the large sheet.

Gluing

The gluing is done in a special shop in which the temperature is maintained at a minimum of about 68° to 70° Fahrenheit. This is necessary to ensure that the glue remains in the proper condition, that is fluid and workable, in the operation of gluing the cotton fabric to the skin. The skin sheet is held by clamps along one edge of a table a little more than a meter wide whose length is slightly greater than the width of the sheet. It is then slightly moistened with water and gently pulled towards the other edge of the table to eliminate most of the wrinkles and is then clamped along that edge too. At this stage each width of skin sheet is inspected for holes which may have escaped patching in the previous operation. To this width of prepared and now repaired skin sheet, the appropriate cotton fabric about one meter wide is glued. The gluing operation may be carried cut in either of two ways and both ways were used in the gasbags of R.101. The first method is called gluing through the cotton and the second gluing on the skin. The first method was used in all bags except the bag NO. 8.A. made for the new bay of the ship. In the first method, the length of cotton is laid on the skin sheet and the glue is applied to the upper face of the cotton and rubbed in by hand and squeegee. In the second method, the glue is applied direct to the skin surface and the cotton fabric previously rolled on a roller is rolled on to the glued surface and as in the former method well pressed down with the hand and squeegee. There is no difference in the quality of the product by either method, but the second one is slightly more rapid. It must be understood that the skin sheet to which the fabric is being glued in this way is the continuous piece made on the skin laying bench and that as it passes over the gluing tables for the attachment width by width of the cotton fabric, each width of the latter is overlapped about an inch on the margin of the preceding panel. This overlapping joint we speak of as a "panel seam." In all the bags except NO. 8.A. these panel seams were covered with a tape of thin cotton fabric and about 1¼″ wide. This taping was omitted in the panel seams of all parts of bag NO. 8.A. This matter is further discussed in connection with the strength of the fabric and of the seams in the fabric in a subsequent paragraph. It will be appreciated that the discontinuous sheet of skin has now been covered with these continuous but overlapping panels of cotton fabric. The glue is of special quality, and in addition to the prime quality of good adhesive power, flexibility is essential. The basis is a high grade hide glue. With appropriate adjustments of the proportion of glue base to water, many high quality glues would be admissible in this work. We have, however, used one throughout, namely Messrs. Cannon's I.L. propeller glue. A typical formula for the glue is the following:

Water	...	About 200 gms.
Glue	...	18 gms.
Creosote	...	0.8 gms.
Glycerine	...	16.5 gms.
Turkey Red Oil	(75% grade)	10.0 gms.

The formula is referred to as typical and not as *the* formula, because the proportion of water is varied to produce the desired working viscosity which varies a little from one purchase of glue to another. The creosote is present as a preservative and to prevent, or at any rate to retard, the growth of molds. The glycerine is by its hygroscopic nature, to render the glue flexible and the turkey red oil indirectly promotes the same end. For Bag NO. 8.A. a different formula was used, in that the turkey red oil was omitted, for it had been discovered that the purpose served by the presence of the oil was rather better served if instead of putting it into the glue, the appropriate amount was introduced into the cotton fabric itself before the gluing. The applied glue was rendered to a large extent waterproof by subsequent application of a weak solution of formaldehyde. This is in the form of a 1 percent aqueous solution was applied by brush to the cotton face of each panel immediately after the gluing operation and while the glue was yet soft. In the gluing shop parlance, this operation is always referred to as "fixing."

Marking and cutting
The material from the gluing shop is laid out on the assembly shop floor where the appropriate form and dimensions are marked on it from drawings. Two further operations are done at this stage. One is the attachment of the various fittings, that is, sleeves, handling patches, etc. Another is that a careful inspection is made of the skin surface for any defects and these are remedied.

Varnishing
This having been done, the sheet is then varnished to within about a 6-inch border all round with the appropriate varnish on each face. On the skin face,

the varnish is a highly [sic] quality proprietary oil varnish. Many will do almost equally well; we have used Messrs. Naylor's extra flexible varnish. On the cotton face the same varnish with the addition of some beeswax and aluminum powder and an appropriate amount of diluents is used. This outer varnish is applied slightly warm. The object of both varnishes is, of course, to increase the waterproofness of the fabric.

Main assembly

The term "main assembly" is used to indicate the joining of the bay by means of the circumferential seams. Reference to the model will show that there are other main seams. All these main seams are of precisely the same construction. Those other than the circumferential ones are usually joined before the varnishing is done. The structure of a main assembly seam can be seen from the drawing and from the sample exhibited. The operations are as follows:

The skin surface which is to enter the overlap is gently abraded with very fine sandpaper. The cotton face which is to enter the overlap is slightly wetted with warm water. Warm seaming glue is then brushed on one face and some of the fixing solution referred to in the section on gluing is applied to the other face. The two faces are then applied and the join well pressed down. This overlap join is then covered as shown in the drawing and the sample with a taping of plain fabric cut on the bias and stuck down with some of the same seaming glue, the fixing solution being afterwards brushed on the outside the whole well pressed down and any excess of glue at the margins cleaned up with a hot damp swab. When thin joint has set, the whole piece is reversed so that the skin face becomes uppermost and the skin surface for a short distance on each side of the edge of the overlap is gently abraded. A narrow bias cut tape is stuck over this edge and over this again a double layer of wet skin, so as to render the skin lining continuous over the main seams. The seam and the marginal 6″ or so previously left unvarnished is now varnished within and without as previously explained for the main area of the fabric. The formula of the seaming glue is given below:

Water	3,600 gms.
Glue	1,000 gms.
Creosote	45 gms.
Glycerine	200 gms.
Turkey Red Oil	1,350 gms.

It is rather more concentrated than the panel glue and has a little less glycerine. The atmosphere in the Assembly Shop is maintained at a fairly high relative humidity about 70 to 80 percent usually, whenever the fabric has to be moved and pulled about very much. This is in order to maintain the flexibility of the fabric and enable it to withstand without damage to skins the unavoidable vigorous handling required in moving the parts and in packing the bag. It is no part of this report to deal with inspection, but it is merely mentioned here that at all stages, the materials and workmanship are under the scrutiny of the Works Inspectors and these in turn under the Inspectors of the AID. For this reason, it is not as a rule necessary to carry out a minute inspection of a completed bag, but all completed bags are inspected before packing.

Main materials

Cotton Fabric Three kinds have been used in these gasbags:

- Bags NOS. 3 to 12 inclusive
- Bag NO. 2 except a portion of the F.E.
- Bag NO. 13 Parts of forward end and forward tapers and part of body
- Bag NO. 14 Forward and after tapers

were made from "D" quality cotton to Specification D.T.D.94. It has a breaking load of about 35 lbs an inch.

- Bags NOS. 1 and 15 and is wholly
- Bags NOS. 2, 13 and 14 in the parts not made of "D" as stated above

were made from a lighter cotton known as "D.X" for which a provisional specification issued for that contract only was used, which is as follows:

Weight 50 gms. per sq. meter
Threads per inch 118, 3 in warp and weft
Strength 500 kgs per meter (mean)
450 kgs per meter (minimum)

Bag NO. 8.A. was made from a new and improved type of fabric known at present as "G" fabric, for which a provisional specification as follows is in use:

Weight Not more than 57 gms. per square meter (uncoiled)

Weight Not more than 64 gms. per square meter with oil

Threads per inch 135 in warp and weft

Strength 30 lbs per inch in warp and weft

Extension 8–12 percent in warp and weft

It will be seen that these fabrics differ in strength and that the weaker fabric has been used for the smaller bags, while the medium fabric (the "G") was used for a very large bag. There is no reason based on the loads which come on the gasbag fabric in use, for choosing a stronger fabric for the larger bags, but in manufacture and in handling, because they are heavier they may get more vigorous treatment and strength in a gasbag fabric is required more in this connection than to meet the stresses which legitimately come on it in use. These are very small indeed. It is no part of gasbag manufacture but rather of design to deal with this quantitatively, but the statement may be made here and no doubt can be confirmed from Design Memoranda that the maximum loads on the fabric in use do not exceed 1 lb. per inch run. It will be seen from the specification given above and allowing nothing for the increased strength given by the skin that there was a very ample margin.

Skins These were bought under the inspection of the AID, visual and hand tests for cleanliness, size and strength being the criteria.

Glue Every batch received from Messrs. Cannon was tested and moreover batches of the composite glue used in the Gluing Shop were periodically tested in two ways. First, for viscosity; second, sample panel seams were frequently made and tested for breaking strength, and in addition panel seams out from the actual work were also tested. Full records of these tests exist in their original form. Such tests were a part of routine inspection.

The strength of the joints or seams

As stated above very frequent tests were made as a part of the inspection of work in progress. These constitute a test of the strength of the bag for if the seam holds, the strength of the finished fabric is realized and if not, then the strength of the weaker part, that is the seam, is measured. The tests on seams were carried out on pieces 3 inches wide and about 8 inches effective length. These were always cut from unvarnished material. Two sets of three, four or five such pieces were prepared for each test and before the test one set was conditioned for not less than seventy-two hours in an atmosphere of 65 percent relative humidity (these constituting the normal or dry test) and the other set was conditioned for not less than seventy-two hours at 95 percent relative humidity (this constituting the wet test). The specification for these tests stated that the piece must not break nor the seam part under a load of less than 20 lbs per inch. This specification was applied throughout, whichever of the three cottons referred to above had been used as the basic fabric of the bag. A special note may be added with regard to the panel joints in Bag NO. 8.A. where the "G" fabric was used. As stated earlier, those panel joints were untaped (the main seams in this bag as in all others were taped with a wide taping). The taping adds nothing to the strength of a join and in an unsewn joint is there merely to prevent the edge lifting. As we had abundant proof that the edges of seams made by us did not lift and as we had observed that other experienced makers of gasbags of this type, that is the Germans, used no tape on such joints, it was omitted, saving a little weight and a manufacturing operation without any decrease in the quality of the product.

Pair of gas bags

Copies of the workshop reports made at the time of reconditioning all the bags during December 1929–March 1930, and of the further reconditioning of Bag 9 only in July–August 1930, are appended.

The defects found in bags after service are:

1. Small holes through fabric and skin.
2. Cracked skins.
3. Skins separated one from another.
4. Both layers of skin lifted from the cotton.
5. Lifting tapes or seam edges.
6. Mold.
7. Fittings, such as sleeves etc. becoming loosened from their attachment to the fabric of the bag.
8. Large rents as distinct from holes referred to in (1). Sometimes there are clean cuts made deliberately during deflation.

Method of repair

1. Clean off outer varnish, apply patch of cotton on the outside with glue. Re-skin the inside and re-varnish the repair region.
2. Re-skin with new wet skins. Varnish over when skins are dry.
3. As (2) unless very trifling. Minute separation of skin from skin is found

in the best newly made fabric and it is left untouched.

4. Remove the separated skins, re-skin over a layer of glue. Varnish when dry.

5. Clear away varnish. Glue edges down. Re-varnish.

6. Action depends on judgment as to how serious it is. If it is bad cut it out and repair by insertion of a new piece of the composite fabric. The method of inserting this is to all intents and purposes similar to the making of a main seam. Several slightly moldy places—R.101's bags were, after consideration and consultation left as they were and specially marked that information as to tendency of mold to spread might be acquired from subsequent inspection of the bags. Mold has to be guarded against in this type of gas bag, but R.101's were scarcely at all affected and tests show that mold that looks rather bad has caused little or no deterioration.

7. Glue then down again or replace them and the fabric around them according to the circumstances.

8. Cut out the fabric about the rent or cut and replace with new fabric as in (6).

In the above work ordinary seaming glue is used for the insertion of new pieces and for re-gluing parts where it would have been used originally. For re-skinning a glue modified by the addition of a little acetic acid is used. The function of the acetic acid is to keep the glue, though nearly cold on the fabric lying on the floor, fluid for long enough for the re-skinning to be carried out. If the glue set too quickly poor adhesion would be the result.

Note on approximate rate of deflation of a gas bag

Each of the large bags of R.101 had four empty necks (or deflation sleeves) about 18″ diameter. When such necks are open there are four clear vents totaling about seven square feet. The time taken for about 70 percent of the gas to escape from a large bag through these openings (for handling purposes the rate of discharge is usually reduced considerably when about 70 percent has been allowed to escape) is or the order of twenty to twenty-five minutes, the top outer covers being turned back for this operation. Some 500,000 cubic feet of gas thus escapes, in the time stated, through seven square feet of opening and under a mean pressure or about 1″ of water.

RAW [Royal Airship Works]

3.11.30.

COLMORE REPORT ON R.101'S LIFT

NOVEMBER 1929

This document was prepared by Reginald Colmore at the request of Sir John Higgins, the Air Member for Supply and Research (AMSR). Colmore was the Acting Director of Airship Development and so in charge of the Royal Airship Works; Higgins was the highest-ranking civil servant in charge of airship development programs at the Air Ministry and reported directly to the Secretary of State for Air, Lord Thomson. Although the report was signed by Colmore, it was written most likely by Richmond with assistance from Rope.

This document was written after R.101's lift and trim trials in late September 1930. R.101's lift was so deficient that "it would be impossible to attempt to operate the ship on the Indian route even for demonstration flights with only this disposable lift available." The document contains two parts: a memo to Higgins outlining the problems with R.101's lift and possible modifications to increase it, and an appendix, labeled "1A," that details the proposed modifications.

The report to Higgins describes how the high atmospheric temperatures in Egypt and India would reduce R.101's already substandard lift to the point where the airship could not carry enough fuel to make the journey safely. The report mentions modifications to R.101 to gain six tons of lift: just enough to travel to India with ten passengers. It then outlines lengthening R.101 to gain nine tons of lift to enable the ship to operate the United

Kingdom–Egypt route throughout the year with what they carefully described as a "useful load" and to also operate a "number of months of the year" from Egypt to India. The report notes that, "it could not, of course, be carried out in time for the first flight as now proposed."

The appendix lists twenty items that could be modified or removed from the ship to gain lift. It reveals the desperation of the Works' team to lighten R.101's load: even a voice pipe that adds thirty pounds to the airship's weight is not too small to consider. The reader curious about how Colmore arrives at his "grand total" of 13,506 lbs for the weight saved should note that under item 11 Colmore chose to use the more conservative 150 lbs shaved instead of the possible 250 lbs.

This document was extracted from item NO. 35 "A M File Flight to India, 522039" in the supplement materials assembled for the Simon Inquiry. The Abbreviation "A M" indicates "Air Ministry." The document is at the National Archives, Kew, Reference AIR 5/904. I have inserted notes in brackets to help clarify any ambiguities.

In accordance with AMSR's instructions the following report on the lift of R.101 in submitted.

The lift and trim test was carried out in the NO. 1 shed at RAW at 6 p.m on September 30th, 1929. The purity of the gas at the time of the test was ninety-seven percent, but the air density was low and the gross lift under the conditions at the time of the test worked out at 146.8 tons. Had the air density been the normal standard, sea level figure, the gross lift would have been 151.6 tons with the same gas purity.

The actual weighed weight of the structure at the time of the test was 110.1 tons, and this figure must be regarded as reliable. The difference between this and the gross lift at the time of the test is 38.5 tons, whereas, the disposable weight actually on board only amounted to 35 tons. There is thus a discrepancy of 3.5 tons which can only be accounted for by the accumulation of dust and dirt on the ship and by the limits of error of the experiment.

We have no further data at present to justify taking any credit for this discrepancy, and it is proposed to work on a disposable lift of thirty-eight tons under standard conditions, with a purity of ninety-seven percent, which it should be practicable to maintain.

It would be impossible to attempt to operate the ship on the Indian route even for demonstration flights with only this disposable lift available. At Karachi during the midsummer months the air density is such that there would be a loss of about seven percent of the gross lift of the airship, or say eleven tons, which would reduce the disposable lift to twenty-seven tons. Even if crew, ballast, etc. were reduced to a minimum, the ship could not leave the ground with more than say seven tons of fuel and even then it would be necessary to leave at the best time of the day.

A number of suggestions have been put before AMSR verbally for improving the lift of the ship, and a statement—IA—is attached for our proposals in detail.

In regard to cost. The labor involved for the modifications to the wiring will cost approximately £1,700, and the material will amount to approximately £200.

The removal of the reefing girders, involving a part renewal of the outer cover forward and aft, will cost approximately £350 labor and £650 material. These are the two largest individual items. It is not possible at the moment to give a firm estimate for the other work proposed, but the total labor and material cost of all the items shown on the attached statement should not exceed £6,000, excluding cost of gas for re-inflation and any work done by crew.

This money can be found without exceeding the total airship estimate for 1929.

You will note that if this work in approved, the disposable lift of the ship will be increased by about six tons, bringing the figure up to forty-four tons.

Considering now the lift which would be available for fuel for a demonstration flight on the Indian route, The disposable lift of forty-four tons might be divided as follows:

Crew & Effects	3½ tons
Moveable furniture not included in fixed weights	1 ton
Emergency ballast	8 tons
Ordinary ballast	2 tons
Spare parts and fittings to be carried in flight	½ ton
Allowance for flying height	5 tons
	20 tons

It is not proposed to carry parachutes for this flight.

This would leave twenty-four tons for fuel and freight.

It would appear sufficient if an allowance was made of one ton per ten passengers for such a flight (including food, luggage etc.). If this is accepted there would be available twenty-three tons for fuel under standard conditions, with ten passengers on board.

Cardington

It is considered it can be assumed that standard conditions or very little worse will be obtainable at Cardington for the commencement of the flight, and that the ship would get away with about twenty-three tons of fuel.

Egypt

The loss of lift owing to the generally lower air density in Egypt may amount to as much as seven-and-a-half tons during the summer months (May to October). Excluding May to October inclusive the loss of lift should not exceed three tons provided the best time of the day is chosen for leaving. Except during the summer months, therefore, the ship should be able to leave Egypt with about twenty tons of fuel.

Karachi

The loss of lift owing to the generally lower air density at Karachi may amount to as much as ten tons during May, June and July. From November to March inclusive the loss of lift should not exceed five to seven tons, and the ship, therefore, should be able to get away from Karachi with say seventeen tons of fuel during these months,

The improvements recommended might be completed by the middle of

February if work can commence on the ship in the course of the next ten days or so, but a certain amount of overtime will be necessary. Also, as I have recently reported, the calls on the Drawing Office staff in connection with the trials of R.101 have proved more than anticipated, and probably Drawing Office work will arise on R.100 after that ship's trials, if not before. If found necessary, therefore, it is hoped that immediate approval would be given to the engagement of additional Drawing Office staff.

If the improvements can be completed by the middle or February, the ship might be ready for the first demonstration flight to India by say the first or second week in March. It should be pointed out, however, that although an intensive effort will be necessary to keep such a date, it is thought we should endeavor to work to this program.

It is proposed to consider now the performance of R.101 on the Indian route with the lift available after the improvements have been completed.

England/Egypt section

Based on our present ideas of fuel consumption and speed, there should be a sufficient margin of fuel to fly the ship to Egypt throughout the year. Between Egypt and England, however, as pointed out above, the lift available for fuel is considerably less, and it is considered an intermediate landing will be necessary on a number of occasions between the months of April and October. Between November and March it should be possible to carry more fuel, but the margin appears small. If the first demonstration flight was carried out in March, it would probably be sufficient if emergency arrangements were made for a landing at Marseilles or Friedrichshafen, in connection with the return journey.

Ismailia/Karachi section

The fuel required on this section is far more difficult to estimate, but a further investigation to endeavour to ascertain more definitely a safe margin for a flight in March is now in hand.

It may be necessary to consider intermediate emergency facilities for refueling and gassing, but I will report further in the course of a few days when the above investigation has been completed, and when further information should be available on fuel consumption as a result of the present endurance flight.

The performance of R.101, even with the improvements proposed, is, unfortunately, still far from satisfactory, and the following possible improvements in connection with the engine installation are therefore put forward.

Astern power

A suggestion has been made that the Meteor engine should be used in place or a Tornado for the astern power of the ship, which would effect a saving of approximately one-half ton. [The Meteor engine, like the Tornado, was built by Beardsmore. Rolls-Royce also offered an engine named Meteor, but this engine was not produced until the 1940s.] It is not clear yet whether the Meteor can be modified to prevent the water pump fouling the suspension struts of the power car. If this can be done the suggestion appears a practical one.

In considering this suggestion it should be mentioned that a saving of approximately one-and-a-half tons could be obtained if a [Rolls-Royce] Condor was fitted in place of a Tornado. The petrol for this engine could be limited to about three times the amount which is already carried in each power car for the Ricardo starting engines, and it could be arranged for the whole of this petrol also to be carried in the car. I do not know whether this would be considered as contrary cxhy120380.0o the decision in regard to the use of petrol engines in hot climates, but there is no technical objection, and we do not think there would be any more risk of fire than from the existing petrol tanks in the power cars.

If it is decided that petrol carried outside the hull of the ship is permissible as a temporary measure, then there is the still more attractive proposition of making use of two Maybach engines which we should like to examine.

Any of the above alterations in addition to saving weight have the merit of providing additional spare Tornados at an earlier date than those at present on order.

In relation to the future operation of the ship as distinct from the first demonstration flight, an important improvement could be obtained by inserting an additional bay in the structure. We do not see any design or operational objection to this.

It is considered that a net gain in lift of nine tons could be obtained by this means, the whole of which would be available for fuel or freight. This would enable the ship to operate on the England/Egypt section throughout the year carrying a useful load, which would also be possible during a number of months of the year on the Egypt/India section.

If it is decided to adopt this proposal, although it could not, of course, be carried out in time for the first flight as now proposed, it would appear desirable to incorporate the new section in the ship as soon as possible afterwards. The earliest date at which the material could be provided and the components got ready for the assembly of the ship, is considered to be June 1930, but to do this it will be necessary to provide additional staff almost immediately. If all components are ready beforehand, it would not be necessary to lay the ship up for more than eight weeks.

R. B. B. Colmore

RAW for DAD [Royal Airship Works for Director of Airship Development]

18.11.1929

Statement 1A

Refit of R.101

Modifications proposed

The following items of work to be carried out on the re-fit of R.101 are suggested principally with the object of reducing the fixed weights. In some cases, however, the experience gained in the operation of the ship up-to-date shows that the changes proposed would lead to greater simplicity and reliability of operation. The modifications to the gasbag wiring, Item 17, will necessitate deflating each bag of the ship in turn. In view of this and the fact that it may be found desirable to remove some or all of the power cars in turn from the ship, it is definitely recommended that on coming into the shed, the ship should be slung on cradles and completely deflated. This would also permit of a close inspection of the structure to see what have been the effects, if any, of the flying which the ship has so far carried out.

It is not considered that complete deflation need cause any additional delay if, as far as possible, work is completed in the various bays consecutively so that re-inflation does not have to wait necessary until all work is done.

Item 1 Removal of access to the top of Frame 5. The work on the look-out at Frame 5 has never been completed, and to do so would mean additional weight. The Flying Staff now consider that this position can be dispensed with. All ladders and platforms above the D longitudinal port side would be removed, and also the voice pipe.

Weight saving:

On ladders and platforms **170 lbs**

On voice pipe **84 lbs**

Item 2 The covers to the engine cylinders are at present somewhat heavy, being made in thick-cast aluminum and are not easy to remove; an operation which must be carried out before every flight. AD/RDE has agreed to their abolition. A light sheet aluminum cover which could be easily removed will be substituted to keep rain from the engine.

Weight saving **145 lbs**

Item 3 The Triplex glass provided in the windows of the promenade has not been found to provide a very good outlook as the glass is not sufficiently uniform; on the other hand, the Cellon windows appear quite effective. It is proposed to substitute Cellon windows in the place of the glass.

Weight saving **417 lbs**

Item 4 Remove two WCs [water closets]. The present number is considered unnecessarily large, and it is proposed to remove two with their partitions, etc.

Weight saving **130 lbs**

Item 5 Reduction in amount of fuel stowage. It is now evident that the ship even when modified cannot have sufficient lift to take fuel in all the storage tanks which have been provided. The absolute maximum storage which can be contemplated as ever able to be carried is twenty-seven tons. Working to this figure, it is possible to remove tanks equivalent to the storage of eight-and-a-half tons of fuel.

Weight savings on tanks and slings **800 lbs**

Item 6 The lubricating oil for the engines is at present carried in somewhat awkward shape tanks in the bottom of the power cars. These tanks in the present gauge of material have given a certain amount of trouble. They also lead to a somewhat complicated piping system. It is proposed to substitute a single tank in each car which is practically cylindrical in shape placed on the deck at the side of the engine. The deck which will be built above these tanks gives the engineers better access to the engines and the existing deck. The oil piping system will also be simplified.

Weight saving **190 lbs**

Item 7 The present transfer system relies on the use of two compressors, a compressed air main throughout the ship and certain high pressure transfer tanks. It is thought that considerable amount of weight could be saved by substituting a system of electrically driven pumps. It is probable also that these would be easier to operate. Quotations for the necessary electric motors promise delivery in six to seven weeks. Difficulties have been experienced in obtaining a quotation for suitable pump, but it is thought that this might be made at RAW.

Weight saving **500 lbs**

Item 8: Piping Supports It is considered that the number of these may be slightly reduced, and also a lighter design of support may be employed.

Weight saving **50 lbs**

Item 9 The oil temperatures on the Tornado engines have been found to be quite low in flight at full power even when half the oil cooling surface at present provided has been out of action. It is considered that by a re-arrangement of the oil system, the amount of cooling surface and also of oil piping could be reduced which, together with the new oil tank referred to above, would provide a considerably simplified arrangement.

Weight saving **150 lbs**

Item 10: Modification to steam radiators The operation of the engine cooling system as at present designed, has not proved very suitable. The radiators are mounted a considerable way above the engine, but the original reason for this no longer holds. The design of a radiator itself has given trouble partly owing to the manner in which it is mounted and also due to the arrangement of [the] relief valve. It is proposed to move the radiators down to positions immediately above the engine oars and to sling them in a different manner. The drain from the radiators would run direct to the separators in the power cars and not through the reserve water tank.

Considering first the radiators at Frames 4 and 11, although the weight saving would not be great, the reliability would be very materially increased.

Weight saving **80 lbs**

Considering next the radiator at Frame 8 which is used for passenger car heating, certain modifications are discussed below under the heading of "ventilation." It is strongly recommended, however, that, at any rate for the flight to India, any question of passenger car heating should be abolished. At present, it necessitates the radiator being below the level of the engines and in consequence, the condensed water being pumped back. The engines in question are both thrown out of action if there is any failure in the pumping system, and to a certain extent this has proved a source of unreliability so far. The radiator and pump are difficult to get at as at present mounted, although a certain amount could be done to simplify this in the alteration to the ventilating system referred to below. If the heating is abolished, however, it is proposed to substitute triangular radiators over the power cars in question exactly similar to the radiators employed in the other cars.

Weight saving **200 lbs**

Item 11: Ventilating system The present system of combined ventilating and heating for the passenger quarters entails the use of an electric fan, and a considerable amount of power to drive it. It is thought that the same degree of ventilation could be attained by the use of air scoops. If the heating is retained (vide the above paragraph) and therefore no weight saving is claimed under that heading, the weight saving on the new system would be 250 lbs. If the above saving is claimed, however, the weight saving may be taken as 150 lbs.

Item 12 So far there has been no opportunity to test the controls of the ship in rough weather, although it is hoped to gain further experience on this point before the ship goes into the shed. The indications so far in ordinary weather show the steering without the operation of the servo gear to be remarkably easy and it is hoped therefore that it will be possible to decide to remove the servo gear.

Weight saving **400 lbs**

Item 13: Reefing Girders It is now considered that the cover from the bow to Frame 1 and between Frames 13 and 15 is adequately supported without the use of reefing boom girders and that they could therefore be removed.

Weight saving **1,280 lbs**

This would entail making new covers for the portions of the hull referred to.

Item 14 It is now considered unnecessary to have engine room telegraphs in the control room as well as in the control car. It is proposed therefore to remove the former.

Weight saving **30 lbs**

Item 15 It is proposed to incorporate the voice pipe leading forward to the bow in the passengers handrail along the corridor.

Weight saving **30 lbs**

Item 16: Simplifications to fuel system The use of pumps for trimming fuel instead of air compressors will lead to considerable simplifications in the arrangement of the fuel system and a reduction in the number of cocks and valves involved. The operation of the system in flight will be greatly simplified thereby. It is not possible to forecast, however, at present what the actual weight saving will be.

Item 17 When the present gasbag wiring system was designed, it was considered a matter of [a] certain amount of speculation as to whether the bag would take up precisely the shape predicted. It was therefore thought desirable to so design the wiring system as to leave ample clearance between the wires and the girders of the hull. It has now been found that the shape taken up agrees extremely closely with the predicted and it is therefore possible to reduce the clearances referred to. This will mean lengthening a certain number of the wires but not all. No new fittings will be required.

Additional lift **6,720 lbs**

Item 18 The platforms on the D longitudinal for access to the valves, as at present constructed, are unnecessarily heavy, and it is proposed to replace them with a new type, a sample of which has already been made.

Weight saving **150 lbs**

Item 19 For early demonstration flights until it has been possible to estimate more closely the margin of fuel required, it is considered justifiable to remove some of the passenger sleeping cabins from the upper deck in Bay 6–7. As these are in self-contained units, this could be done without damage to the passenger accommodation or the decorations etc. If twelve cabins are removed, fourteen double-berth cabins will be left, providing sleeping accommodation for twenty-eight persons. It would be proposed to remove the wooden decking as well as the cabins and to partition off the blank space thus left.

Weight saving **1,200 lbs**

Item 20 It is considered that some economies might be effected in the electrical system. If the servo gear and the ventilating fan are removed as suggested above, no power will be required in the ship except for the electric pumps, which it is proposed to install in place of the compressed air trimming system. The pumps will require a relatively small amount of power and could be connected to the generator which at present serves for cooking. This would enable the power generator to be removed from the ship with all its switches, cable, connectors etc. It is also proposed to remove from the galley the vegetable steamer and hot cupboard, as it is considered that for the number of persons carried on the early long demonstration flights, all the necessary cooking could be carried out on the range.

It is also proposed to remove the tank for hot water in the toilet room. Supplies of hot water could be obtained in lieu from the galley.

Weight saving **630** lbs

The grand total of the weight savings referred to above = **13,506 lbs**

In addition to the above items, there is a certain amount of work found necessary as the result of the flying trials to date. It is not proposed to enumerate all the items, many of them being comparatively small. Amongst the more important may be mentioned:

- Improvements to the rate of discharge of the ordinary water ballast.
- Improvements to the base hose feeding of bags to allow more rapid filling.
- Improvement to the sealing of the outer cover to prevent the leakage of rain and padding of certain girders where there is a tendency to chafe the gasbags when the ship rolls at the Mooring Tower.
- The above improvements may mean a small amount of additional weight which cannot be estimated at present, but which is very unlikely to exceed 500 lbs.

The net gain therefore is approximately six tons.

RAW

Cardington

18th November 1929

Boldface phrases listed below mark either the beginning of a cited sentence or keywords in a sentence. Atherstone's diary entries are cited by date: they can be found in Masefield *To Ride the Storm* 1982, Swinfield *Airship* 2012 and AIR 5/904 document 36. References to the testimony from the Simon Inquiry (described in detail in the Bibliography) are listed by the day of testimony—there were thirteen days of hearings—and a page number. For example, "Inquiry Day 8, 425." Debates in the House of Commons or House of Lords are from *Hansard* and are cited by chamber, date, volume, and column. For example, HC Deb 14 May 1924 vol 173 cc1344–9.

Abbreviations Used

AA *The Advertiser* (Adelaide, South Australia)

AIR The National Archives of the UK departmental code for "Ministry of Defence"

AR *Argus* (Melbourne)

AU *The Australasian* (Melbourne)

AV *Aviation*

BT *The Baltimore Sun*

CAB The National Archives of the UK departmental code for "Cabinet Office"

CDT *Chicago Daily Tribune*

CSM *Christian Science Monitor*

CT *The Canberra Times*

DBG *Daily Boston Globe*

DE *Daily Express*

DEDG *Devon and Exeter Daily Gazette*

DM *Daily Mail*

DT *Daily Telegraph*

DTL *Daily Telegraph* (Launceston, Tasmania)

EC *Essex Chronicle*

EX *Examiner* (Launceston, Tasmania)

GB *Great Britain*

HC *House of Commons*

HL *House of Lords*

ILN *Illustrated London News*

IT *Irish Times*

LAT *Los Angeles Times*

ME *The Mercury* (Hobart, Tasmania)

MG *Manchester Guardian*

MJ *Milwaukee Journal*

NA *News* (Adelaide, South Australia)

NYHT *New York Herald Tribune*

NYT *New York Times*

OB *Observer*

QL *Queenslander*

SC *Scotsman*

ST *Sunday Times*

SU *Sun*

TI *Times of India*

TL *The Times* (London)

WM *Western Mail* (Perth, Western Australia)

WP *Washington Post*

WW *Wireless World*

PROLOGUE: THE PERENNIAL PROMISE OF AIRSHIPS

1 **The milk-white blimp** The story of the escaped JLENS aerostat is well told in BT September 24, 2015, NYT October 28, 2015, and Graham, "Have you seen this blimp?"

3 **For freight** MJ April 17, 1966, 13.

4 **President McKinley promised** Ferguson, *Colossus*, 49.

4 **When the Graf Zeppelin flew** The meaning of a zeppelin to the German people and other details in this chapter are from de Syon, *Zeppelin!*

5 **"What a paradise this land is!"** Chickering, *Imperial Germany*, 1.

6 **"Distance,"** said a British official Pirie, *Air Empire*, 127.

6 **"closer and more constant"** TL October 16, 1928, 9.

6 **Airships "will knit together"** Thomson, *Air Facts*, 144-145.

6 **characterized by George Orwell** Orwell, *My Country Right or Left*, 151-152.

6 **"a temporary and curable disorder"** Darwin, "Imperialism in Decline?"

7 **"An airplane," wrote one advocate** Blessing, "Airships versus Airplanes."

7 **India, said Prime Minister Disraeli** This paragraph and the following comments on India are based on Morris, *Farewell the Trumpets*.

9 **no more than a rehash** and other quotes from Morpurgo, *Barnes Wallis*, 122.

10 **A colleague of R.101's officers** Cave-Browne-Cave, "R.101 and Other Airships— The Process of Development," 1962.

CHAPTER ONE: THE DEBUT OF THE GREAT BRITISH AIRSHIP

17 **cars were jammed** CDT October 14, 1929, 8.

18 **like a worm** SC October 14, 1929, 9.

18 **"Did we do it?"** Graves and Hodge, *The Long Weekend*, 230.

18 **It declared that flying** McKenzie, *The Mystery of the Daily Mail*, 51.

18 **Henry Hawker of the Sopwith Company** Headlines about Hawker form Graves and Hodge, *The Long Weekend*, 13.

19 **Illustrated Magazine** Gordon, "His Majesty's Airship."

19 **"a marvel of engineering skill"** ILN March 9, 1929, 384.

19 **"simplicity of the joints"** *Flight* August 30, 1928.

20 **like banana oil** *Time* November 3, 1930.

21 **"between 1926 and the Day of Judgment"** *The Aeroplane* August 30, 1930.

21 **earned one shilling and sixpence an hour** MG October 4, 1929, 12.

24 **"as lightly as thistledown"** Masefield, *To Ride the Storm*, 123.

24 **Substituting helium for hydrogen** Khoury, *Airship Technology*, discusses this on page 506. It mentions that Richard Van Treutren (in *Airship*, March 2002) noted that the relative lift valves of helium and hydrogen are frequently misrepresented. Helium at standard conditions (100% purity, 29.92 in Hg, and 32°F) has 93% the lift of hydrogen. This misleads: it implies that a helium-filled airship will carry 93% of the payload of the same ship filled with hydrogen. In reality at normal operating conditions, the difference of the standard gross lift is nearly 10% due to the lower purity with which helium operations are conducted. As the temperature of the air mass in which the airship operates increases, a further disparity is introduced which increases the lift advantage of hydrogen. Also, in substituting helium for hydrogen in an airship, the structural weight of the ship is constant, service load including the fuel is constant (for the same range) and the entire loss of lift must come out of the only remaining variable—the payload. The entire loss of lift reduces the payload by 50%, not 7%. C. P. Burgess provided a formula showing an airship's useful load decreased by 31% and the loss of commercial load by an astonishing 59%. See Burgess, *Airship Design*.

24 **cost about £180,000** *The Future of Helium* reports that 1,000 cubic feet of helium cost $174 in ~1925 dollars. Thus, for an airship of 5,000,000 cubic feet (about the size of R.101) helium would cost $870,000. The exchange rate at the time was £1 = $4.87, so the helium for R.101 would be £178,645—about £180,000.

25 **cost £2,500** HC Deb 24 March 1927 vol 204 c563.

25 **"To the uninstructed mind"** Cave-Browne-Cave, "Rigid Airships and Their Development," 1920.

25 **An officer of R.100 noted** Meager, *My Airship Flights*, 16.

28 **"utter boredom"** Abbatiello, *Anti-Submarine Warfare*,104.

28 **"a calm, cool, analytical man"** Masefield, *To Ride the Storm*, 74.

29 **could withstand a thirty-ton pull** For details on the tower see notes for page 32.

30 **"most gratifying"** Swinfield, *Airship*, 261 and Masefield, *To Ride the Storm*, 123.

31 **dial Bedford 2255** SU October 13, 1929, 7.

31 **"Tim"** Walmsley, *R.101*, 118.

31 **swing, roll, rise and fall with the wind** TL October 9, 1929, 11.

31 **"beautifully"** SC October 14, 1929, 9.

31 **"was beginning to shake down very quickly"** Swinfield, *Airship*, 261.

31 **"secondhand"** Swinfield, *Airship*, 263.

31 **"Very tired but happy"** Masefield, *To Ride the Storm*, 122.

32 **Major Scott's invention of the mooring tower** For Scott's thoughts on the mooring tower see Scott "Handling and Mooring of Airships," 1929 and Scott "The Development of Airship Mooring," 1926; and for details of the tower see *The Engineer*, March 11, 1927 (No. 1), *The Engineer*, March 11, 1927 (No. 11), and *The Engineer*, March 18, 1927.

CHAPTER TWO: AIRBORNE AT LAST

35 **"rotten"** Swinfield, *Airship*, 267.

35 **"Good luck to you boys!"** SC October 15, 1929, 9.

35 **"Good luck Scottie!"** Swinfield, *Airship*, 291.

35 **shadow flicker** "Aboard the airship *Hindenburg*," 1965–1966.

36 **schoolchildren waved their handkerchiefs** SC October 15, 1929, 9.

36 **pressure height** For general discussions of "pressure height" see Khoury, *Airship Technology*, 12; Higham, *British Rigid Airship*, XX; Burgess, *Airship Design*, 287; and Hartcup, *Achievement of the Airship*, 20.

37 **Months earlier** Swinfield, *Airship*, 268.

37 **Harry Leech** For details on Leech see *Flight*, November 7, 1930; MG October 6, 1930, 13; DEDG October 7, 1930, 8; SC December 22, 1930, 11; *http://www.short-stownheritage.co.uk/#/r101-crash-survivors/4553605481* (Shortstown Heritage web site); and his biography in Appendix C on page 209 of this book.

38 **most pampered car** DM September 27, 1924, 7.

38 **"I owe more"** Campbell, *Speed on Wheels*, 102.

38 **lack of vibration** Swinfield, *Airship*, 261.

38 **small platform in space** Roxbee "Cardington," 1999.

38 **"wonderfully good"** and other quotes from Atherstone in this paragraph from Swinfield, *Airship*, 261; Masefield, *To Ride the Storm*, 126.

39 **"give them [Londoners] one good look"** DE October 15, 1929.

39 **rhythmic clanking** MG November 19, 1929, 11.

39 **Prince of Wales zipped by** DM October 15, 1929, 13.

39 **Thomson, the Air Minister, abandoned** Masefield, *To Ride the Storm*, 127.

41 **lent a grace** Liddell Hart, "Lord Thomson," 1930.

41 **"I can foresee"** HL Deb 21 May 1924 vol 57 cc557-600.

42 **"outstanding success"** *Aeroplane*, June 12, 1929.

42 **"Before so very long"** Masefield, *To Ride the Storm*, 75.

43 **a meal of** QL October 24, 1929, 26.

43 **about £230 a year** Clark, *The National Income*, 57.

43 **Atherstone emigrated to Australia** Details of Atherstone in Australia are drawn from AIR 2/305, "File on Atherstone."

44 **They had already toured** NA February 8, 1927.

44 **Atherstone lectured** ME June 6, 1927.

44 **"Flying Ball"** and descriptions of dresses AU August 27, 1927.

45 **"was practically nonexistent"** AR July 30, 1927.

45 **"a complete absence"** DTL August 13, 1927.

46 **"Three degrees up"** TL October 17, 1929, 16.

46 **eight-degree tilt …ten degrees** Ventry and Koleśnik, *Airship Saga*, 127.

46 **We think of an airship as a simple thing to fly** Details in these eight paragraphs are from Upson, *Directional Stability*.

48 **cheery Yorkshireman…dour Arthur Bell** Chamberlain, *Airships—Cardington*, 156; the author notes on page viii of this book that "…Cook, Bell and Binks I knew rather better by virtue of having been welcomed in their homes during the last year."

49 **"Well done!"** QL October 24, 1929, 26.

49 **"We had a very satisfactory flight"** and other quotes from Scott are from SC October 15, 1929, 9 and QL October 24, 1929, 26.

49 **the airship's raison d'être** Details on flying to India, including quotes, are from Kenworthy, *The Listener*, 1930.

51 **"unduly optimistic"** Swinfield, *Airship*, 258.

51 **"Compared to the airplane"** Thomson, *Air Facts*, 123–124.

52 **"fresh breeze"** HL 20 Nov 1929 vol 75 cc617-22.

52 **Atherstone railed** All quotes from Swinfield, *Airship*, 264.

52 **"down flat"** Swinfield, *Airship*, 268.

CHAPTER THREE: AN INEPT COMMANDER TAKES CHARGE

55 **"Pay out main wire 600 feet"** The dialogue and steps used to moor an airship at the Royal Airship Works are detailed in Meager, *My Airship Flights*, 155.

56 **"catch hold of the beast"** Scott "Handling and Mooring of Airships," 1929.

57 **"false lift"** See, for example, Warner, *Aerostatics*, 88.

58 **"Well done Scottie!"** Swinfield, *Airship*, 191.

58 **Scott had commanded the airship R.34** The story of R.34 is well told in Abbott, *Airship* and in capsule in Higham, *British Rigid Airship*, 182–188.

58 **demanded rum** Higham, *British Rigid Airship*, 185.

58 **"no one"** Scott "Handling and Mooring of Airships," 1929

59 **"incidence of risks which must always be entailed in"** *The Engineer*, March 11, 1927 (No. 11).

59 **authoritative yet soft voice** DE October 15, 1929; WM November 21, 1929, 4.

59 **Scott explained** TL October 19, 1929, 12.

60 **Lord Thomson then chimed in** MG October 19, 1929, 13.

60 **two water storage systems** These are fully described in Chamberlain, *Airships—Cardington*, 177.

61 **Eight years earlier** The story of R.36 is well-told in Castle, *British Airships*, 35 and Masefield, *To Ride the Storm*, 61–63.

61 **The Times best captured** TL March 21, 1921, 9.

62 **the sensitive Irwin** Walmsley, *R.101*, 118; Masefield, *To Ride the Storm*, 71.

62 **"a sick man"** Masefield, *To Ride the Storm*, 62 quoting Cave-Brown-Cave.

62 **Scott would drink…"cost us"** Scott's drinking habits are well-described in Swinfield, *Airship*, 177–178.

63 **So public where these affairs** Swinfield, *Airship*, 191.

63 **"I am probably"** Richmond, "Some Modern Developments in Rigid Airship Construction," 1928.

63 **Scott commanded** This third flight, including the future Elizabeth II's wave, is described in MG November 2, 1929, 13.

64 **dived on to the ground** Masefield, *To Ride the Storm*, 133.

64 **Afterward Scott explained** SC November 4, 1929, 10.

65 **Atherstone advocated** All quotes in this paragraph and the next from Swinfield, *Airship*, 261–259.

65 **"breakfast, lunch and tea"** TL October 19, 1929, 12.

65 **Thomson revealed to reporters** MG October 19, 1929, 13.

66 **The delay, claimed Thomson** MG October 19, 1929, 13.

66 **Thomson had told reporters** TL October 19, 1929, 12.

66 **He was annoyed** Inquiry Day 7, 378.

66 **In his diary** All quotes in this paragraph from Swinfield, *Airship*, 264.

CHAPTER FOUR: INSIDE THE GREAT AIRSHIP

69 **"Quite a crowd"** Swinfield, *Airship*, 265.

69 **to 97 percent of capacity…he removed loose articles** Masefield, *To Ride the Storm*, 146.

70 **he removed loose articles** Swinfield, *Airship*, 265.

70 **"It was obvious"** Swinfield, *Airship*, 265.

70 **To Atherstone this unnecessary flight** Swinfield, *Airship*, 264.

70 **"gas bladders"** HC Deb 12 March 1928 vol 214 cc1533-607.

71 **"Anyone," declared an MP** HC Deb 18 March 1930 vol 236 cc1925-2006.

71 **The only luxury seen** MP observations and quotations throughout this chapter are from MG November 25, 1929, 9 and ST November 24, 1929, 15.

73 **embarkation tickets** TL November 25, 1929, 11.

74 **"This movement of passengers"** This quotation and those in the next two paragraphs are from a patent written by Richmond and Scott: Richmond UK Patent 281748.

75 **Mr. Albert Savidge** For details on Savidge and sources of quotes from him in this and the next paragraph see MG October 7, 1929, 14 and DE October 3, 1929.

75 **one crew member estimated** Meager, *My Airship Flights*, 199.

75 **appeared in a print advertisement** This ad is reproduced in Countryman, *R.100 in Canada*, 104.

75 **drawing caricatures** Walmsley, *R.101*, 123.

76 **to quote Lord Thomson** Thomson, *Air Facts*, 124.

76 **write letters** Note paper and envelopes described in TL November 25, 1929, 11.

76 **glass could not be made uniform** AIR 5/904 document 35.

77 **"awful shut-in feeling"** *Aeroplane*, October 8, 1930.

77 **an internal report** AIR 5/904 document 27.

78 **pinnacle of Giblett's meteorological work** His most significant works are Giblett "Line-Squalls," 1927 and Giblett, "The structure of wind over level country," 1932.

79 **"Electrical storms"** Scott "Airship Piloting," 1920.

79 **On this lay the latest copy** This copy was found near the wreckage of R.101: *Wireless World*, October 15, 1930.

79 **Morse code** For a clear discussion of the advantage of codes over voice see King, *Amelia Earhart's Shoes*, 293-294.

80 **ship's position using bearings** Meager describes this procedure well in Meager, *My Airship Flights*, 175-176. See also Robinson "Wireless Navigation," 1924 and Johnston, *Proceedings World Engineering Congress*.

80 **green flags on a large wall map** MG August 16, 1930, 19.

81 **The electrical equipment** "Electrical Equipment of HM Airship R.101," 1930.

81 **"as well cooked"** MG October 7, 1929, 14.

82 **"as roomy as a big yacht"** *The Aeroplane*, May 29, 1929.

82 **"spick and span"** Meager, *My Airship Flights*, 199.

82 **served the Members a feast** MG November 24, 1929, 17.

82 **"home truths"** Swinfield, *Airship*, 265.

82 **Irwin noticed...tables needed a batten** AIR 5/904 document 40.

83 **"The weather conditions"** MG November 24, 1929, 17.

83 **One drunk Member** Masefield, *To Ride the Storm,* 147.

84 **As further protection** Richmond UK Patent 281748.

85 **By evening the Members departed** Swinfield, *Airship,* 265.

85 **Although Atherstone thought some features** Swinfield, *Airship,* 267.

85 **Their terrifying roar** Meager, *My Airship Flights,* 149; Shute, *Slide Rule,* 79.

85 **vibrated violently** Chamberlain, *Airships—Cardington,* 121.

85 **vibrations split open** Inquiry Day 7, 380.

86 **"The speed"** Swinfield, *Airship,* 267.

86 **"I investigated"** Swinfield, *Airship,* 266.

86 **"Neither Irwin nor I"** Swinfield, *Airship,* 266.

87 **The data revealed a startling truth** AIR 5/904 document 35.

88 **"imperialist orgy"** *Popular Imperialism and the Military,* 214.

88 **This second modification** The quotations in these last two paragraphs are from Swinfield, *Airship,* 271.

CHAPTER FIVE: PROBLEMS WITH THE CLOTH COVER

89 **Rope returned to his workshop** Rope's test are well-described in Masefield, *To Ride the Storm,* 206.

90 **"There is no margin of safety"** Rope's memo, quoted throughout this chapter, is reproduced in Masefield, *To Ride the Storm,* 206.

90 **the cloth cover must possess** Details about preparing the cloth cover are described in Dyer "Airship Fabrics," 1921.

90 **Works' technical staff spent months** For details of attempts to find new materials for the cover see Richmond, "The Development of Rigid-Airship Construction."

91 **"the best mathematical brain"** Meager, *My Airship Flights,* 202.

92 **Another said** Sir Alfred Puglsey quoted in Masefield, *To Ride the Storm,* 74.

92 **"He's got two loves"** Masefield, *To Ride the Storm,* 74.

92 **"so modest and retiring"** Sir Alfred Puglsey quoted in Masefield, *To Ride the Storm,* 74.

93 **"Does civil aviation pay?"** HL Deb 03 June 1930 vol 77 cc1341–68.

93 **"Civil aviation," he began** HL Deb 03 June 1930 vol 77 cc1341–68.

94 **a twenty-three-day, 13,400-nautical-mile** NYT June 1, 1930, 1.

95 **"after seven years of depression"** Meyer, *Airshipmen, Businessmen, and Politics,* 132.

95 **"I've just got one solution left"** Vaeth, *Graf Zeppelin.,* 44.

96 **"No genuine German"** Meyer, *Airshipmen, Businessmen, and Politics,* 132.

96 **"its spiritual and technological strength"** Meyer, *Airshipmen, Businessmen, and Politics,* 132.

97 **In his speech to the House of Lords** HL Deb 03 June 1930 vol 77 cc1341–68.

98 **They treated the airship like a critically ill patient** The triage is detailed in AIR 5/904 document 35, which is reproduced in this book as Appendix F, page 255.

99 **A crew member watched** Meager, *My Airship Flights*, 188.

99 **"Slight damage to the fabric"** MG June 24, 1930, 13.

CHAPTER SIX: THE AIRSHIP FLIES AGAIN

101 **its role in the RAF Display** Specific details of the 1930 RAF Display are from MG June 29, 1930, 17; general background on the Displays drawn from *Putnam Aeronautical Review* and IT June 3, 1927, 7.

102 **Irwin ordered the rudder coxswain** The flight to the RAF Display is described in Meager, *My Airship Flights*, 190. Irwin's thoughts on the problems are in AIR 5/904 document 40.

103 **The Graf Zeppelin had overheated** This event is discussed in NYHT June 23, 1930, WP June 23, 1930, 1, CDT June 23, 1930, 7, and NYT June 23, 1930, 1.

103 **awed 150,000 spectators** MG June 29, 1930, 17.

104 **"It is as much"** MG November 11, 1930, 9.

104 **"bent"** MG November 11, 1930, 9.

104 **Better, he said** Meager, *My Airship Flights*, 190.

104 **He now worried** AIR 5/904 document 40.

104 **"the least satisfactory part"** Richmond "The Development of Rigid-Airship Construction," 1930.

105 **when spread flat covers 30,000 square feet** Inquiry Day 9, 376 reports the volume of gas bag NO. 4 as 416,000 cubic feet. If this bag were a cube it would have a surface area of 33,390 square feet; if it were a sphere the surface area would be 26,938 square feet. A bag's shape is between that of a cube and a sphere, so I report here the bag's surface area as 30,000 square feet. A typical oxen "skin" is 30 inches by 6 inches: about 1.25 square feet. This means that a single bag takes about 24,000 skins, which I rounded to 25,000. Each bag has a double wall, hence 50,000 skins.

105 **a million and a half** Richmond "The Development of Rigid-Airship Construction," 1930.

105 **"Bedfordshire yokels"** *The Aeroplane*, May 29, 1929.

106 **the bag cost over £8,000** Cave-Browne-Cave, "Rigid Airships and Their Development," 1920 reports that a "complete set of gas bags" cost £40,000. He was talking about R.33 which had nineteen gas bags. The total capacity of R.33 was 1,950,000 cubic feet. This means that it cost in 1920 about 0.0205 pounds/cubic foot. Gas bag NO. 4 had a volume of about 416,000 cubic feet so a rough estimate of the cost is £8,533 pounds; I rounded this to £8,000, although note that R.101 was built ten years later.

107 **sang, talked, and whistled** Meager, *My Airship Flights*, 206.

107 **To test for smaller leaks** AIR 5/905 document 74.

107 **more holes** Descriptions of what Irwin observed are in AIR 5/904 document 40 and AIR 5/905 document 74.

108 **"Even allowing"** AIR 5/904 document 40.

108 **"thorough inspection"** AIR 5/905 document 74.

109 **"the average person"** *Flight* December 12, 1935.

109 **"if it was necessary"** Inquiry Day 9, 499.

109 **pink chit** Inquiry Day 10, 522.

109 **This legal document** AIR 5/904 document 38.

110 **The padding worried him** Inquiry Day 9, 511.

110 **Though he always addressed his report** This document is described, including its red lettering, in Inquiry Day 9, 509; the document is reproduced in Masefield, *To Ride the Storm*, 224-225.

CHAPTER SEVEN: RADICAL SURGERY

113 **a letter to a friend** This letter is reproduced in Masefield, *To Ride the Storm*, 190-193.

114 **"That quiet, dark little man"** SC October 14, 1929, 9.

114 **His colleagues at the Works** Masefield, *To Ride the Storm*, 42, 390, Chamberlain, *Airships—Cardington*, 115.

114 **"I am one of the most fortunate of men"** Leasor, *The Millionth Chance*, 99.

114 **his "baby"** SC October 6, 1930, 10.

114 **These ships would feature** Richmond, "The Development of Rigid-Airship Construction." and Masefield, *To Ride the Storm*, 194.

115 **It was so simple** TL April 28, 1930, 8.

115 **Within an hour** Richmond and Rope describe their ride in the *Graf Zeppelin* in AIR 5/12 "Report by Lt. Col. Richmond and S/Ldr. Rope on their visit to Friedrichshafen, and Graf Zeppelin flight, 1930." This item is reproduced in this book as Appendix D, page 215.

116 **novel and radical metal framework** Richmond, "R.101," 1929.

117 **"erection work"** Richmond, "The Development of Rigid-Airship Construction."

117 **Richmond's exacting specifications** Richmond, "R.101," 1929.

117 **"all the fuel and water stowage"** Richmond, "Some Modern Developments in Rigid Airship Construction," 1928.

118 **The Times reported** TL August 19, 1930, 7.

118 **The high regard** *Flight* June 8, 1944.

118 **"Anything Inferior Detected"** *Flight*, February 18, 1937.

118 **Outram had VIP status** *Flight* January 8, 1932.

119 **When the Daily Mail** *Flight* August 15, 1930.

119 **"distinguished cargo"** *Flight* October 22, 1925.

119 **He was the courageous man** Armored car: Masefield, *To Ride the Storm*, 59; feared flying: Masefield, *To Ride the Storm*, 243 quoting Sydney Nixon a colleague of Colmore's; innovative antisubmarine patrols: SC July 29, 1930, 9.

120 **"I have every hope"** Colmore's letter is reproduced in Masefield, *To Ride the Storm*, 258-261.

120 **"inherently sound"** Masefield, *To Ride the Storm*, 58.

120 **Colmore loudly objected** Masefield, *To Ride the Storm*, 220.

121 **"I am sure you will agree"** Masefield, *To Ride the Storm*, 226.

121 **"more and more new problems"** *Flight* May 5, 1927.

121 **Every year the number** *Flight* May 8, 1931.

121 **Outram believed** *Report of the R.101 Inquiry*, 51.

121 **"As you yourself realize"** Masefield, *To Ride the Storm*, 226.

122 **installed 4,000 more two-ply fabric patches** *Report of the* R.101 *Inquiry*, 47.

122 **no better, it seemed to him** Swinfield, *Airship*, 270.

122 **"a totally unjustified risk."** Masefield, *To Ride the Storm*, 229.

122 **"really good"** AIR 5/904 document 36.

122 **"glaring defects"** Masefield, *To Ride the Storm*, 301.

123 **"functioned perfectly"** Masefield, *To Ride the Storm*, 300.

123 **four-page memo** AIR 5/904 document 27.

123 **"is to start to India"** Masefield, *To Ride the Storm*, 301.

CHAPTER EIGHT: DEPARTURE FOR INDIA

127 **Scott knew** Inquiry Day 10, 551.

127 **like Irwin that the lengthened ship handled better** Inquiry Day 10, 550.

128 **fresh food for the flight** Meager, *My Airship Flights*, 160.

128 **As Scott waited** Scott's actions and quotes from *Flight* October 10, 1930.

128 **slightly slurred** Masefield, *To Ride the Storm*, 337.

128 **non-executive Admiral** Scott's reaction to this status and the press briefing mentioned in the paragraphs that follow are described in AIR 5/13.

129 **"We don't need these tins"** Masefield, *To Ride the Storm*, 336.

130 **One crew member joked** Chamberlain, *Airships—Cardington*, 146.

130 **Woodis Rogers** For an example of Rogers's verse see Rogers "Note on Major Dobson's Paper on Meteorology," 1921.

130 **The crew balanced the lifting force** For details of the amounts loaded see Inquiry Day 2, 103.

130 **When he wore his Sidcot suit** Meager, *My Airship Flights*, 164.

130 **allowed only fifteen pounds...Crown's Emigration Authorities** AIR 5/904 document 27.

130 **Binks said goodbye** SC October 9, 1930, 9.

131 **cask carefully apportioned** Masefield, *To Ride the Storm*, 479.

131 **Meanwhile, Harry Leech** All details in this paragraph are from SU November 8, 1930, 10.

131 **accompanied by his wife and elderly mother** Leasor, *The Millionth Chance*, 14.

131 **as he wrote a friend** Masefield, *To Ride the Storm*, 194.

131 **a speech at the British Association for the Advancement of Science** NYHT September 9, 1930, 12 and Richmond "The Development of Rigid-Airship Construction," 1930.

131 **allowance of forty-four pounds** Masefield, *To Ride the Storm*, 479.

131 **medal of St. Christopher** SC October 6, 1930, 10.

132 **"a rather long time"** AIR 5/904 document 36.

132 **Thomson turned to his aide** Masefield, *To Ride the Storm*, 43.

132 **"It looks," the man said** Masefield, *To Ride the Storm*, 42.

132 **"To ride the storm"** Bibesco, *Lord Thomson*, 175.

132 **Just then a slight breeze blew** AIR 5/905 document 63.

133 **Thomson, a skillful orator** Thomson's proposal to the Imperial Conference is described in Masefield, *To Ride the Storm*, 276; the proposed locations of mooring towers is described on page 198.

133 **"sitting there as part of a bubble"** Masefield, *To Ride the Storm*, 218.

134 **"I was going to work"** Masefield, *To Ride the Storm*, 43.

134 **Thomson's baggage** Masefield, *To Ride the Storm*, 340–341.

134 **"My precious carpet"** Masefield, *To Ride the Storm*, 43.

134 **Flight Instructions firmly noted** Flight Instruction #32 referred to throughout this chapter is from AIR 5/904 document 27.

134 **all 254 pounds** Masefield, *To Ride the Storm*, 479–480.

134 **"Good-bye"** Leasor, *The Millionth Chance*, 14.

134 **an exhausted Noel Atherstone** *Flight* October 10, 1930.

135 **"semiready and in a nearly totally** Swinfield, *Airship*, 271.

135 **Floating into Quebec** *Flight*, August 8, 1930 and Shute, *Slide Rule*, 116.

136 **"flap and panic"** Swinfield, *Airship*, 271.

136 **Flight Instruction #32** AIR 5/904 document 27.

137 **"The future of airships"** AIR 5/904 document 36.

137 **"powers that be"** Swinfield, *Airship*, 271.

137 **Air Ministry advanced** NYT September 18, 1930, 5 and AIR 2/305.

137 **"Typical," he thought** Swinfield, *Airship*, 268.

137 **"luck will figure"** AIR 5/904 document 36.

137 **"the ship's captains"** Swinfield, *Airship*, 274

137 **three watchkeepers** Hayward, *Air Navigation*, 26.

138 **The crew and passengers were now isolatoes** Chapter 27 of *Moby Dick*.

139 **spotlight was shone on the last engine** Details of the last engine to start are in *Aeroplane*, October 8, 1930.

139 **"Prepare to slip"** The dialogue and sequence of steps for departure are described in Meager, *My Airship Flights*, 160.

139 **liquid-filled gauge** These gauges are described in Meager, *My Airship Flights*, 160.

140 **regular, muffled beat** MG November 19, 1929, 11.

140 **oblong luminous rectangle** ST November 3, 1929, 17.

140 **silhouetted figures waved…signaled with flashlights** Chamberlain, *Airships— Cardington*, 149.

CHAPTER NINE: TO RIDE THE STORM

141 **Not satisfactory," thought Joe Binks** The actions and thoughts of Binks, Bell, Disley and Leech in this chapter are drawn from their testimony at the Simon Inquiry published in the *Minutes of Proceedings at Public Inquiry into the Loss of the Airship R.101.* 2 vols. Large chunks of their testimony is reproduced in Chapter Twenty-Four of Masefield, *To Ride the Storm.* Only quotations and details not from these sources are cited for this chapter.

141 **monster of an engine** For details of these engines see *The Engineer*, September 21, 1928 and *Flight* November 15, 1928.

142 **Arthur "Ginger" Bell** Walmsley, *R.101*, 140.

142 **plywood flooring bending** ST November 24, 1929, 15.

144 **doubled as the ship's electrician** Meager, *My Airship Flights*, 198; TL November 4, 1930, 19.

144 **three huge aluminum core cables** "Electrical Equipment of HM Airship R.101," 1930.

145 **pulling a handle to jettison** *Flight* November 15, 1928.

145 **Unlike a gasoline-powered engine** For details on these engines and quotes from the inventor see *The Engineer*, September 21, 1928 and Robinson, *Heavy-Oil Engines.*

147 **shared bunk, number thirteen** EC October 10, 1930, 2.

147 **Bell picked out the plasticine** Chamberlain, *Airships—Cardington*, 156.

148 **broadcast of Elgar's "Pomp and Circumstance"** MG October 4, 1930, 14.

148 **Ambrose and his Orchestra** MG October 4, 1930, 14.

149 **calcium phosphide flare dropped** The use of these flares for navigation is described by Meager, *My Airship Flights*, 175; see also Hughes, *History of Air Navigation*, 76.

149 **resemblance to Charlie Chaplin** Walmsley, *R.101*, 104.

155 **Union Jack on the flag was partly burned** DM August 29, 1931.

155 **like a giant spider web** TL October 6, 1930, 14.

156 **mooring pendant...caked with mud** TL October 6, 1930, 14.

156 **ground was littered...strewn on the ground** MG October 6, 1930, 9.

156 **hiss of rain** TI October 25, 1930, 13.

CHAPTER TEN: THE CAUSES OF R.101'S CRASH

161 **in a cemetery a half-mile from the Royal Airship Works** Details of the burial are in TL October 13, 1930, 12 and MG October 13, 1930, 9. These and other news reports are well summarized in Leasor, *The Millionth Chance*, 187–194.

164 **"was an easy"** SC June 30, 1930, 8.

164 **"the work of placing these reinforcing strips"** Masefield, *To Ride the Storm*, 304.

164 **Key members...noticed problems** The source for this paragraph and the three that follow is Shute, *Slide Rule*, 123.

165 **Irwin told Booth a day or so before** Inquiry Day 10, 556.

166 **"I thought," said Higgins to Irwin** This quote and those below are from AIR 5/13.

167 **"I wonder," Atherstone thought** Swinfield, *Airship*, 264.

168 **Yet Thomson objected** All events and quotes in this paragraph from Inquiry Day 7, 377-378.

168 **Thomson told delegates at the Fourth Imperial Press Conference** All quotes from Masefield, *To Ride the Storm*, 218.

169 **quote a zeppelin expert** HL Deb 03 June 1930 vol 77 cc1341–68.

169 **"slow and sure policy"** Quotes and description of events in this and the next paragraph are from AIR 5/904 document 35.

170 **"ready to go to India** Inquiry Day 8, 425.

170 **"I told the Secretary of State [Thomson]," Higgins reported** Inquiry Day 8, 426.

170 **Reginald Colmore, cautioned** AIR 5/904 document 35.

171 **He always carried in his pocket** MG December 6, 1930, 5.

171 **"the importance attached"** AIR 5/904 document 35.

171 **"if the ship did not succeed"** Cave-Browne-Cave, "R.101 and Other Airships— The Process of Development," 1962. This is a first person report of a conversation with Colmore. Masefield in *To Ride the Storm* dismisses this report, see page 8.

171 **That departure date "was biased," said Booth** Inquiry Day 9, 557.

171 **quietly arranged** MG December 6, 1930, 5.

172 **"All were agreed"** Pugsley, "Airship," 1966.

172 **Director of Civil Aviation hailed** Masefield, *To Ride the Storm*, 318.

172 **Richmond studied chemistry** Morpurgo, *Barnes Wallis*, 110.

172 **His engineering experience** *The Engineer* October 10, 1930, 402.

172 **"violated the essential feature"** Cave-Browne-Cave, "Some Airship Personalities," 1966.

172 **"balance the gaps"** Roxbee "Cardington," 1999.

172 **"supplemented"** Pugsley, "Airship," 1966.

172 **Harold Roxbee, an engineer at the Works** Roxbee "Cardington," 1999.

173 **"I regard R.101"** Masefield, *To Ride the Storm*, 9.

173 **in private he expressed reservations** Hartcup, *Achievement of the Airship*, 182.

173 **Barnes Wallis designed** Quotes in this and the next paragraph from Morpurgo, *Barnes Wallis*.

174 **"I got the impression"** "Report of Admiral Stromeyer," 42.

175 **"He was undoubtedly"** *Flight* September 1, 1921.

175 **"the first ship of purely British design"** *Flight* June 9, 1921.

175 **"the cream of the airship services"** *Flight* September 1, 1921.

175 **The disaster robbed Britain** Chamberlain, *Airships—Cardington*, 111.

176 **a task described by R. V. Southwell** TL October 10, 1930, 8.

176 **double as watchkeepers** Guignard, *Aeromedical Aspects*, 16.

EPILOGUE: STORIES OF THE SURVIVORS AND
THE FATE OF BRITISH AIRSHIPS

177 **engines used by Sir Malcolm Campbell** See Campbell, *Speed on Wheels*.

177 **who died in December 1973** The *Civil Registration Index of Births, Marriage and Death for England and Wales* lists in the Bedford district "Bell, Athur Victor born 31Au1898 Bedford" vol. 4A, page 157. It does not list an exact date of death, but notes that he died in December 1973.

178 **June 1974, aged eighty-two** Chamberlain, *Airships—Cardington*, viii.

178 **After Noel Atherstone's death** Details about Atherstone's finances are from AIR 2/305.

178 **Susanna Atherstone remarried** See *http://www.thepeerage.com*.

178 **She preserved Atherstone's diaries** Swinfield, *Airship*, 257.

179 **MacDonald told the House of Commons** HC Deb 14 May 1931 vol 252 cc1391–487.

179 **a salvage team had removed** DM December 4, 1931, 5 and *Flight* December 11, 1931.

180 **And for the politicians** See, for example, Pirie, *Air Empire*.

181 **Remnants of Britain's airship program** For a description of the remaining parts of the RAW see *Civil Engineering Heritage*.

181 **charred ensign displayed** DM August 29, 1931.

181 **His wife, Doreen** For details of her projects see DT September 5, 2003.

182 **hacked to pieces** IT October 6, 1930, 7.

182 **They promised** MG October 18, 1930, 14.

182 **Britain in two consignments** MG December 18, 1930, 11.

182 **a cargo of processed food and meat** Robins, *The Ships that Came to Manchester*, Chapter Five.

182 **They used it to create** SC June 15, 1933, 9.

APPENDICES

187 **ships cost the British government £1,825,000** *The Aeroplane* August 30, 1930.

216 **Helium, explained a U.S. military officer** "Exportation of Helium Gas" *Hearing before the Committee on Interstate and Foreign Commerce of the House of Representatives, Sixty-Sixth Congress, Second Session, on H.R. 12376*, May 21, 1920.

245 **"showed a complete loss of strength"** Doree, C. and J. W. W. Dyer. "Some Effects of the Action of Ultraviolet Light on Cotton Fabrics," 1917.

I have divided the sources I consulted in writing this book into four categories: a) newspapers, b) magazines, c) documents from the British Archives, and d) books, journal articles, and patents. I cite those that I used frequently in short-title form in the notes.

A significant source for this book was the materials gathered for an investigation led by Sir John Simon into the causes of R.101's crash. The investigation's formal title is *The Public Inquiry into the Loss of Airship R.101*, called here the "Simon Inquiry." This inquiry held thirteen days of hearings. The first hearing was held on October 29, and the final hearing on December 12, 1930. This book used three sets of materials generated by this inquiry: (1) the final report, *Report of the R.101 Inquiry*. London: His Majesty's Stationery Office, 1931; (2) the testimony from the thirteen days of hearings, published as *Minutes of Proceedings at Public Inquiry into the Loss of the Airship R.101*. 2 vols. London: Institution of Civil Engineers (Great Britain), 1930; and (3) the supplemental documents from the inquiry, which are described below under "British Archives." Both the report and the transcripts contain useful information, but the richest details about the events of R.101's only year of operation are in the inquiry's never-published supplemental documents.

Newspapers

These articles are organized alphabetically by newspaper title and then chronologically for each title. It is not standard to cite page numbers for newspapers because the location of articles varies by edition. Here, though, page numbers are given for many of the articles: those with page numbers are from ProQuest Historical Newspapers™ or Gale Databases *Times OnLine*. Australian newspaper were found in the Trove database, which is a collaboration between the National Library of Australia and Australia's State and Territory libraries. In all these databases the edition is standardized, so these page numbers will help readers find the specific articles without excessive searching. Articles without page numbers are typically either from microfilm or from bound copies.

The Advertiser (Adelaide, South Australia)
"Airship Routes: England to Australia in 11 Days, Arrival of British Mission," June 29, 1927.

Argus (Melbourne)
"Airship Navigation: Imperial Liners," July 30, 1927.

The Australasian (Melbourne)
"Society Doings in Sydney," August 27, 1927.

The Baltimore Sun
Willman, David. "$2.7 billion later, Pentagon's high-tech blimps fail to deliver on promise," September 24, 2015.

The Canberra Times
"Air Service: Britain to Australia," September 2, 1927.

Chicago Daily Tribune
"Speeds 146.16 Miles An Hour in Auto; Record," September 24, 1924, 3.
Root, Waverly. "Britain Holds Breath as R.101 Takes Air Today," October 14, 1929, 8.

"Britain Fast Linking Her Far Flung Lands with Sky Lanes," February 24, 1930, 3.

"Britain to Build new Monster of Sky for Service to America," May 13, 1930, 5.

"Zep Runs Away and Leaves its Skipper Behind: Airship Breaks Loose at Hamburg Fete," June 23, 1930, 7.

The Christian Science Monitor

"Canada's Air Activities," June 12, 1928, 22.

"British Airship has Successful Maiden Flight," October 14, 1929, 4.

"An Imperial Conference," June 24, 1930, 18.

"R.100 to Seek Tiny Migrants in Mid-Ocean," July 29, 1930, 1.

Daily Boston Globe

"Bad Weather Balks Trial of Big Airship," October 3, 1929, 29.

"R.100 To Cross Ocean to Canada this Spring," March 22, 1930, 9.

Daily Express

"Luxury of Travel in the R.101," October 3, 1929.

"Astonishing R.101 Scenes," October 14, 1929.

"Flying over the R.101," October 15, 1929.

"Major Scott's Story," October 15, 1929.

"Mooring Heard by Listeners-In," October 15, 1929.

"Thousands Watch R.101 on House Tops," October 15, 1929.

Daily Mail

"Most Pampered Motor-Car: Never Moves Itself Except to Race," September 27, 1924, 7.

"Big Airship Failure," September 24, 1929, 13.

"Big Airship Failure," September 25, 1929, 10.

"What it was Like in R.101," October 15, 1929, 13.

"Everything Going on Well with the R.100," July 29, 1930, 1.

"R.100's Dash to Reach Home by Tonight," August 15, 1930, 1.

"The Mystery of the Number R.101 Carried," October 6, 1930, 1.

"R.101's Ensign Unveiled," August 29, 1931, 11.

"Breaking Up R.100: A Steamroller to Flatten Out the Debris," December 4, 1931, 5.

"His Plans for New Speed Bid," January 21, 1932, 12.

"Sir Malcolm Campbell: How Britain Made My Record Possible," March 18, 1932, 6.

"Jan Coster Reporting," August 18, 1949, 3.

Daily Telegraph

"Lucy Rope," [Obituary] September 5, 2003.

Daily Telegraph (Launceston, Tasmania)

"Airship Services," August 13, 1927.

Devon and Exeter Daily Gazette

"Broadcasting," October 4, 1930, 3.

"The Biggest Airship: The Coming Flight, Interesting Details," October 4, 1930, 8.

"Bringing Home the Dead," October 7, 1930, 8.

Essex Chronicle

"Essex Men in Airship Disaster," October 10, 1930, 2.

Examiner (Launceston, Tasmania)

Hoare, Samuel. "British Airship: My Flight in R.101," January 3, 1930, 12.

Irish Times

"Aeroplanes Dance to Music: Maneuvers to Tunes by Wireless," June 3, 1927, 7.

"The Largest Airship," August 24, 1928, 8.

"Great Airship Launched," October 14, 1929, 7.

"London Letter," October 15, 1929, 6.

"100 MPs to Fly in R.101; Lord Thomson's Invitations," October 16, 1929, 7.

"An Irishman's Diary," October 28, 1929, 4.

"R.101 in a Gale: A Severe Test," November 12, 1929, 10.

"Tales of the Storm," November 12, 1929, 10.

"Airship's Gale Triumph," November 13, 1929, 7.

"R.101," November 19, 1929, 6.

"R.101's Successful Tests: Cruise of Thirty Hours over British Isles," November 19, 1929, 7A.

"Back to Cadington: A Foggy Welcome," November 19, 1929, 7B.

"A Splendid Trip: Airship Behaved Splendidly," November 19, 1929, 7C.

"Flight of R.101 postponed," November 25, 1929, 8.

"The Press Conference," July 2, 1930, 6.

"Empire Press Conference: Souvenir Records of Speeches," July 24, 1930, 5.

"Work of Salvage," October 6, 1930, 7.

Los Angeles Times

"Atlantic Trip of R.100 Will Be Made Later," May 29, 1930, 20.

Shiver, Jube. "A Blimp Project Gets a Lift," August 4, 1997.

Manchester Guardian

Robertson, F. A. "The World's Largest Airship: Progress of Construction: New Methods in Building: Preparing for Empire Service," August 24, 1928, 6.

"HM Airship R.101: Huge Liner of the Air Ready for Trials," October 3, 1929, 11.

"The 'Groundsmen' for R.101: Unemployed Signed on," October 4, 1929, 12.

"Women's Rush for Airship Posts," October 7, 1929, 14.

"R.101 Still in Hangar: Airship Launch Again Postponed," October 8, 1929, 11.

"Launching of the R.101: The World's Biggest Airship," October 13, 1929, 17.

"Court & Personal: Two Royal Airmen," October 16, 1929, 10.

"R.101's Heavy Fuel," October 18, 1929, 11.

"R.101 Mooring Delay: Ropes Caught in Trees," October 19, 1929, 13.

"R.101 Does Seventy Miles an Hour," November 2, 1929, 13.

"Partial Eclipse: Sun mistaken for Airship by Londoners," November 2, 1929, 13B.

"R.101's Night Flight: Sharp Turns at 62 Miles an Hour, Slight Mishap at Mooring Mast," November 4, 1929, 9.

"The R.101 Trip Ballot; 80 places for 150 MP applicants; Three Women Lucky," November 7, 1929, 11.

"Gale Over Whole Country," November 12, 1929, 11.

"Worst Gale of the Year," November 12, 1929, 13.

"R.101 Trip for MPs: Unequal Risk for the Parties!" November 14, 1929, 11.

"Airship's 31 Hours' Flight," November 19, 1929, 11.

"Today's R.101 Flight: Eager MPs, Good Weather Forecast," November 23,

1929, 13.

"Bad Luck on the R.101: MPs Trip Again Held up. Another Gale. Explanation by Air Minister: Difficultly of Getting Back," November 24, 1929, 17.

"A Question of Lift: How it is Affected by Rain," November 24, 1929, 17.

"Unlucky MPs: Visit to R.101, but No Flight; Collapse of Lift; 100 Stairs Climbed in Wind and Rain," November 25, 1929, 9.

"Still Greater Airships?" November 29, 1929, 11.

"R.100's Flight To Canada," May 17, 1930, 15.

"R.101 at the Mast: First Flights After Recent Alternations," June 24, 1930, 13.

"R.101 Cruise: Visit to RAF Pageant at Hendon Today," June 28, 1930, 15.

"Pageantry of the Sky," June 29, 1930, 17.

"The Hendon Air Pageant," June 30, 1930, 4.

"R.100 Gets Order to Go," July 29, 1930, 11.

"The Homecoming of the R.100," August 16, 1930, 19.

"Wireless Notes and Programmes," October 4, 1930, 14.

"Over French Coast at St. Quentin," October 5, 1930, 17.

"An Anglo-French Inquiry," October 6, 1930, 9.

"Engineer Who Escaped: Mr. Leech Describes the Crash," October 6, 1930, 9.

"Englishman's Story: Rescuer Who Got into a Cabin," October 6, 1930, 9.

"Story of the Disaster," October 6, 1930, 9.

"Mr. H. J. Leech, the Airship Works Expert," October 6, 1930, 13.

"The Return to Cardington," October 13, 1930, 9.

"Wreck of R.101," October 14, 1930, 14.

"The R.101 Contract for Removal of Wreckage," October 18, 1930, 14.

"Engine Log of R.101," October 31, 1930, 18.

"Did R.101 Dive Twice?" November 4, 1930, 20.

"Rushing R.101," November 7, 1930, 9.

"Many Holes in the R.101's Gas Bags," November 8, 1930, 11.

"Lord Thomson's Will," November 10, 1930, 6.

"Was R.101 Fit for India Flight?" November 11, 1930, 9.

"R.101 Inquiry Resumes," December 4, 1930, 2.

"Dr. Eckener's Theory of R.101 Disaster," December 5, 1930, 18.

"R.101 Inquiry Closed," December 6, 1930, 5.

"The Last of R.101," December 18, 1930, 11.

"Bringing Home R.101 Wreckage," December 23, 1930, 5.

The Mercury (Hobart, Tasmania)

"Sky Liners of the Future: Luxurious Air Travel," June 6, 1927.

Milwaukee Journal

"Proposed Nuclear Blimp: Would Carry 400 Passengers in Luxury, Contain a Plane to Ferry Them," April 17, 1966, 13.

New York Herald Tribune

"Trans-Atlantic Mooring Mast to be at Montreal: $375,000 Tower Planned on Site to Cost $175,000; Service to Start in Year," July 1, 1927, 1.

"Britain Plans Giant Airship as Third in R.100 Class," May 13, 1930, 3.

"*Graf Zeppelin* to Make Tours Over Europe During Summer," June 1, 1930, C4.

"Zeppelin Nears Azores; Due in Spain Tonight," June 4, 1930, 1.

"Zeppelin Breaks Away: Pursued By 46 in Planes: Sun's Heat Makes Craft Unmanageable at Hamburg; Captain Left, on Ground," June 23, 1930.

"R.100 Takes Off for Sea Flight Home Tonight," August 13, 1930, 3.

"Feathers to Aid Future Airship, Scientist Holds: R.101 Designer Tells British Association New Type of Cover Will Promote Speed," September 9, 1930, 12.

New York Times

"British Airliner Marvel of Luxury," October 3, 1929, 8.

"Prince Qualifies as Pilot: British Heir Passes Final Test, Making 'Perfect' Landings," October 8, 1929, 28.

"Britain Launches Largest Airship," October 13, 1929, 20.

"Drill Shows Parachute Shortage," October 15, 1929, 3.

"London Hails R.101 on Her First Flight," October 15, 1929, 3.

"Rain Again Halts Air Trip of MPs," November 24, 1929, 6.

"R.100 Set to Fly to Canada," May 17, 1930, 7.

"R.100 Delayed a Month," May 28, 1930, 20.

"Zeppelin Lands After Battling Squalls," June 1, 1930, 1.

"Zeppelin Log Nears 100,000-Mile Total," June 1, 1930, 25.

"Log of the *Graf Zeppelin* on Transoceanic Flight," June 4, 1930, 12.

"*Graf Zeppelin* Breaks Loose at Hamburg; Subordinate Officer Lands Craft at Berlin," June 23, 1930, 1.

"Officers of R.100 Long with Airships," July 29, 1930, 3.

"R.100 Speeding Home with Favoring Wind," August 15, 1930, 1.

"R.100 Finds Britain in Cricket Fever," August 13, 1930, 13.

"R.101 to Fly Next Week in India Flight Tests," September 18, 1930, 5.

"Rats in R.101 Seen as Factor in Crash," October 26, 1930, 13.

"Says R.101 Leaked at Alarming Rate," November 8, 1930, 7.

"Eckener Testifies Today. R.101 Inquiry to Be Resumed—Son Born to Widow of Officer," December 3, 1930, 12.

"Leech Will Aid Campbell," December 21, 1930, 5.

Bromwich, Jonah. "Runaway Military Surveillance Blimp Drifts from Maryland to Pennsylvania," October 28, 2015.

News (Adelaide, South Australia)

"Empire Air Services: Experts on Way to Australia," February 8, 1927.

Queenslander

"'Silver Fish' Maiden Voyage of R.101," October 24, 1929, 26.

The Scotsman

"British Airship: Launch Next Year," August 24, 1928, 9.

"World's Largest Airship," October 5, 1929, 9.

"Air Traffic Control," October 5, 1929, 15.

"Sunday Scenes: Mr. Landsbury's Alledged Motor Offense," October 14, 1929, 9.

"Lunch Served on Board," October 15, 1929, 9.

"Over London: Watched by Thousands," October 15, 1929, 9.

"Welcome Home Broadcast," October 15, 1929, 9.

"R.101's trial flights," October 16, 1929, 8.

"Another Flight: R.101 Cruises over Central England," October 19, 1929, 13.

"King Sees R.101," November 2, 1929, 10.

"Mooring Mast Mishap," November 4, 1929, 10.

"Over Falkirk," November 18, 1929, 9.

"Over Edinburgh," November 18, 1929, 9B.

"On Board R.101: Letter Writing Visitors," November 25, 1929, 11.

"Town's Gift to R.101: Bedford as an International Air Port," February 27, 1930, 8.

"Making Room for 'Sister': R.101 leaves mooring mast for shed," June 30, 1930, 8.

"Last Night's Scenes at Cardington," July 29, 1930, 9.

"Weather Reports to be Supplied While Crossing Atlantic," July 29, 1930, 9.

"Who's Who on Board," July 29, 1930, 9.

"To Broadcast from Airship," July 31, 1930, 9.

"R.101 Crashes in France on Way to India," October 6, 1930, 9.

"An Auspicious Start," October 6, 1930, 10.

"The Navigator," October 6, 1930, 10.

"R.101 Disaster," October 6, 1930, 10.

"Smoking on Airship," October 6, 1930, 10.

"Survivor's Graphic Story," October 9, 1930, 9.

"We are Down, Lad," October 13, 1930, 9.

"R.101 Survivor: To Join Captain Campbell in New Speed Record Attempt," December 22, 1930, 11.

"R.101's Scrap Metal Used: New German Airship to be Ready Next Year," June 15, 1933, 9.

The Sun

"British Dirigible Moors to Mast," October 13, 1929, 7.

"Letters to the Editor," November 8, 1930, 10.

The Sunday Times

"R.101's First Night Flight," November 3, 1929, 7.

"Weather Stops MPs Flight," November 17, 1929, 24.

"Lunch but no Flight: Disappointed MPs," November 24, 1929, 15.

"Zeppelin Comes and Goes," April 27, 1930, 18.

The Times (London)

"Sleeping Cabin In New Airship, Late R.36," March 21, 1921, 9.

"R.38's Voyage. Atlantic Flight Plans," July 23, 1921, 8.

"Disaster to R.38," August 25, 1921, 8.

"The Wreck of R.38," August 26, 1921, 10.

"The Loss of R.38," February 24, 1922, 6.

"Case Against Airships: Air Ministry's Policy Criticized," September 21, 1927, 8D.

"Review of *This Airship Business*," January 27, 1928, 19E.

"The Imperial Conference," October 16, 1928, 9.

"The R.101: Airship Nearing Completion," May 27, 1929, 11.

"Airships: First Flights Next Month," September 4, 1929, 10.

"R.101: State Airship Completed," October 3, 1929, 11.

"R.101: Arrangement for Mooring," October 9, 1929, 11.

"R.101 Delayed by Wind," October 10, 1929, 16.

"The R.101: Successful launch," October 14, 1929, 11.

"The R.101: State Airship's First Flight," October 15, 1929, 16.

"R.101: Success of Test Flight," October 16, 1929, 14.

"R.101 in a Strong Wind," October 17, 1929, 16.

"R.101: Plans for Today's Cruise," October 18, 1929, 16.

"R.101: A Long Day's Flight," October 19, 1929, 12.

"R.101 at Full Speed: Circling Over Sandringham," November 2, 1929, 9.

"R.101's First All-Night Flight," November 4, 1929, 9.

"The R.101: Plans for MPs Cruise on Saturday," November 14, 1929, 14.

"R.101: Flight of Over 1,000 Miles," November 19, 1929, 16.

"Peers and MPs in R.101," November 25, 1929, 11.

"Weight savings in R.101," December 2, 1929, 10.

"*Graf Zeppelin's* Visit," April 28, 1930, 8.

"R.101 Over London: Visit to Hendon Pageant Today," June 2, 1930, 12.

"R.101 at Mooring Mast: Plans for Improvement in Speed," June 24, 1930, 11.

"Yesterday's Weather," June 30, 1930, 16.

"Story of the Flight: Calm and Secure Travel," August 18, 1930, 12.

"Lengthening of R.101," August 19, 1930, 7.

"Weight Saving in R.101: Lift Increased to 172 Tons," August 20, 1930, 10.

"The Imperial Conference: Leaders of the Delegations," September 29, 1930, 16.

"The Imperial Conference: Opening Session Today," October 1, 1930, 12.

"The Imperial Conference: Opening Session," October 2, 1930, 7.

"Great Airship Disaster," October 6, 1930, 14.

Southwell, R. V. "Letter to the Editor: Men of R.101," October 10, 1930, 8.

"Friends' Last Farewell," October 13, 1930, 12.

"R.101: Opening of the Inquiry," October 20, 1930, 9.

"R.101 Inquiry: View of Expert Commission," October 30, 1930, 20.

"Loss of R.101," October 31, 1930, 11.

"Loss of R.101," November 1, 1930, 17.

"Loss of R.101," November 4, 1930, 19.

"R.101 Inquiry: Weather Charts Produced," November 5, 1930, 19.

"Loss of R.101," November 5, 1930, 19.

"Loss of R.101," November 6, 1930, 9.

"Loss of R.101," November 7, 1930, 9.

"Leaks in R.101 Gas Bags," November 8, 1930, 7.

"Timing of the Flight of R.101," November 11, 1930, 19.

"The R.100," November 17, 1931, 14.

"End of R.100," December 4, 1931, 11.

"Miss Ellen Wilkinson: A vivid personality," February 7, 1947, 7.

Times of India

"Current Topics: The Perfect MP; The New Air Secretary by One Who Knows Him," February 14, 1924, 8.

"The Imperial Press Conference," June 2, 1930, 10.

"The Parliament of Press," July 19, 1930, 10.

"A Day of National Mourning," October 7, 1930, 7.

"Squadron Leader Rope," October 7, 1930, 9.

"Graphic Account of the Loss of Airship R.101," October 25, 1930, 13.

Washington Post

"Captain Chases Graf On Runaway Flight," June 23, 1930, 1.

"Britain's New Giant of Skies Begins Her Flight to Montreal," July 29, 1930, 1.

"Pilot Blames Storm For R.101 Disaster: Sister of Leech Recalls He was Pessimistic Over Flight," October 6, 1930, 1.

"R.101 Survivors Describe Death Plunge of Dirigible," November 1, 1930, 7.

Western Mail (Perth, Western Australia)

"People of the Week," November 21, 1929, 4.

Magazines

These articles are organized alphabetically by magazine title and then chronologically for each title.

The Aeroplane

"A Comparative Examination of the Future of the Rigid Airship and the Aeroplane," January 9, 1929, 40.

Gray, C. G. "On Seeing the Big Airship," May 29, 1929, 865.

"On Politicians and Aviation," June 12, 1929, 958.

"The R.101," October 8, 1930, 793.

Flanders, L. Howard. "Some Notes on Alternations in the R.101," October 8, 1930, 804A.

Aviation

"Machinery Installation of R.101," November 15, 1928, 988.

"The British State Airship R.101," October 26, 1929, 850–853.

The Engineer

"The Cardington Airship Shed and Mooring Tower No. I," March 11, 1927, 230–231.

"The Cardington Airship Shed and Mooring Tower No. II," March 11, 1927, 258–260.

"The Cardington Airship Shed and Mooring Tower No. III," March 18, 1927, 288–296.

"Heavy Oil Engines for Aircraft and Railways," September 21, 1928, 314.

"The British Airship," September 20, 1929, 293.

"His Majesty's Airship R.101," October 4, 1929, 361.

"R.101 Airship Disaster," October 10, 1930, 395–400, 402–404.

Flight

"Airship Pioneers," November 9, 1916, 979.

"Ten Years Ago," September 20, 1917, 977.

"Personals," January 17, 1918, 78.

"The British Air Services," May 16, 1918, 546.

"Personals," May 15, 1919, 651.

"ZR.2 (R.38): A Visit to the Royal Airship Works," June 9, 1921, 387.

"The R.38 Disaster," September 1, 1921, 589–592.

"Notices to Airmen," January 12, 1922, 23.

"Notices to Airmen," January 26, 1922, 54.

"Handley Page 'Hampstead' Delivered," October 22, 1925, 696.

"The Royal Aero Club of the UK," May 6, 1926, 273.

"An Interesting Dinner," May 5, 1927, 281.

"A Very Jolly Affair: AID Puts Away the Micrometer and Microscope for One Evening," April 26, 1928, 293.

Robertson, F. A. "Airships: His Majesty's Airship R.101," August 30 1928, 741–746.

"Machinery Installation of R.101," November 15, 1928, 988.

"Electric Cooking Equipment for R.101," July 11, 1929, 667.

"R.100 Starts for Montreal," August 1, 1930, 872–873.

"R.100 Flies to Montreal," August 8, 1930, 891–894.

"Miss Amy Johnson honoured," August 15, 1930, 916.

"Return of R.100," August 22, 1930, 952–953.

"The Lost of HM Airship R.101," October 10, 1930, 1107.

"Honours for R.101 Survivors," November 7, 1930, 7.

"R.101 Inquiry: Leakage from Gas Bags," November 14, 1930, 1238.

"Pensions and Gratuities to R.101 Dependents," November 14, 1930, 1239.

"AID Annual Dinner," May 8, 1931, 411.

"Breaking up R.100," December 11, 1931, 1210.

"Airisms from the four winds," January 8, 1932, 39.

"The Seventh Success," May 6, 1932, 406.

"The Approved Inspectors' Dinner at Sheffield," December 14, 1933, 1273.

"The Ninth," May 3, 1934, 433.

"Co-Efficiency of Expansion," December 12, 1935, 621.

"The Lion and the Lamb," February 18, 1937, 174.

"Death of Col. Outram," June 8, 1944, 609.

"Cody Controversy [Letter from W. G. Gibson]," September 5, 1958, 430.

The Illustrated London News

"A Flying 'Hotel:' The Remarkable Passenger Quarters in Britain's New Giant Airship, R.101," March 9, 1929, 384.

"Window on the World," October 4, 1930, 583.

Popular Science Monthly

Rosendahl, Charles E. "Flying with an Airship Captain," March 1930, 40.

Teed, P. L. "British Airship Policy," August 30, 1930, 458.

Time

"Patched Show," October 13, 1930, 24.

"Aeronautics: R.101's Rats," November 3, 1930, 42.

Wireless World

"R.101," October 15, 1930, 432.

British Archives

Documents from the British Archives—more formally "The National Archives of the UK"—are cited in the notes with the alphanumeric code used by the archives and, if appropriate, a page number. For example, AIR 3/205, 2.

Note that AIR 5/903, 5/904, 5/905, and 5/906 listed below contain the supplemental documents from the Simon Inquiry. They are numbered 1 to 110, but there are only 108 documents: numbers 96 and 101 were assigned no documents—they are described as "blank" in the document list prepared for the inquiry. These supplemental documents are cited in the notes with the document number and title. For example, AIR 5/904, document 38, "Inspection Report of R.101 (McWade)."

List of Documents Consulted

The National Archives of the UK, AIR 3/205 AIRSHIPS: Airships—All Types (CODE A, 6/1): Engagement of Lt. Cdr. Atherstone as additional Flying Officer for Airship crew. (1927–1934).

The National Archives of the UK, AIR 5/12, "Report by Lt. Col. Richmond and S/Ldr. Rope on their visit to Friedrichshafen, and *Graf Zeppelin* flight, 1930."

The National Archives of the UK, AIR 5/13, "Responsibilities of Captain for R.101: Position of Major Scott and F/Lt. Irwin."

The National Archives of the UK, AIR 5/903, Public Inquiry into the loss of Airship R.101: Papers of Sir John Simon, G.C.S.I., K.C.V.O., K.C., M.P.: Documents submitted to the Court of Inquiry, NOS. 1–20. With list of documents NOS. 1–110.

The National Archives of the UK, AIR 5/904, Public Inquiry into the loss of Airship R.101: Papers of Sir John Simon, G.C.S.I., K.C.V.O., K.C., M.P.: Documents submitted to the Court of Inquiry, NOS. 21–50.

The National Archives of the UK, AIR 5/905, Public Inquiry into the loss of Airship R.101: Papers of Sir John Simon, G.C.S.I., K.C.V.O., K.C., M.P.: Documents submitted to the Court of Inquiry, NOS. 51–80.

The National Archives of the UK, AIR 5/906, Public Inquiry into the loss of Airship R.101: Papers of Sir John Simon, G.C.S.I., K.C.V.O., K.C., M.P.: Documents submitted to the Court of Inquiry, NOS. 81–109.

The National Archives of the UK, CAB 24/162/47, "Civil Air Transport," Memorandum by Samuel Hoare, November 1923.

The National Archives of the UK, CAB 24/165/4, "Airship Development," Memorandum by C. B. Thomson, February 11, 1924.

Books, Journal Articles, and Patents

Abbatiello, John J. *Anti-Submarine Warfare in World War I: British Naval Aviation and the Defeat of the U-Boats.* London: Routledge, 2006.

Abbott, Patrick. *Airship: The Story of R.34 and the First East-West Crossing of the Atlantic by Air.* New York: Scribner, 1973.

"Aboard the airship *Hindenburg*: Louis P. Loechner's diary of its maiden flight to the United States." *The Wisconsin Magazine of History* 49, no. 2 (Winter, 1965–1966): 101–121.

Admiralty Handbook of Wireless Telegraphy 1931. London: His Majesty's Stationery Office, 1932.

Beauchamp, Kenneth G. *A History of Telegraphy: Its Technology and Application.* London: Institution of Electrical Engineers, 2001.

Beloff, Max. *Britain's Liberal Empire: 1897–1921.* London: MacMillan, 1987.

Bibesco, Princess Marthe. *Lord Thomson of Cardington: A Memoir and Some Letters.* London: Jonathan Cape, 1932.

Blessing, Arthur R. "Airships versus Airplanes." *North American Review* 226 (July 1928): 53.

Bullard, Thomas R. *Rigid Airships: A Check-List.* (Privately printed: Oak Park, Illinois, 1987).

Bunting, W. L. and H. L. Collen. *A Geography of the British Empire.* Cambridge: Cambridge University Press, 1916.

Burgress, Charles P. *Airship Design.* New York: Ronald Press Company, 1927.

Campbell, Malcolm. *Speed on Wheels.* London: Sampson Low, Marston, 1949.

Castle, Ian. *British Airships 1905–30.* Oxford: Osprey, 2009.

Cave-Browne-Cave, T. R. "Rigid Airships and Their Development." *The Aeronautical Journal 120 (1920): 143–184.*

———. "R.101 and Other Airships—The Process of Development." *Journal of the Royal Aeronautical Society* 66 (August 1962): 489–498.

———. "Some Airship Personalities." *Journal of the Royal Aeronautical Society* 70, no. 661 (1966): 52–53.

Chamberlain, Geoffrey. *Airships-Cardington: A History of Cardington Airship Station and its Role in World Airship Development.* Lavenham, Suffolk: Terence Dalton Limited, 1984.

Chickering, Roger. *Imperial Germany and the Great War, 1914–1918.* Cambridge: Cambridge University Press, 2014.

Civil Engineering Heritage: Eastern and Central England. Civil Engineering Heritage Series. Edited by E. A. Labrum. London: Thomas Telford Ltd, 1993.

Countryman, Barry. *R.100 in Canada.* Erin, Ontario: The Boston Mills Press, 1982.

Darwin, John. "Imperialism in Decline? Tendencies in British Imperial Policy Between the Wars." *The Historical Journal* 23 (no. 3, September 1980) 657–679.

de Syon, Guillaume. *Zeppelin! Germany and Airships 1900–1939.* Baltimore: The Johns Hopkins University Press, 2002.

Doree, C. and J. W. W. Dyer. "Some Effects of the Action of Ultraviolet Light on Cotton Fabrics." *Journal of the Society of Dyers and Colourists* 33 (1917): 17–19.

Durst, C. S. "The Loss of R.101." *The Meteorological Magazine* 65 (1930): 226–230.

Dyer, J. W. W. "Airship Fabrics." *The Aeronautical Journal* 25 (July 1921): 332–356.

"Electrical Equipment of HM Airship R.101." *Aircraft Engineering* 2 (January 1930): 4.

Ferguson, Niall. *Colossus: The Price of America's Empire.* New York: Penguin, 2004.

The Future of Helium as a Natural Resource. Edited by William J. Nuttall, Richard Clarke, Bartek Glowacki. London: Routledge, 2012.

Gates, Barrington. "R.101." *New Statesman* 1 (April 11, 1931): 244.

Giblett, M. A. "Line-Squalls." *Journal of the Royal Aeronautical Society* 31 no. 198 (June 1927): 509– 549.

———. "The structure of wind over level country." *Geophysical Memoirs* VI, no. 54 (1932).

Gordon, Adrian. "His Majesty's Airship R.101: Its triumph of Aeronautical Design." *The World Today* 55 (April 1929): 551–556.

Graham, David A. "Have you seen this blimp?" *The Atlantic.* October 28, 2015. *http://www.theatlantic.com/national/archive/2015/10/have-you-seen-this-blimp/412897/.*

Graves, Robert and Alan Hodge. *The Long Weekend: A Social History of Great Britain 1918–1939.* New York: Norton, 1963.

Grimwood, Terry, "R.101—The Kesgrave Connection," published at *http://www.comberenterprises.co.uk/apps/WikkaKCW/KesgraveHistoryR101,* undated.

Guignard, J. C. and P. F. King. *Aeromedical Aspects of Vibration and Noise.* AGARDograph no. 151. Neuilly-sur-Seine, France: NATO Advisory Group for Aerospace Research, 1972.

Hartcup, Guy. *The Achievement of the Airship: A History of the Development of Rigid, Semi-rigid, and Non-rigid Airships.* Newton Abbot: David & Charles, 1974.

Hayward, Terry. "Airship Navigation." Chapter 2 in *Air Navigation: From Balloons to Concorde*. Edited by Walter Blanchard. West Sussex: Woodfield Publishing, 2006.

Higham, Robin. *The British Rigid Airship, 1908–1931: A Study in Weapons Policy*. Westport, Connecticut: Greenwood Press, 1975. First published 1961 by G. T. Foulis.

Hodgson, John Edmund. *The History of Aeronautics in Great Britain, From the Earliest Times to the Latter Half of the Nineteenth Century*. London: Oxford University Press, 1924.

Hughes, Arthur J. *History of Air Navigation*. London: George Allen & Unwin, 1946.

Hutchinson, Kenneth. *High Speed Gas: An Autobiography*. London: Duckworth, 1987.

Johnston, E. A. "Ernest Livingston Johnston—Air Navigator." *Journal of Navigation*, 49 (1996): 317–331.

Johnston, E. L. "The Atlantic Flight of R.100." *Aircraft Engineering* 2 (November 1930): 287.

———. "The Practical Application of Navigation (Paper No. 262)." In vol. 5 *Proceedings World Engineering Congress Tokyo 1929*, 375–391, Tokyo: World Engineering Congress, 1931.

Jones, Derek. *Shortstown: The Home of the Airship*. (Privately printed).

Kenworthy, J. M. "To India and Back by Air." *The Listener* 3 (March 5, 1930): 399.

Kerisel, Jean. *Of Stones and Man: From the Pharaohs to the Present Day*. Boca Raton, Florida: CRC Press, 2005.

Khoury, G. A. *Airship Technology*. 2nd ed. Cambridge: Cambridge University Press, 2012.

King, Thomas, Randall Jacobson, Karen R. Burns, and Kenton Spading. *Amelia Earhart's Shoes: Is the Mystery Solved?* Lanham, Maryland: AltaMira Press, 2004.

Leasor, James. *The Millionth Chance: The Story of R.101*. New York: Reynal and Company, 1957.

Liddell Hart, B. "Lord Thomson." *The Fortnightly Review* 128 (November 1, 1930): 577–583.

"Lieut.-Col. V. C. Richmond, OBE" [Obituary]. *Nature* 126 (October 18, 1930): 619.

Masefield, Peter G. *To Ride The Storm: The Story of the Airship R.101*. London: William Kimber, 1982.

McKenzie, Fred A. *The Mystery of the Daily Mail*. London: Associated Newspapers, 1921.

Meager, George. *Leaves from my Logbook.* Akron, Ohio: Wingfoot Lighter-Than-Air Society, 1961.

———. *My Airship Flights 1915–1930.* London: William Kimber, 1970.

Meyer, Henry Cord. *Airshipmen, Businessmen, and Politics 1890–1940.* Washington: Smithsonian Institution Press, 1992.

Minutes of Proceedings at Public Inquiry into the Loss of the Airship R.101. 2 vols. London: Institution of Civil Engineers (Great Britain), 1930.

Morpurgo, J. E. *Barnes Wallis.* New York: St. Martin's Press, 1972.

Mowat, Charles Loch. *Britain Between the Wars: 1918–1940.* Chicago: University of Chicago, 1955.

Orwell, George. *My Country Right or Left 1940–1943.* Vol 2, *The Collected Essays, Journalism and Letters of George Orwell.* Edited by Sonia Orwell and Ian Angus. London: Penguin, 1970.

Pigott, Peter. *Taming the Skies: A Celebration of Canadian Flight.* Toronto: Dundurn, 2003.

Pirie, Gordon. *Air Empire: British Imperial Civil Aviation, 1919–39.* New York: Manchester University Press, 2009.

Popular Imperialism and the Military: 1850–1950. Edit by John Mackenzie. Manchester: Manchester University Press, 1992.

Pugsley, A. "Airship." *Journal of the Royal Aeronautical Society* 70 (1966): 44–51.

Putnam Aeronautical Review. Edited by John Motum. Annapolis, Maryland: Naval Institute Press, 1990.

"Report of Admiral Stromeyer Regarding Visit of the InterAllied Commission to the Airship Building Works in Rheinau on July 8, 1920." In *Key to the Development of the Super-Airship,* edited by Frederick S. Hardesty. New York: 1930.

Report of the R.101 Inquiry. London: His Majesty's Stationery Office, 1931.

Richmond, V. C. "Organisation of a Colonial Airship Service." *The Aeronautical Journal* 25, no. 131 (November 1921): 588–615.

———. "A Review of the Present Position with Regard to Airship Research and Experiment." *The Journal of the Royal Aeronautical Society* 30, no. 190 (October 1926): 547–586.

———. "Some Modern Developments in Rigid Airship Construction." *Transactions of the Naval Architects* 70 (1928): 173–209.

———. "R.101." *The Journal of the Royal Aeronautical Society* 33, no. 224 (August 1929): 686–723.

———. "The Development of Rigid-Airship Construction." *Engineering* 130, no. 3374 (September 12, 1930): 341–344 and 130, no. 3376 (September 26, 1930): 412–414.

————, and F. M. Rope. 1928. Construction of Airships. US Patent 1,683,490, filed December 15, 1927, and issued September 4, 1928.

————, and G. H. Scott. 1926. Improvements in or relating to the Construction of Rigid Airships. UK Patent 281748, filed August 11, 1926, and issued December 12, 1927.

Robins, Nick. *The Ships that Came to Manchester*. The Hill, Stroud, Gloucestershire: Amberley Publishing, 2015.

Robinson, J. "Wireless Navigation." *Journal of the Royal Society of Arts* 72, no. 3735 (June 20, 1924): 516–531.

Robinson, William. *Heavy-Oil Engines of Akroyd Type*. London: Blackie & Son, 1931.

Rogers, Woodis. "Note on Major Dobson's Paper on Meteorology." *Aeronautical Journal* 25 (May 1921): 234.

Roxbee, Harold (Lords King Norton). "Cardington." *The Aeronautical Journal* 103, no. 1022 (April 1999): 187–189.

Scott, G. H. "Airship Piloting." *Aeronautics* 19, no. 373 (December 9, 1920): 414–418.

————. "The Development of Airship Mooring." *Journal of the Royal Aeronautical Society* 30, no. 188 (August 1926): 459–481.

————. "Handling and Mooring of Airships." *The Journal of the Royal Aeronautical Society* 33, no. 227 (November 1929) 1034–1049.

————. "The Mechanical Handling of Airships." *Aircraft Engineering* 2 (September 1930): 235.

Shute, Nevil. *Slide Rule: The Autobiography of an Engineer.* New York: William Morrow & Company, 1954.

Swinfield, John. *Airship: Design, Development, and Disaster.* Annapolis, Maryland: Naval Institute Press: Annapolis, 2012.

Teed, P. L. "The Lift of Hydrogen." *Aviation and Aeronautical Engineering* 8 (May 15, 1920): 328–330.

————. "Airships in Horizontal Flight." *Aircraft Engineering* 3, no. 27 (May 1931): 107–108.

Tennekes, Henk. *The Simple Science of Flight: From Insects to Jumbo Jets*. Cambridge: MIT, 2009.

Thomson, Christopher Birdwood [Lord Thomson]. *Air Facts and Problems*. New York: Doran, 1927.

Upson, Ralph H. "Directional Stability and Control of Airships." *Aviation and Aeronautical Engineering* 8 (April 1, 1920): 200 and 8 (April 15, 1920): 238.

Vaeth, J. Gordon. *Graf Zeppelin: The Adventures of an Aerial Globetrotter.* New York: Harper & Brothers, 1958.

Ventry, Arthur F., and Eugène Koleśnik. *Airship Saga: The History of Airships Seen Through the Eyes of the Men Who Designed, Built and Flew Them.* Poole, Dorset: Blandford Press, 1982.

Walmsley, Nick Le Neve. *R.101: A Pictorial History.* Stroud, Gloucestershire, UK: The History Press, 2000.

"The Work of the AID Test House and Techniques for Maintaining Production Quality." *The Institution of Production Engineers Journal* 32, no. 6 (June 1953): 256.

INDEX

Note on the Type

This book is set in Adobe Caslon, a superb digital rendering of the typeface designed by the great English type designer William Caslon (1692–1766). Caslon began his career as an engraver of pistols and muskets, eventually moving into letter founding, which brought him fame in his lifetime. Over a period of twenty years he produced every letter carefully, cutting each by hand. Some designers take a dim view of this individuality, but despite this professional disdain, the typeface remains one of the best loved. It was used in the printed version of the Declaration of Independence. In the version used here, Adobe Caslon, type designer Carol Twombly (1959–) has captured the unique character and charm of this eighteenth-century typeface.

An early twenty-first-century typeface complements the book's body type: Mr. Eaves Sans graces the opening of each chapter—chapter titles and drop capitals—and the page headers. It was designed in 2009 by Zuzana Licko (1961–) of Emigre Fonts. She created this sans-serif typeface as a companion to her serif typeface Mrs. Eaves, a late twentieth-century revival of Baskerville. The most notable features of Mr. Eaves Sans are in the roman lower case letters *a*, *e*, and *g*, as well as in subtle details such as the angled lead in strokes, the counter forms of the *b*, *d*, *p*, and *q*, and the flared leg of the capital *R*, the tail of the *Q*.

Lightning Source UK Ltd.
Milton Keynes UK
UKHW012354071021
391837UK00001B/87